AN INTRODUCTION TO

LINEAR ALGEBRA

FOR SCIENCE AND ENGINEERING

AN INTRODUCTION TO LINEAR ALGEBRA FOR SCIENCE AND ENGINEERING

Dominic G. B. Edelen

Professor of Mathematics and Astronomy
Center for the Application of Mathematics
Lehigh University

Anastasios D. Kydoniefs

Assistant Professor
Center for the Application of Mathematics
Lehigh University

AMERICAN ELSEVIER PUBLISHING COMPANY, INC.
New York London Amsterdam

AMERICAN ELSEVIER PUBLISHING COMPANY, INC.
52 Vanderbilt Avenue, New York, N.Y. 10017

ELSEVIER PUBLISHING COMPANY
335 Jan Van Galenstraat, P.O. Box 211
Amsterdam, The Netherlands

International Standard Book Number 0-444-00127-1

Library of Congress Card Number 72-75447

Second Printing, 1975

Manufactured in the United States of America

To Erica and Maro

Contents

Preface

This book has been written as a first course in linear algebra for students of science and engineering. It is addressed to the student rather than to the instructor and is the outgrowth of initial drafts which have been class tested over a two year period.

At each stage, the theory is first motivated by posing specific questions or by uncovering specific needs. The theory is then developed by a systematic quest for *efficient* methods for solving concrete problems. This is followed by detailed examples which are fully worked out.

A distinctive feature of the book is the use of one basic procedure, Gauss elimination, and one basic concept, namely closure under addition and multiplication by numbers. These two ingredients are used almost exclusively for computational purposes and for the development of the theory of linear independence, matrices, and linear systems of algebraic equations. In this way, the student is required to grasp only one basic method. The method itself is given in the format of an algorithm for the reduction of a matrix to row-echelon form. This algorithm can be easily translated into a computer program if desired. Thus, for example, the existence and the computation of inverses of nonsingular matrices is analyzed by converting the problem to one of row reduction of an augmented matrix. Similarly, row reduction of matrices is used to answer questions concerning linear independence of vectors, subspaces, bases for subspaces, the rank of a matrix, etc.

Although the text is oriented toward obtaining efficient methods of solving problems, the full theory is given. We have simply rearranged the topics so that the student is required to master only what is actually needed in order to solve given classes of problems. Having solved these problems, the student is then shown that he has proven a number of important results along the way. He is also shown that the theory usually provides very simple checks on his calculations and where the error is most likely to be if he has made one.

A definite attempt has been made to present the theory so that it may be used as a starting point for more advanced courses. For example, careful but not explicit distinction has been made between a vector space and its dual. In this way, the student can still use what he has learned when the vector space and its dual are not as simply related as they are for finite dimensional spaces. An n-dimensional vector space is identified with the space of column vectors with n entries. On the other hand, row vectors are generated by the operation of the matrix transpose and are basically identified with coefficients of linear systems.

The major topics not treated in this book are automorphisms of vector spaces and changes of basis. In our opinion, these ideas tend to cloud the essential concepts at this level of presentation. Their elimination provides time for the inclusion of a number of additional topics in matrix algebra and matrix manipulation which are esssential for students of science and engineering: simultaneous diagonalization of pairs of quadratic forms; construction of families of commuting matrices, families of positive definite matrices, and families of symmetric matrices which remain symmetric under matrix multiplication; representation of matrices in terms of canonical sums and as products of elementary row matrices and a canonical upper-triangular matrix; polar decomposition; Cayley-Hamilton theorem; etc.

Three kinds of problems are included at the end of each lecture. The first kind consists of computational problems which require only straightforward applications of the theory. A sufficient number of such problems is provided for at least two semesters of work without repetition. As an aid to the students who work by themselves, the answers to about half of these problems are provided at the end of the book. The second kind consists of theoretical problems which test the student's ability to use the theory to obtain simple and direct extensions of previous results. The third kind consists of more difficult theoretical problems which extend and supplement the material given in the text. Sequences of problems are given which culminate in major extensions of the theory or in proofs of the few key results that are not given in the text. A more comprehensive treatment of linear algebra is thus accessible if the instructor covers these problems in class. Appropriate hints are given for the more difficult problems.

Linear algebra is given in a number of different colleges and universities in the first two or three years of a science, engineering, mathematics, or computer science curriculum. Some institutions combine it with the calculus or with analytic geometry, others combine it with a first course in differential equations, and sometimes it is combined with the first course in computer science and/or computer applications. Since the question of what constitutes the appropriate place in the curriculum for a first exposure to linear algebra is still open to debate and experimentation in many universities, a text of a supplementary nature appears to be useful. This would provide the desired versatility to allow incorporation in the curriculum without drastic changes of proven texts or syllabi. Accordingly, the first eight lectures of this text can be used as a supplement of three weeks on linear algebra. This will cover linear homogeneous and inhomogeneous systems of equations, subspaces, linear dependence, rank, dimension, and vector and matrix algebra. The first sixteen lectures can be used as a six or eight week course on linear algebra which also includes determinants, eigenvectors and eigenvalues of matrices, quadratic forms, representations of matrices, etc. The full text can be used as an eight to twelve week course in conjunction with a course on differential equations or partial differential equations. The additional material consists of the application of the theory to systems of linear inhomogeneous differential equations of the first order with constant coefficients and an introduction to the concepts of control theory.

Since this book is an introduction to linear algebra, it is by necessity restricted in scope and content. Advanced students of science and engineering will require additional knowledge in a number of specific and general areas. A list of books is therefore given at the end of the text which may be used for further reading and study. The first part of the list gives texts which develop the theory and its ramifications on several distinct levels of sophistication; the second part gives texts which deal with applications of linear algebra.

The authors are indebted to their colleagues in the Center for the Application of Mathematics for their comments and interest in this project and to the instruction staff for Math-205 for their cooperation in class testing much of the material. They also wish to acknowledge the care, patience, and perseverance of Mrs. Fern Sotzing and especially Mrs. Kaija Siftar in typing the drafts of this book.

DOMINIC G. B. EDELEN
ANASTASIOS D. KYDONIEFS

Bethlehem, Pa.

LECTURE 1

Linear Systems of Equations

Three simple problems • Equivalence of systems of equations • The three rules which give equivalent systems • Study of the first problem: a unique solution • Study of the second problem: no solution • Study of the third problem: infinitely many solutions • Problems

We begin our study of linear algebra by considering three problems. Although these problems may appear very simple on first examination, they will lead to results which will indicate that we have to be very careful so that we don't jump to unwarranted conclusions. Once the need for caution is realized, linear algebra will then unfold by asking and answering a sequence of very simple questions.

The three problems are as follows: Find all triplets of real numbers x_1, x_2, x_3, by means of the known operations of arithmetic, that satisfy the simultaneous systems of equations of

PROBLEM 1

$$\begin{aligned} x_1+x_3&=0,\\ x_2-x_3&=1,\\ x_1+2x_2+x_3&=1; \end{aligned}$$

PROBLEM 2

$$\begin{aligned} x_1+x_3&=0,\\ x_2-x_3&=1,\\ x_1+2x_2-x_3&=1; \end{aligned}$$

PROBLEM 3

$$\begin{aligned} x_1+x_3&=0,\\ x_2-x_3&=1,\\ x_1+2x_2-x_3&=2. \end{aligned}$$

The equations of these problems appear to be very similar; in fact, the equations of the second problem differ from those of the first only in one entry in the third equation, and the equations of the third problem differ from the equations of the second problem in only one entry in the last equation. The similarity in the appearance of these systems of equations is deceptive, however, as we shall see shortly.

The requirements on the problem are that we use the operations of arithmetic. We could then just proceed haphazardly, as with two simultaneous equations in two unknowns encountered in high school. Order in such operations is useful, however, particularly when it leads to a well defined algorithm (or program, if you wish) that handles the details of the calculations for us. Before proceeding with the three given problems, we shall take a short sidetrack and establish three rules, or operations, that will do what we want. These three rules will actually form the basis for almost all of the calculations that we will have to make in order to solve problems in this course.

Since the rules we are going to establish can be used in many settings and for solving many kinds of problems, it is useful to give them a fairly general context. Suppose that we are given a system of m equations of the form

$$\begin{aligned} f_1(x_1, x_2, \ldots, x_n) &= b_1, \\ f_2(x_1, x_2, \ldots, x_n) &= b_2, \\ &\cdots\cdots \\ f_m(x_1, x_2, \ldots, x_n) &= b_m, \end{aligned} \tag{1.1}$$

that we propose to solve for the n quantities $x_1, x_2, \ldots, x_n$. By **solve,** we mean that we determine all collections of n numbers $x_1, x_2, \ldots, x_n$ such that when any one of these collections of n numbers is substituted into the above system of m equations, the left-hand sides of the given equations have exactly the values that appear on the right-hand sides of the given equations. Any one such collection of n numbers with this property is called a **solution** of the Eqs. (1.1). The three rules provide a means by which we can replace the given system of equations, Eqs. (1.1), by another system that is equivalent to the given system. By two systems of equations being **equivalent**, we mean simply that every solution of the first system is a solution of the second system and that every solution of the second system is also a solution of the first system. Stated another way, two systems of equations are equivalent only if we neither gain solutions or lose solutions by replacing one system by the other system.

The three rules we use to find a system of equations that is equivalent to a given system of equations are as follows:

1. Interchange any two equations of the given system.
2. Multiply an equation of the given system by a nonzero number.
3. Add to an equation of the given system an equation that is formed by multiplying another equation of the system by a number.

An application of any one of these three rules to a given system will yield a new system of equations. What we have to do is to make sure that the new system is equivalent to the old system.

The new system that is formed by use of the first rule is obviously equivalent to the given system, for the order in which the equations appear in the system (1.1) does not matter.

Suppose that we pick the ith equation of the given system (1.1) to apply the second rule to. The ith equation of the given system is

$$f_i(x_1, x_2, \ldots, x_n) = b_i, \tag{1.2}$$

while the ith equation that is obtained by rule two for the new system would be

$$a\, f_i(x_1, x_2, \ldots, x_n) = a\, b_i, \quad a \neq 0. \tag{1.3}$$

All of the other equations in the new system are exactly the same as the corresponding equations of the old system since we have only applied rule two to the ith equation of the old system. If $x_1, x_2, \ldots, x_n$ satisfy Eq. (1.2), then they will also satisfy Eq. (1.3). This conclusion is true whether or not the number a is zero or nonzero. Since all other equations of the two systems are the same, any solution of the old system (1.1) will be a solution of the new system. In going the other way, however, if the number a were zero, then every $x_1, x_2, \ldots, x_n$ would satisfy Eq. (1.3), for Eq. (1.3) would reduce to $0=0$. It is for this reason that we require the number a to be nonzero in rule two. With the number a nonzero, we can divide both sides of Eq. (1.3) by a and thereby obtain Eq. (1.2). Thus, if $x_1, x_2, \ldots, x_n$ satisfies Eq. (1.3), then this same n-tuple of numbers will satisfy Eq. (1.2). Thus, since all of the other equations of the new system are identical with those of the old system, the two systems are equivalent.

In order to verify that the third rule will lead to an equivalent system of equations, we select two equations from the original system, say the ith equation and the jth equation:

$$\begin{aligned} f_i(x_1, x_2, \ldots, x_n) &= b_i, \\ f_j(x_1, x_2, \ldots, x_n) &= b_j. \end{aligned} \tag{1.4}$$

When rule three is used, the ith and the jth equations of the new system would be

$$\begin{aligned} f_i(x_1, x_2, \ldots, x_n) &= b_i, \\ f_j(x_1, x_2, \ldots, x_n) + a\, f_i(x_1, x_2, \ldots, x_n) &= b_j + a\, b_i, \end{aligned} \tag{1.5}$$

and the other equations of the new system would be identical to the corresponding equations of the old system. If $x_1, x_2, \ldots, x_n$ is a solution of Eqs. (1.4), then it also satisfies Eqs. (1.5). On the other hand, if x_1,

$x_2, \ldots, x_n$ is a solution of Eqs. (1.5), then we may subtract $a\, b_i$ from the second equation of Eqs. (1.5) so as to obtain

$$f_j(x_1, x_2, \ldots, x_n) + a\, f_i(x_1, \ldots, x_n) - a\, b_i = b_j.$$

Substituting from the first equation of (1.5) we then have

$$f_j(x_1, x_2, \ldots, x_n) = b_j,$$

together with the first of Eqs. (1.5); that is, we recover Eqs. (1.4). Thus, $x_1, x_2, \ldots, x_n$ satisfies Eqs. (1.4) whenever it satisfies Eqs. (1.5). Since the remaining equations of the old system are identical with the remaining equations of the new system, the two systems are equivalent.

We will now use the three "basic" rules to solve the problems posed at the beginning of this lecture. The system of equations given in problem 1 can be replaced by an equivalent system obtained by replacing the third equation of the system by itself minus the first equation of the system (by rule 3):

$$\begin{aligned} x_1 + x_3 &= 0, \\ x_2 - x_3 &= 1, \\ 2x_2 &= 1. \end{aligned}$$

Solving the third equation of this system for x_2 and then substituting this result into the first two equations we obtain the solution $x_1 = 1/2$, $x_2 = 1/2$, $x_3 = -1/2$. Hence, there is one and only one triplet of numbers, namely $(1/2, 1/2, -1/2)$ that satisfies the system of equations of problem 1. The student should note that all that we have used are the operations of arithmetic, for the three rules really are just a systematization of several of the operations of arithmetic. The reason why the three rules lead to such simplification is that the equations under study are *linear equations* in each of the three unknowns x_1, x_2, x_3. A fuller appreciation of the utility of the three rules will come when we have to solve more complex problems.

For the moment, however, let us turn to problem 2. If we replace the third equation of the system of problem 2 by itself minus the first equation (by rule 3), we obtain the equivalent system

$$\begin{aligned} x_1 + x_3 &= 0, \\ x_2 - x_3 &= 1, \\ 2x_2 - 2x_3 &= 1. \end{aligned}$$

Hence, if we replace the third equation of this system by itself minus twice the second equation (by rule 3) we obtain the equivalent system

$$\begin{aligned} x_1 + x_3 &= 0, \\ x_2 - x_3 &= 1, \\ 0 &= -1. \end{aligned}$$

The last equation of this equivalent system says that in order that the system be satisfied, we must have $0=-1$. Since this is clearly not true, there exist no numbers x_1, x_2, x_3, that satisfy the system of equations given in problem two. Thus, even though the systems in problem 1 and problem 2 differ only in a single entry in the third equations of the two systems, their solutions are quite different—problem 1 has exactly one solution while problem 2 has no solutions.

Starting with the equations of problem 3, we obtain an equivalent system (by application of rule 3 twice) through replacing the third equation by itself, minus the first equation, minus two times the second equation:

$$\begin{aligned} x_1+x_3&=0, \\ x_2-x_3&=1, \\ 0&=0. \end{aligned}$$

Thus, the system of problem 3 is equivalent to the system comprised of the two equations

$$x_1+x_3=0, \qquad x_2-x_3=1.$$

For every real number x_3, this system has the solution

$$x_1=-x_3, \qquad x_2=1+x_3.$$

Written another way, the collection of all solutions to the system of equations of problem 3 is given by

$$x_1=-\beta, \qquad x_2=1+\beta, \qquad x_3=\beta,$$

where β can assume any value we please. Thus the system of equations of problem 3 has not just one solution, it has infinitely many solutions.

The apparent similarity of the systems of equations given in problems 1 through 3 has indeed been proven deceptive. Problem 1 has one and only one solution; problem 2 has no solution whatever; while problem 3 has infinitely many solutions. The manner in which we have obtained these properties of the solutions of the three problems—namely, the application of the three rules whereby a system may be replaced by an equivalent system—has given us an algorithm for solving systems of three linear equations in three unknowns. At this point, it should be clear to the student that if we are to be able to make headway with more complicated problems (such as fifteen linear equations in seventeen unknowns) we are going to have to obtain systematic methods for deciding just what to expect for solutions and how to obtain the solutions with the least effort. Such a systematic method is indeed available, and it is provided by the study of linear algebra. This study will also provide us with a very efficient algorithm for actually solving problems. This algorithm will give us the information that will be needed in answering a number of important questions that arise in the theory of linear algebra.

We shall start the study of linear algebra in the next lecture. As is almost invariably the case, a new subject requires a new system of notation, for the notation should do the work for you whenever possible. The student is asked to bear with us for a little while until the notation becomes familiar. After this point has been reached, the use and economy of the notation will speak for itself.

Problems

1.1 A **complex number** z can be written in the form

$$z = a + ib, \qquad i^2 = -1,$$

where a and b are real numbers called, respectively, the **real** and **imaginary part** of z. Often, the notation

$$a = \text{Re}(z), \qquad b = \text{Im}(z),$$

is used. The complex number $0 + i0$ will be denoted simply by 0. Two complex numbers $z_1 = a_1 + ib_1$ and $z_2 = a_2 + ib_2$ are **equal**, $z_1 = z_2$, if and only if $a_1 = a_2$ and $b_1 = b_2$. Thus $a + ib = 0$ if and only if $a = b = 0$, that is $a^2 + b^2 = 0$. If z_1 is not equal to z_2 we write $z_1 \neq z_2$. *Complex numbers are not ordered.* That is, the inequality $z_1 < z_2$ has no meaning for complex numbers. The addition and multiplication of complex numbers is defined by

$$(a_1 + ib_1) + (a_2 + ib_2) = (a_1 + a_2) + i(b_1 + b_2);$$
$$(a_1 + ib_1)(a_2 + ib_2) = (a_1a_2 - b_1b_2) + i(a_1b_2 + a_2b_1).$$

Consequently, the difference and quotient are given by

$$(a_1 + ib_1) - (a_2 + ib_2) = (a_1 - a_2) + i(b_1 - b_2);$$
$$\frac{a_1 + ib_1}{a_2 + ib_2} = \frac{(a_1 + ib_1)(a_2 - ib_2)}{(a_2 + ib_2)(a_2 - ib_2)} = \frac{a_1a_2 + b_1b_2}{a_2^2 + b_2^2} + i\,\frac{a_2b_1 - a_1b_2}{a_2^2 + b_2^2}.$$
$$a_2^2 + b_2^2 \neq 0.$$

We note that the division is defined if and only if the denominator is different from zero. It is easily proved, as in the case for real numbers, that *a product of complex numbers is zero if and only if one of the factors is zero.* The **conjugate** of a complex number $z = a + ib$ is the number $\bar{z} = a - ib$.

Let $z = x + iy$. In a plane orthogonal cartesian system of axes the number z can be represented by the point (x, y). In this representation the x-axis and y-axis will be called, respectively, the **real** and **imaginary axis.** If the real axis is taken as the polar axis, the polar angle θ of a point (x, y) will be called the **argument** of the corresponding complex number $z = x + iy$ and it will be denoted by $\theta = \arg(z)$. The **measure**

$$|z| = (x^2 + y^2)^{\frac{1}{2}} = (z\,\bar{z})^{\frac{1}{2}}$$

of z and its argument, $\arg(z)$, are the polar coordinates of z. It is easily seen that

$$|z_1 z_2| = |z_1||z_2|.$$

Moreover, the following **triangle inequalities** are readily proved

$$|z_1 + z_2| \leq |z_1| + |z_2|, \quad |z_1 - z_2| \leq ||z_1| - |z_2||.$$

Verify:

(a) $(3 + i) - i(4 - 5i) = - 2 - 3i$

(b) $2i(4 - 2i) + 4 - 6i = 8 + 2i$

(c) $\dfrac{1 + 2i}{5 - 4i} = -\dfrac{3}{41} + i\dfrac{14}{41}$

(d) $\dfrac{2i}{3 + i} = \dfrac{1}{5} + i\dfrac{3}{5}$

(e) $5i(- 5 + i) + 6i = - (5 + 19i)$

(f) $\overline{\left(\dfrac{1 + i}{3 + 4i}\right)} = \dfrac{1}{25}(7 + i)$

(g) $(\overline{z_1 \pm z_2}) = \bar{z}_1 \pm \bar{z}_2, \quad (\overline{z_1 z_2}) = \bar{z}_1 \bar{z}_2, \quad (\overline{z_1 / z_2}) = \bar{z}_1 / \bar{z}_2$

(h) $|1 + i| = \sqrt{2}, \quad \arg(1 + i) = \dfrac{\pi}{4} + 2k\pi, \ k = 0, \pm 1, \pm 2, \ldots$

(i) $|1 - i\sqrt{3}| = 2, \quad \arg(1 - i\sqrt{3}) = -\dfrac{\pi}{3} + 2k\pi, \quad k = 0, \pm 1, \pm 2, \ldots$

(j) $|z_1 \cdots z_n| = |z_1| \cdots |z_n|$

(k) $|z_1 + \cdots + z_n| \leq |z_1| + \cdots + |z_k|.$

1.2. Use the three "basic" rules to reduce the following system to an equivalent system of the **upper triangular form:**

$$\begin{aligned} a_{11}x + a_{12}y + a_{13}z &= b_1 \\ a_{22}y + a_{23}z &= b_2 \\ a_{33}z &= b_3. \end{aligned}$$

State the rule used at each step and obtain all possible solutions:

(a) $\begin{aligned} x_1 + x_2 + x_3 &= 4 \\ x_1 - x_2 + x_3 &= 2 \\ 2x_1 + x_2 - x_3 &= 1 \end{aligned}$

(b) $\begin{aligned} x_1 + 2x_2 - x_3 &= 5 \\ 2x_1 - 3x_2 + x_3 &= 0 \\ 3x_1 + 16x_2 + x_3 &= 21 \end{aligned}$

(c) $\begin{aligned} x_1 + 2x_2 + x_3 &= 2 \\ 2x_1 - 5x_2 + x_3 &= 11 \\ 3x_1 + 2x_2 - x_3 &= - 10 \end{aligned}$

(d) $\begin{aligned} x_1 - 2x_2 + x_3 &= 1 \\ 2x_1 + x_2 - x_3 &= 2 \\ 5x_2 - 3x_3 &= 0 \end{aligned}$

(e) $\begin{aligned} x_1 + x_2 + x_3 &= 1 + 4i \\ - x_1 + x_2 - x_3 &= - 1 \\ x_1 - x_2 - x_3 &= - (1 + 2i) \end{aligned}$

(f) $\begin{aligned} ix_1 + 3x_2 - 2ix_3 &= 8 + 3i \\ 2x_1 + (- 1 + i)x_2 + (2 + 3i)x_3 &= - 11 + 8i \\ x_1 + x_2 + x_3 &= 1 + 5i \end{aligned}$

1.3 Determine α so that each system will have at least one solution and then obtain all solutions of each system

(a)
$$\begin{aligned} x_1 + 3x_2 - x_3 &= 1 \\ 2x_1 - x_2 + x_3 &= \alpha + 2 \\ -x_1 + 11x_2 - 5x_3 &= 5 \end{aligned}$$

(b)
$$\begin{aligned} 2x_1 - x_3 &= -1 \\ x_1 + 3x_2 - 14x_3 &= \alpha - 25 \\ x_1 - x_2 + 4x_3 &= 11 \end{aligned}$$

(c)
$$\begin{aligned} 2x_1 + x_2 + x_3 &= 6 \\ x_1 - x_2 - x_3 &= -3 \\ x_1 &= \alpha \end{aligned}$$

(d)
$$\begin{aligned} 3x_1 + 9x_2 - 15x_3 &= 6 \\ 2x_1 + 6x_2 - 10x_3 &= 4 \\ 4x_1 + 12x_2 - 20x_3 &= 1 + \alpha \end{aligned}$$

(e)
$$\begin{aligned} x_1 + x_2 + 2x_3 &= 2 + 3i \\ x_1 - x_2 + x_3 &= 1 - \alpha i \\ 4x_1 - 3x_2 + 5x_3 &= 5 \end{aligned}$$

(f)
$$\begin{aligned} 2x_1 + 3x_2 + x_3 &= -5 + 4i \\ ix_1 + x_2 - x_3 &= -(3 + 2i) \\ x_1 + \frac{4}{2+i}x_2 &= \alpha\frac{4-i}{2+i} \end{aligned}$$

1.4. Prove that the following systems have no solutions:

(a)
$$\begin{aligned} x_1 + x_2 - 3x_3 &= 1 \\ 2x_1 - x_2 + x_3 &= 2 \\ -3x_2 + 7x_3 &= 3 \end{aligned}$$

(b)
$$\begin{aligned} x_1 + x_2 - 3x_3 &= 1 \\ 2x_1 - x_2 + x_3 &= 2 \\ 3x_1 - 2x_3 &= 1 \end{aligned}$$

(c)
$$\begin{aligned} 2x_1 + 3x_2 - x_3 &= 0 \\ x_1 - 3x_2 + x_3 &= 1 \\ -3x_2 + x_3 &= 3 \end{aligned}$$

(d)
$$\begin{aligned} -x_1 + 2x_2 - x_3 &= 0 \\ x_1 + 8x_2 + x_3 &= 9 \\ x_1 + 3x_2 + x_3 &= 5 \end{aligned}$$

(e)
$$\begin{aligned} x_1 - x_2 + 3x_3 &= 1 \\ x_1 - 5x_2 - x_3 &= 4 \\ 2x_1 - 6x_2 + 2x_3 &= 6 \end{aligned}$$

(f)
$$\begin{aligned} 2x_1 - 11x_2 + 11ix_3 &= 10 \\ 2ix_1 - 3x_2 + ix_3 &= 7 \\ (1-i)x_1 - 4x_2 + 5ix_3 &= 1 \end{aligned}$$

1.5. Construct a system of three equations with three unknowns such that it has

(a) one and only one solution
(b) more than one solution
(c) no solutions.

In each case reduce the system to an equivalent system in upper triangular form.

LECTURE 2

Vector Spaces and Subspaces

V_n, the collection of all ordered n-tuples of real numbers • Elements of V_n • Equality of elements of V_n • The sum of two elements of V_n • Closure under the operation $+$ • Multiplication of an element of V_n by a real number • Closure under multiplication by numbers • The real linear space $(V_n; +, \cdot)$ • Representation of an element of V_n by means of the elementary basis elements of V_n • Definition of a subspace of V_n • Linear combinations of elements of V_n • Spanning sets of a subspace • Possible redundancy of a spanning set • Geometric interpretations • Problems

The first thing we want to do is to introduce a system of notation which will efficiently handle ordered collections of numbers, such as the collections of three numbers x_1, x_2, x_3 that occurred in the problems that we solved in the previous lecture.

Let n be a given positive integer. We shall use V_n to denote the collection of **all** ordered n-tuples of real numbers. The word "all" in the above statement is very important, as we shall see presently. The following notation will be used to denote ordered n-tuples of numbers that comprise V_n:

$$\mathbf{x} = \begin{Bmatrix} x_1 \\ x_2 \\ \cdot \\ \cdot \\ \cdot \\ x_n \end{Bmatrix}, \qquad \mathbf{a} = \begin{Bmatrix} a_1 \\ a_2 \\ \cdot \\ \cdot \\ \cdot \\ a_n \end{Bmatrix}.$$

Thus, a bold face letter will represent an ordered n-tuple where the n-tuple of numbers is arranged in a column (with n entries, naturally). In general, $\mathbf{x}$, $\mathbf{y}$, $\mathbf{z}$ will be used to denote ordered n-tuples of variables, while $\mathbf{a}$, $\mathbf{b}$, $\mathbf{c}$ will be used to denote ordered n-tuples of given real numbers. With this notation, we say that $\mathbf{x}$ is a variable **element** of V_n and that $\mathbf{a}$ is a given element of V_n. Thus, $\mathbf{x}$, $\mathbf{y}$, $\mathbf{z}$ and $\mathbf{a}$, $\mathbf{b}$, $\mathbf{c}$ have approximately the same meanings as they had in the mathematics you have seen up to this time, the exception being that these symbols now stand for whole n-tuples rather than for just simple elements.

The first thing that we must agree upon is this: what do we mean by equality of elements of V_n? If **x** and **y** are elements of V_n, that is

$$\mathbf{x}=\begin{Bmatrix} x_1 \\ x_2 \\ \cdot \\ \cdot \\ \cdot \\ x_n \end{Bmatrix}, \qquad \mathbf{y}=\begin{Bmatrix} y_1 \\ y_2 \\ \cdot \\ \cdot \\ \cdot \\ y_n \end{Bmatrix},$$

then **x** is **equal** to **y**, which we write as $\mathbf{x}=\mathbf{y}$, if and only if the n equalities,

$$x_1=y_1, \ x_2=y_2, \ . \ . \ . \ , \ x_n=y_n, \tag{2.1}$$

are satisfied. Thus, two elements of V_n are equal if and only if each of their corresponding pairs of entries is equal in the usual meaning of equality for numbers. This definition of equality enables us to deal with a system of n ordinary equalities like (2.1) by means of the single equality $\mathbf{x}=\mathbf{y}$ in the new notation. This indeed represents an economy, but a rather obvious one.

The next thing we do is to define what we mean by adding two ordered n-tuples together. If **x** and **y** are elements of V_n, that is

$$\mathbf{x}=\begin{Bmatrix} x_1 \\ \cdot \\ \cdot \\ \cdot \\ x_n \end{Bmatrix}, \qquad \mathbf{y}=\begin{Bmatrix} y_1 \\ \cdot \\ \cdot \\ \cdot \\ y_n \end{Bmatrix},$$

then we define the **sum** of **x** and **y** to be the n-tuple of numbers **z** that is given by the n equalities

$$z_1=x_1+y_1, \ z_2=x_2+y_2, \ . \ . \ . \ , \ z_n=x_n+y_n. \tag{2.2}$$

The definition of equality can now be used to write the system of n equalities (2.2) in the concise form

$$\mathbf{z}=\mathbf{x}+\mathbf{y},$$

where **z** is the n-tuple of numbers

$$\mathbf{z}=\begin{Bmatrix} z_1 \\ \cdot \\ \cdot \\ \cdot \\ z_n \end{Bmatrix}.$$

Like the definition of equality, this definition of addition reduces the notion of the sum of two elements of V_n to an ordered system of n distinct sums of real numbers; that is, it is modeled directly on the concept of addition of real numbers. The student should carefully note that we have only defined equality and addition for elements of V_n. In particular, the addition of an element of V_n and an element of V_m is *not defined* when $n \neq m$. You must therefore always check to make sure that you only add elements from the same V_n together, or that you only claim equality for elements of V_n.

The definition of addition of two elements of V_n has a very important property. We note that $\mathbf{z}=\mathbf{x}+\mathbf{y}$ is always an ordered n-tuple of numbers if both $\mathbf{x}$ and $\mathbf{y}$ are ordered n-tuples of numbers. Since V_n is the collection of *all* ordered n-tuples of real numbers, it follows that $\mathbf{x}+\mathbf{y}$ *always belongs to* V_n *if both* $\mathbf{x}$ *and* $\mathbf{y}$ *belong to* V_n. Thus, we can never get outside of V_n by performing additions of elements from V_n—addition of elements gives nothing less and nothing more than another element of V_n. This property is customarily expressed by saying that V_n is **closed** under the given definition of the operation $+$. In order to point out that this property depends on the definition that we have given for the operation $+$, it is better to introduce the following notation: $(V_n;\ +)$ where V_n denotes the collection of all ordered n-tuples of real numbers and $+$ is defined by Eq. (2.2). We then say that $(V_n;\ +)$ **is closed under the operation** $+$. We note in passing, just so that there is no confusion on this point, that being able to add two elements of V_n together to get another element of V_n allows us to add together any number of elements of V_n to get another element of V_n.

Another operation that we shall need is that of multiplying an element of V_n by a real number. If $\mathbf{x}$ is an element of V_n and c is a real number, then **multiplication by the real number** c,

$$\mathbf{z}=c\,\mathbf{x},$$

is defined by

$$z_1=c\,x_1,\ z_2=c\,x_2,\ \ldots,\ z_n=c\,x_n. \tag{2.3}$$

Since $\mathbf{z}$ is again an ordered n-tuple of real numbers, $\mathbf{z}$ is an element of V_n; that is, the multiplication of any element of V_n by a real number gives an element of V_n. This property is stated by saying that V_n is **closed under multiplication by real numbers**. In order to point out that this property depends on the definition that we have given for multiplication by real numbers, we introduce the following notation: $(V_n;\ \cdot)$ where V_n denotes the collection of all ordered n-tuples of real numbers and $\cdot$ denotes the operation of multiplication by real numbers defined by Eq. (2.3). We then say that $(V_n;\ \cdot)$ is closed under the operation $\cdot$ of multiplication by real numbers. If we combine the two operations that we have defined in the notation $(V_n;\ +,\ \cdot)$, then we say that $(V_n;\ +,\ \cdot)$ *is closed under the operation* $+$ *of addition and under the operation* $\cdot$ *of multiplication by real numbers.*

The student should carefully note that we have only defined the multiplication of an element of V_n by something that does not belong to V_n (assuming that $n \neq 1$, since for $n=1$ we have nothing new), namely multiplication by real numbers. Later, we will introduce a "bigger" algebra, called matrix algebra, where a new kind of multiplication will be defined. Even in the bigger algebra, though, we will not be able to multiply two elements of V_n together.

The definitions of addition and multiplication given by Eqs. (2.2) and (2.3) have been built upon the corresponding definitions for addition and multiplication of real numbers. The properties of real numbers under addition and multiplication allow us to obtain the properties of $(V_n; +, \cdot)$ that can be obtained by the various combinations of these two operations. We leave the demonstration of the truth of these properties to the student as exercises.

For all $\mathbf{x}$, $\mathbf{y}$, and $\mathbf{z}$ in V_n, we have

$$\mathbf{x}+\mathbf{y}=\mathbf{y}+\mathbf{x}, \tag{2.4}$$

$$\mathbf{x}+(\mathbf{y}+\mathbf{z})=(\mathbf{x}+\mathbf{y})+\mathbf{z}. \tag{2.5}$$

There exists an element $\mathbf{0}$ of V_n, called the **zero element** of V_n such that

$$\mathbf{x}+\mathbf{0}=\mathbf{x}. \tag{2.6}$$

This element is given by

$$\mathbf{0}=0\,\mathbf{y}, \tag{2.7}$$

where $\mathbf{y}$ is any element of V_n.

For every element $\mathbf{x}$ of V_n there exists an element denoted by $-\mathbf{x}$ such that

$$\mathbf{x}+(-\mathbf{x})=\mathbf{0}. \tag{2.8}$$

The element $-\mathbf{x}$ is given by

$$-\mathbf{x}=(-1)\mathbf{x}. \tag{2.9}$$

For every $\mathbf{x}$ and $\mathbf{y}$ in V_n and for any real numbers a and b we have

$$a(\mathbf{x}+\mathbf{y})=a\,\mathbf{x}+a\,\mathbf{y}, \tag{2.10}$$

$$(a+b)\mathbf{x}=a\,\mathbf{x}+b\,\mathbf{x}, \tag{2.11}$$

$$a\,(b\,\mathbf{x})=(ab)\,\mathbf{x}, \tag{2.12}$$

$$1\,\mathbf{x}=\mathbf{x}. \tag{2.13}$$

The method we have used here is to define V_n as the collection of all ordered n-tuples of real numbers and then to define the operations of addition and multiplication by real numbers. In this way we come up with the system $(V_n; +, \cdot)$ that is closed under the two operations $+$ and $\cdot$ and which has the properties given by equations (2.4) through (2.13). The essential idea here is that V_n is **closed** under the operations $+$ and $\cdot$ that are defined by Eqs. (2.2) and (2.3). Systems such as $(V_n; +, \cdot)$ that are closed under the operations $+$ and $\cdot$ are so important in mathematics that they have been given a special name: $(V_n; +, \cdot)$ is called a **vector space** or a **real linear space**. An element of V_n is often called a **vector** (of order n).

The student who is thoroughly familiar with the properties of real numbers will realize that the properties of the operations $+$ and $\cdot$ that satisfy the Eqs. (2.4) through (2.13) give a full definition of these operations even if the particular rules given by Eqs. (2.2) and (2.3) are not used. It would thus have been possible to define $+$ and $\cdot$ as operations that satisfy the conditions (2.4) through (2.13). For the purposes of these lectures, it is sufficient to just give the definitions (2.2) and (2.3) and then to prove the relations (2.4) through (2.13) since we are dealing with very specific quantities, namely ordered n-tuples of real numbers. For theoretical purposes, it is sometimes better to go the other way. We would then consider the collection K of all "things" with a given property (in our case K would be the collection of all ordered n-tuples of real numbers) and two operations $+$ and $\cdot$ that satisfy the conditions (2.4) through (2.13). This would give us the system $(K; +, \cdot)$. If $(K; +, \cdot)$ is closed under the two operations, then we say that $(K; +, \cdot)$ is a linear space. For example, if we take C to be the collection of all continuous functions $f(x)$ for $0 \leq x \leq 1$, if we define $+$ by $f(x) + g(x) = h(x)$ for each x in $0 \leq x \leq 1$, and if we define $(a\, f)(x) = af(x)$ for each x in $0 \leq x \leq 1$, then $(C; +, \cdot)$ forms a linear space. By this we mean that $(C; +, \cdot)$ is closed under the operations $+$ and $\cdot$ and that these operations satisfy the conditions (2.4) through (2.13). The system $(C; +, \cdot)$ is, however, something quite different from the system $(V_n; +, \cdot)$ that we study in this series of lectures. Other examples of this abstract approach are given in the problems, together with the construction of the **complex vector spaces** $(C_n; +, \cdot)$. A complex vector space is like $(V_n; +, \cdot)$ except that its elements are n-tuples of complex numbers and we are allowed to multiply by complex numbers rather than just real numbers.

In order to see one reason why the idea of closure is so important, we consider a particular example that is also of importance in the general theory of $(V_n; +, \cdot)$. We define n elements of V_n in the following way:

$$\mathbf{e}_1 = \begin{pmatrix} 1 \\ 0 \\ 0 \\ \cdot \\ \cdot \\ \cdot \\ 0 \end{pmatrix}, \quad \mathbf{e}_2 = \begin{pmatrix} 0 \\ 1 \\ 0 \\ \cdot \\ \cdot \\ \cdot \\ 0 \end{pmatrix}, \quad \ldots, \quad \mathbf{e}_n = \begin{pmatrix} 0 \\ 0 \\ 0 \\ \cdot \\ \cdot \\ \cdot \\ 1 \end{pmatrix}. \tag{2.14}$$

Let $\mathbf{x}$ denote an arbitrary element of V_n, so that

$$\mathbf{x}=\begin{Bmatrix} x_1 \\ x_2 \\ x_3 \\ \cdot \\ \cdot \\ \cdot \\ x_n \end{Bmatrix}, \tag{2.15}$$

where $x_1, x_2, x_3, \ldots, x_n$ are n real numbers. Since V_n is closed under addition and multiplication by real numbers, we know that

$$\mathbf{y}=x_1\,\mathbf{e}_1+x_2\,\mathbf{e}_2+\ \ldots\ +x_n\,\mathbf{e}_n \tag{2.16}$$

is also an element of V_n since each $\mathbf{e}_i$ $(i=1, \ldots, n)$ belongs to V_n and $x_1, x_2, \ldots, x_n$ are real numbers. When we use the definitions of addition and multiplication by real numbers given by Eqs. (2.2) and (2.3), the equality (2.16) becomes

$$\mathbf{y}=x_1\begin{Bmatrix} 1 \\ 0 \\ 0 \\ \cdot \\ \cdot \\ \cdot \\ 0 \end{Bmatrix}+x_2\begin{Bmatrix} 0 \\ 1 \\ 0 \\ \cdot \\ \cdot \\ \cdot \\ 0 \end{Bmatrix}+\ \ldots\ +x_n\begin{Bmatrix} 0 \\ 0 \\ 0 \\ \cdot \\ \cdot \\ \cdot \\ 1 \end{Bmatrix}$$

$$=\begin{Bmatrix} x_1 \\ 0 \\ 0 \\ \cdot \\ \cdot \\ \cdot \\ 0 \end{Bmatrix}+\begin{Bmatrix} 0 \\ x_2 \\ 0 \\ \cdot \\ \cdot \\ \cdot \\ 0 \end{Bmatrix}+\ \ldots\ +\begin{Bmatrix} 0 \\ 0 \\ 0 \\ \cdot \\ \cdot \\ \cdot \\ x_n \end{Bmatrix}=\begin{Bmatrix} x_1 \\ x_2 \\ x_3 \\ \cdot \\ \cdot \\ \cdot \\ x_n \end{Bmatrix}.$$

When we use the definition of equality in V_n and Eq. (2.15), we see that Eq. (2.16) gives

$$\mathbf{y}=x_1\,\mathbf{e}_1+x_2\,\mathbf{e}_2+\ \ldots\ +x_n\,\mathbf{e}_n=\mathbf{x}. \tag{2.17}$$

Since $\mathbf{x}$ was an arbitrary element of V_n, what we have shown is that *any element* $\mathbf{x}$ *of* V_n *can be represented as the sum of the n given elements* $\mathbf{e}_1$, $\mathbf{e}_2, \ldots, \mathbf{e}_n$ *provided each of these elements is multiplied by an appropriate real number. The appropriate real number that multiplies* $\mathbf{e}_i$ *is just the ith real number from the n-tuple of real numbers that specifies* $\mathbf{x}$ [see Eq. (2.15)].

We now define a concept which really brings out the importance of the closure of $(V_n; +, \cdot)$ under the operations of addition and multiplication by real numbers. A collection of elements of V_n that is closed under the operations of addition and multiplication by real numbers is said to constitute a **subspace** of V_n. (We should really say that we have a subspace of $(V_n; +, \cdot)$ since the closure property of the subspace is with respect to the operations $+$ and $\cdot$ of $(V_n; +, \cdot)$. The simpler nomenclature, subspace of V_n, is sufficient for these lectures since we will only use the operations of addition and multiplication by numbers that are defined by Eqs. (2.2) and (2.3).) It might appear that we have only repeated the definition of $(V_n; +, \cdot)$. This is not the case, however. Consider the collection Z consisting of all elements of V_n that can be written in the form

$$\mathbf{z} = \begin{pmatrix} z_1 \\ z_2 \\ 0 \\ 0 \\ \cdot \\ \cdot \\ \cdot \\ 0 \end{pmatrix},$$

where z_1 and z_2 are arbitrary real numbers. Another way of defining Z is to say that Z consists of all elements of V_n whose first two entries are arbitrary real numbers and whose remaining entries are all zero. In order to tell whether Z forms a subspace of V_n, we have to check to see if the collection Z is closed under the operations of addition and multiplication by numbers that have been defined for elements of V_n. If $\mathbf{u}$ and $\mathbf{v}$ are two elements of Z then there are real numbers u_1, u_2, v_1, v_2, such that

$$\mathbf{u} = \begin{pmatrix} u_1 \\ u_2 \\ 0 \\ 0 \\ \cdot \\ \cdot \\ \cdot \\ 0 \end{pmatrix}, \qquad \mathbf{v} = \begin{pmatrix} v_1 \\ v_2 \\ 0 \\ 0 \\ \cdot \\ \cdot \\ \cdot \\ 0 \end{pmatrix}.$$

We therefore have

$$\mathbf{u} + \mathbf{v} = \begin{pmatrix} u_1 + v_1 \\ u_2 + v_2 \\ 0 \\ 0 \\ \cdot \\ \cdot \\ \cdot \\ 0 \end{pmatrix}.$$

Since u_1+v_1 and u_2+v_2 are themselves real numbers, we see that $\mathbf{u}+\mathbf{v}$ belongs to Z whenever $\mathbf{u}$ belongs to Z and $\mathbf{v}$ belongs to Z; that is, the first two entries of $\mathbf{u}+\mathbf{v}$ are real numbers and the remaining entries of $\mathbf{u}+\mathbf{v}$ are all zero. Similarly, if c is any real number, then

$$c\,\mathbf{u}=c\begin{pmatrix} u_1 \\ u_2 \\ 0 \\ 0 \\ \cdot \\ \cdot \\ \cdot \\ 0 \end{pmatrix}=\begin{pmatrix} cu_1 \\ cu_2 \\ 0 \\ 0 \\ \cdot \\ \cdot \\ \cdot \\ 0 \end{pmatrix},$$

and hence Z is closed under multiplication by numbers. Since Z is closed under the operations + and $\cdot$, the collection Z forms a subspace of V_n. The collection Z is not all of V_n by any means, however. For instance, Z does not contain the element $\mathbf{e}_3$ and this element belongs to V_n. It should now be clear that a subspace of V_n can indeed be different from all of V_n.

Perhaps a better way to see what is involved in the definition of a subspace is to see what is not a subspace. In order to do this in the simplest manner, we note that *every subspace contains the vector* $\mathbf{0}$. This follows from the fact that a subspace is closed under multiplication by real numbers and zero is a real number; if $\mathbf{x}$ belongs to a subspace then $0\,\mathbf{x}=\mathbf{0}$ also belongs to that subspace. Let T be the collection of all elements of V_n that have the form

$$\mathbf{u}=\begin{pmatrix} 1 \\ u_2 \\ 0 \\ \cdot \\ \cdot \\ \cdot \\ 0 \end{pmatrix};$$

that is, T consists of all vectors that have one as the first entry, an arbitrary number as the second entry, and the remaining entries are all zero. If T forms a subspace of V_n, then it must be closed under multiplication by real numbers. However, $0\,\mathbf{u}=\mathbf{0}$, and $\mathbf{0}$ does not have one as the first entry. Hence T is not closed under multiplication by real numbers so that it is not a subspace of V_n. Let K denote the collection of all elements of V_3 of the form

$$\mathbf{u}=\begin{pmatrix} u_1 \\ u_2 \\ u_1u_2 \end{pmatrix},$$

where u_1 and u_2 are arbitrary real numbers. K is thus the collection of elements of V_3 whose third entries are the product of the first two entries. If **u** and **v** are elements of K, then

$$\mathbf{u}+\mathbf{v}=\begin{Bmatrix} u_1+v_1 \\ u_2+v_2 \\ u_1u_2+v_1v_2 \end{Bmatrix}.$$

However, the product of the first two entries of $\mathbf{u}+\mathbf{v}$ would be $(u_1+v_1)(u_2+v_2)$, which is different from $u_1u_2+v_1v_2$ for arbitrary real numbers u_1, u_2, v_1, v_2. Thus, the third entry of $\mathbf{u}+\mathbf{v}$ is not equal to the product of the first two entries of $\mathbf{u}+\mathbf{v}$, and hence K is not closed under addition.

Since V_n is closed under addition and multiplication by real numbers, the sum of any two elements of V_n always belongs to V_n and the multiplication of any element of V_n by a real number belongs to V_n. Thus, the sum of any two elements of the collection K always belongs to V_3, it is just that it does not belong to K. Stated another way, if a collection of elements of V_n does not form a subspace, we can get outside of the collection by addition of elements or by multiplication by real numbers, or both. We will, however, never get outside of V_n by performing these operations.

As you might guess, the notion of a subspace is important when we come to solving problems associated with systems of linear equations. In fact, we shall show in the next lecture that the collection of all elements of V_n whose entries satisfy a system of linear homogeneous equations will always form a subspace of V_n. The time spent in mastering the concept of a subspace is thus time well spent if you want to fully understand what you are doing when you solve problems in linear algebra.

Another way of seeing how closure enters into the definition of a subspace is by using the closure requirement itself to specify a subspace. Suppose that we are given a finite number of elements of V_n, say $\mathbf{a}_1, \mathbf{a}_2, \mathbf{a}_3, \ldots, \mathbf{a}_p$. By a **linear combination** of these given vectors, we mean a vector of the form

$$\mathbf{u}=c_1\,\mathbf{a}_1+c_2\,\mathbf{a}_2+\ \ldots\ +c_p\,\mathbf{a}_p, \tag{2.18}$$

where $c_1, c_2, c_3, \ldots, c_p$ are real numbers. If we define A to be the collection of *all* linear combinations of $\mathbf{a}_1, \mathbf{a}_2, \mathbf{a}_3, \ldots, \mathbf{a}_p$, then A forms a subspace of V_n. This conclusion follows by noting that any multiplication of Eq. (2.18) by a real number gives a new vector that is again a linear combination of $\mathbf{a}_1, \ldots, \mathbf{a}_p$ and that the sum of two linear combinations of $\mathbf{a}_1, \ldots, \mathbf{a}_p$ is again a linear combination of $\mathbf{a}_1, \ldots, \mathbf{a}_p$. That is, A is closed under addition and multiplication by real numbers so it forms a subspace of V_n. A subspace of V_n that is generated in this way is said to be **spanned** by the vectors $\mathbf{a}_1, \ldots, \mathbf{a}_p$ that are used to construct the linear combinations. A set of vectors which spans a given subspace is called a

spanning set of the subspace. For instance, the subspace Z whose elements are of the form,

$$\mathbf{z}=\begin{Bmatrix} z_1 \\ z_2 \\ 0 \\ \cdot \\ \cdot \\ \cdot \\ 0 \end{Bmatrix},$$

is spanned by the pair of vectors $\mathbf{e}_1$, $\mathbf{e}_2$; that is,

$$\mathbf{z}=z_1\,\mathbf{e}_1+z_2\,\mathbf{e}_2.$$

The set of vectors that spans a subspace is not unique unless the subspace consists of the single vector **0**. We can not therefore speak of *the* spanning set of a subspace, we have to say *a* spanning set of a subspace. For instance, another spanning set for the subspace Z of V_n is given by

$$\begin{Bmatrix} 1 \\ 1 \\ 0 \\ 0 \\ \cdot \\ \cdot \\ \cdot \\ 0 \end{Bmatrix}, \begin{Bmatrix} 1 \\ -1 \\ 0 \\ 0 \\ \cdot \\ \cdot \\ \cdot \\ 0 \end{Bmatrix}, \text{ that is } \begin{Bmatrix} z_1 \\ z_2 \\ 0 \\ 0 \\ \cdot \\ \cdot \\ \cdot \\ 0 \end{Bmatrix} = \left(\frac{z_1+z_2}{2}\right)\begin{Bmatrix} 1 \\ 1 \\ 0 \\ 0 \\ \cdot \\ \cdot \\ \cdot \\ 0 \end{Bmatrix} + \left(\frac{z_1-z_2}{2}\right)\begin{Bmatrix} 1 \\ -1 \\ 0 \\ 0 \\ \cdot \\ \cdot \\ \cdot \\ 0 \end{Bmatrix}.$$

The subspace Z is also spanned by the vectors

$$\begin{Bmatrix} 1 \\ 1 \\ 0 \\ 0 \\ \cdot \\ \cdot \\ \cdot \\ 0 \end{Bmatrix}, \begin{Bmatrix} 1 \\ -1 \\ 0 \\ 0 \\ \cdot \\ \cdot \\ \cdot \\ 0 \end{Bmatrix}, \begin{Bmatrix} 3 \\ 5 \\ 0 \\ 0 \\ \cdot \\ \cdot \\ \cdot \\ 0 \end{Bmatrix}, \begin{Bmatrix} \pi \\ 8 \\ 0 \\ 0 \\ \cdot \\ \cdot \\ \cdot \\ 0 \end{Bmatrix}, \begin{Bmatrix} -6 \\ -2\pi \\ 0 \\ 0 \\ \cdot \\ \cdot \\ \cdot \\ 0 \end{Bmatrix}.$$

The last spanning set for Z given above is obviously redundant since Z is also spanned by just the first two vectors. A spanning set for a subspace may be highly redundant, as in the last example. Such redundancy is obviously very inefficient and hence we shall look for a simple and efficient algorithm that will eliminate all redundancy in a spanning set. Elimination of such (hidden) redundancies lies at the heart of linear algebra and is the motivation for the study of much of the algebraic structure that will be developed in this series of lectures.

Let B be the subspace of V_3 that is spanned by the two vectors

$$\begin{Bmatrix}1\\1\\0\end{Bmatrix}, \quad \begin{Bmatrix}-1\\2\\0\end{Bmatrix}.$$

We then know that B consists of all linear combinations of these two vectors. It is then natural to ask a question such as the following: does the vector $\begin{Bmatrix}2\\5\\0\end{Bmatrix}$ belong to B? From the definition of a spanning set, the vector $\begin{Bmatrix}2\\5\\0\end{Bmatrix}$ will belong to B if and only if there exist two real numbers c_1 and c_2 such that

$$\begin{Bmatrix}2\\5\\0\end{Bmatrix}=c_1\begin{Bmatrix}1\\1\\0\end{Bmatrix}+c_2\begin{Bmatrix}-1\\2\\0\end{Bmatrix}=\begin{Bmatrix}c_1-c_2\\c_1+2c_2\\0\end{Bmatrix},$$

since any element of B is a linear combination of the vectors that span B. The definition of equality in V_3 then gives the requirements

$$2=c_1-c_2, \qquad 5=c_1+2c_2.$$

In other words, in order to decide whether a given vector belongs to a subspace that is spanned by a given collection of vectors, we have to solve a system of simultaneous linear algebraic equations. Whether this can or can not be done tells us when the given vector does or does not belong to the subspace spanned by the given collection of vectors. Thus, in order to answer such a simple question about whether a vector belongs to a subspace or not, we are again led to the problem of solving systems of linear algebraic equations. The study of methods of solving systems of linear equations is thus demanded by the theory that underlies the subject as well as by the need for methods to solve given problems. In the problem under study here, the answer is that we can indeed solve the two equations: $c_1=3$, $c_2=1$; that is

$$\begin{Bmatrix}2\\5\\0\end{Bmatrix}=3\begin{Bmatrix}1\\1\\0\end{Bmatrix}+\begin{Bmatrix}-1\\2\\0\end{Bmatrix}.$$

A geometric interpretation of algebraic concepts is often useful in fixing these concepts and in showing their interrelations in a visual context. Since our aim is to provide such a visual context, we shall restrict the interpreta-

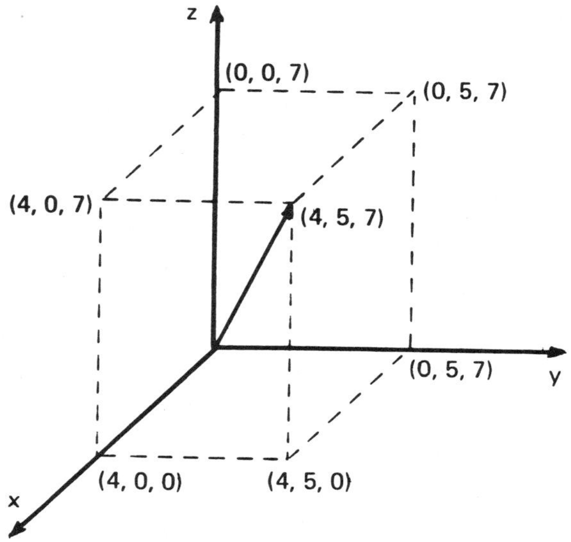

Figure 2.1

tions to two and three dimensions. The extension to four and higher dimensions is then straightforward by a systematic use of analytic geometry.

Let E_2 and E_3 denote the usual 2-dimensional and 3-dimensional number spaces referred to a given Cartesian coordinate system. A point P in E_3 is labeled by the three real numbers (p_1, p_2, p_3) which are the coordinates of the point P with respect to the given Cartesian coordinate system (i.e., as in ordinary analytic geometry with $x=p_1$, $y=p_2$ and $z=p_3$). *An element* **a** *of* V_3 *is identified with a directed line segment in* E_3 *("fixed vector") that starts at the origin* (0, 0, 0) *and ends at the point with coordinates* (a_1, a_2, a_3). Figure 2.1 shows this identification. Please note very carefully that the directed line segment in E_3 that represents an element of V_3 always starts at the origin and no place else. This is very important. It is often the case in physics that a "vector" is just plopped down anywhere in E_3. Such a "vector" has nothing whatever to do with elements of V_3. A plopped down vector (free vector) requires six numbers to describe it; that is, three numbers for the point where it starts and three numbers for the point where it ends. It is not until you bring in the notion of "parallel vectors" and use this notion to construct equivalence classes that these equivalence classes can be identified with elements of V_3. The simple fact of the matter is that V_3, and every subspace of V_3, is closed under addition and multiplication by numbers, and hence the zero vector of V_3 (the origin in E_3) belongs to V_3

and to every subspace of V_3. If the directed line segment in E_3 that represents an element of V_3 didn't start at the origin, then this important property of closure in V_n would not carry over to arrows in E_3. In prosaic terms, we can think of V_3 as the "porcupine" of all arrows in E_3 that start at the origin.

Equality of two elements **a** and **b** of V_3 corresponds to the fact that the fixed vectors that represent **a** and **b** in E_3 lie exactly one on top of the other.

The sum of two elements **a** and **b** of V_3, that is,

$$\begin{Bmatrix} a_1+b_1 \\ a_2+b_2 \\ a_3+b_3 \end{Bmatrix},$$

corresponds to the fixed vector in E_3 that starts at the origin and stops at the point with coordinates $(a_1+b_1,\ a_2+b_2,\ a_3+b_3)$. Thus, the sum of two fixed vectors in E_3 is obtained by the "parallelogram law": construct the parallelogram in E_3 with adjacent sides **a** and **b**, then the diagonal of the parallelogram is $\mathbf{a}+\mathbf{b}$. Figures 2.2 and 2.3 show the operation of addition in E_2 and in E_3. The sum of two fixed vectors always lies in the plane that is defined by the two fixed vectors.

The multiplication of an element **b** of V_3 by a number c is represented in E_3 by a fixed vector that starts at the origin and ends at $(cb_1,\ cb_2,\ cb_3)$. This is shown in Fig. 2.4. Thus, every multiple $c\mathbf{b}$ of a vector **b** in V_3 corresponds to a fixed vector in E_3 that lies on the same line through the origin as the given fixed vector **b** and its direction is the same or opposite to the direction of **b** accordingly as c is positive or negative. The vectors **b** and c**b** are said to be **parallel vectors**.

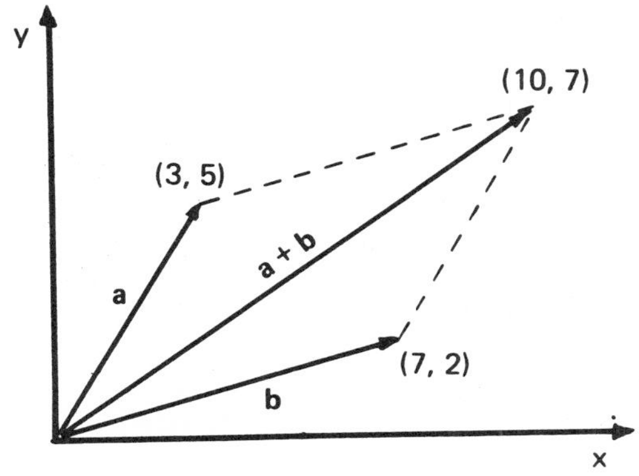

Figure 2.2

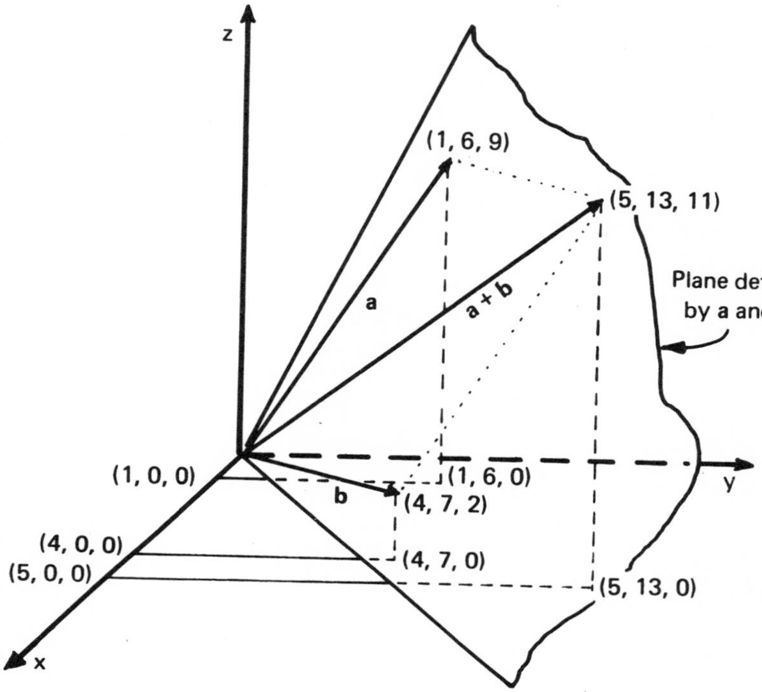

Figure 2.3

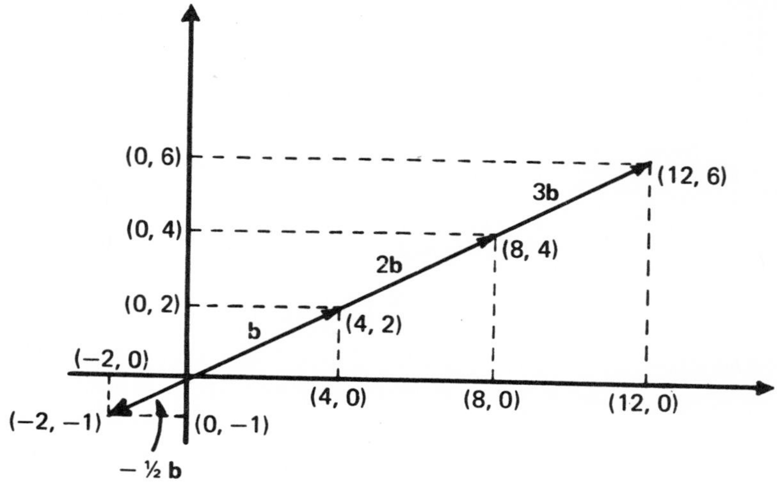

Figure 2.4

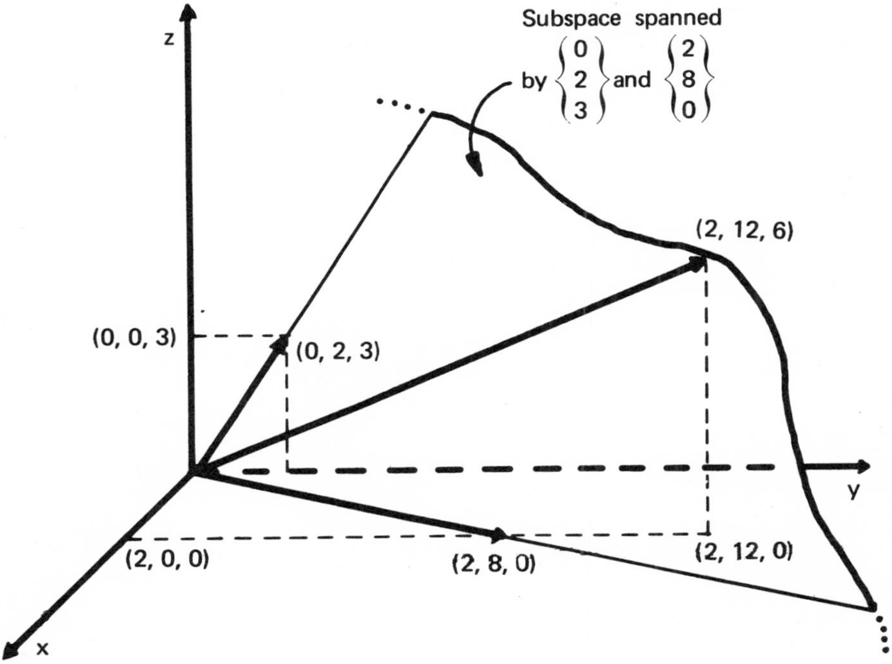

Figure 2.5

Since a subspace of V_3 is closed under addition and multiplication by numbers, a subspace of V_3 corresponds to all arrows in E_3 that end at one of the following places: (1) the origin itself, (2) a line through the origin, (3) a plane through the origin, (4) all of E_3. Figure 2.5 shows the picture of the subspace that is spanned by $\begin{Bmatrix} 0 \\ 2 \\ 3 \end{Bmatrix}$ and $\begin{Bmatrix} 2 \\ 8 \\ 0 \end{Bmatrix}$. This subspace is also spanned by $\begin{Bmatrix} 0 \\ 2 \\ 3 \end{Bmatrix}$ and $\begin{Bmatrix} 2 \\ 12 \\ 6 \end{Bmatrix}$. It is also seen to be generated by the sum of the subspaces spanned by $\begin{Bmatrix} 0 \\ 2 \\ 3 \end{Bmatrix}$ and $\begin{Bmatrix} 2 \\ 8 \\ 0 \end{Bmatrix}$.

What should be apparent to the student at this point is that the algebra of the porcupine of all arrows in E_3 that emanate from the origin is in a one-to-one correspondence with $(V_3; +, \cdot)$.

Problems

2.1. Let

$$\mathbf{z} \equiv \begin{Bmatrix} z_1 \\ \cdot \\ \cdot \\ \cdot \\ z_n \end{Bmatrix}, \quad \mathbf{w} \equiv \begin{Bmatrix} w_1 \\ \cdot \\ \cdot \\ \cdot \\ w_n \end{Bmatrix},$$

be ordered n-tuples of complex numbers. We define the + and · operation in the same way as for real n-tuples, that is

$$\mathbf{z} + \mathbf{w} = \begin{Bmatrix} z_1 \\ \cdot \\ \cdot \\ \cdot \\ z_n \end{Bmatrix} + \begin{Bmatrix} w_1 \\ \cdot \\ \cdot \\ \cdot \\ w_n \end{Bmatrix} = \begin{Bmatrix} z_1 + w_1 \\ \cdot \\ \cdot \\ \cdot \\ z_n + w_n \end{Bmatrix}, \quad \alpha\mathbf{z} = \begin{Bmatrix} \alpha z_1 \\ \cdot \\ \cdot \\ \cdot \\ \alpha z_n \end{Bmatrix},$$

where α is a complex number. Prove that:

(i) If the + and · operation are defined as above, the formulae (2.4) through (2.13) (where **x**, **y**, **z** will denote complex n-tuples and a, b complex numbers) are valid for the set C_n of all ordered n-tuples of complex numbers.

Because of the above property (C_n; +, ·) is a **vector space over the complex numbers** and its elements are **complex vectors.** A subset of (C_n; +, ·) which is closed under the same operations is a **subspace** of C_n. A **linear combination** of the elements $\mathbf{z}_1, \ldots, \mathbf{z}_p$ of C_n is the vector

$$\mathbf{z} = a_1\mathbf{z}_1 + \ldots + a_n\mathbf{z}_n,$$

where $a_1, \ldots, a_n$ are complex numbers. If each element of a subset C of C_n is a linear combination of $\mathbf{z}_1, \ldots, \mathbf{z}_p$ then $\mathbf{z}_1, \ldots, \mathbf{z}_p$ is a **spanning set** of C. The **conjugate** of a complex vector **z** is the complex vector $\overline{\mathbf{z}} = \begin{Bmatrix} \overline{z}_1 \\ \cdot \\ \cdot \\ \cdot \\ \overline{z}_n \end{Bmatrix}$.

Prove that:

(ii) $\mathbf{z} + \overline{\mathbf{z}}$ is a vector with real entries

(iii) $\mathbf{z} - \overline{\mathbf{z}} = i\mathbf{a}$ where **a** is a vector with real entries.

2.2. Obtain $\mathbf{x} + 2\mathbf{y}$, $3\mathbf{x} - \mathbf{y}$ and $\mathbf{x} - i\mathbf{y}$ when **x** and **y** are given, respectively, by

(a) $\begin{Bmatrix} 0 \\ 1 \\ 2 \\ 3 \end{Bmatrix}, \begin{Bmatrix} 1 \\ 2 \\ 3 \\ 4 \end{Bmatrix}$; (b) $\begin{Bmatrix} 1 \\ 3 \\ 0 \\ 1 \end{Bmatrix}, \begin{Bmatrix} 10 \\ -3 \\ 2 \\ -4 \end{Bmatrix}$; (c) $\begin{Bmatrix} -5 \\ 2 \\ 1 \\ 3 \end{Bmatrix}, \begin{Bmatrix} 5i \\ 1+i \\ -3 \\ 1-i \end{Bmatrix}$;

(d) $\begin{Bmatrix} 1+2i \\ -1 \\ -i \\ 5 \end{Bmatrix}, \begin{Bmatrix} 2 \\ -i \\ 3 \\ 4 \end{Bmatrix}$; (e) $\begin{Bmatrix} -2 \\ 4 \\ 6 \\ -5 \end{Bmatrix}, \begin{Bmatrix} 5 \\ -6 \\ 4 \\ 0 \end{Bmatrix}$; (f) $\begin{Bmatrix} 1 \\ 0 \\ 2 \\ 1 \end{Bmatrix}, \begin{Bmatrix} -5 \\ 4 \\ 3 \\ -2 \end{Bmatrix}$.

2.3. Calculate $\mathbf{x}$ such that $\mathbf{y} + 2\mathbf{x} = \mathbf{z}$ when $\mathbf{y}$ and $\mathbf{z}$ are given, respectively, by

$$\text{(a)} \begin{Bmatrix}1\\2\end{Bmatrix},\begin{Bmatrix}3\\-4\end{Bmatrix};\quad \text{(b)} \begin{Bmatrix}-7\\18\end{Bmatrix},\begin{Bmatrix}3\\15\end{Bmatrix};\quad \text{(c)} \begin{Bmatrix}6\\13\end{Bmatrix},\begin{Bmatrix}0\\12\end{Bmatrix};$$

$$\text{(d)} \begin{Bmatrix}1\\2\\3\end{Bmatrix},\begin{Bmatrix}0\\0\\4\end{Bmatrix};\quad \text{(e)} \begin{Bmatrix}3\\-5\\7\end{Bmatrix},\begin{Bmatrix}8\\-13\\6\end{Bmatrix};\quad \text{(f)} \begin{Bmatrix}1\\6\\13\end{Bmatrix},\begin{Bmatrix}7\\-6\\14\end{Bmatrix}.$$

2.4. Determine whether the vector $\mathbf{b}$ belongs to the subspace of V_3 spanned by the vectors $\mathbf{a}_1$, $\mathbf{a}_2$ when $\mathbf{a}_1$, $\mathbf{a}_2$, and $\mathbf{b}$ are given, respectively, by

$$\text{(a)} \begin{Bmatrix}1\\2\\-3\end{Bmatrix},\begin{Bmatrix}0\\3\\0\end{Bmatrix},\begin{Bmatrix}4\\-1\\-6\end{Bmatrix};\quad \text{(b)} \begin{Bmatrix}0\\-3\\-4\end{Bmatrix},\begin{Bmatrix}5\\13\\7\end{Bmatrix},\begin{Bmatrix}5\\4\\5\end{Bmatrix};\quad \text{(c)} \begin{Bmatrix}-7\\10\\0\end{Bmatrix},\begin{Bmatrix}0\\13\\5\end{Bmatrix},\begin{Bmatrix}-7\\23\\5\end{Bmatrix};$$

$$\text{(d)} \begin{Bmatrix}3\\7\\-8\end{Bmatrix},\begin{Bmatrix}11\\-18\\6\end{Bmatrix},\begin{Bmatrix}-5\\31\\-24\end{Bmatrix};\quad \text{(e)} \begin{Bmatrix}7\\-8\\13\end{Bmatrix},\begin{Bmatrix}3\\17\\5\end{Bmatrix},\begin{Bmatrix}-11\\33\\-21\end{Bmatrix},$$

$$\text{(f)} \begin{Bmatrix}i\\2\\1+i\end{Bmatrix},\begin{Bmatrix}5\\3i\\7\end{Bmatrix},\begin{Bmatrix}9\\8i\\13+i\end{Bmatrix}.$$

2.5. If $\mathbf{z} \in C_n$ then $\mathbf{z} = \mathbf{a} + i\mathbf{b}$ where $\mathbf{a}$ and $\mathbf{b}$ are vectors with real entries.

2.6. If a, b, c are given and z_1, z_2 are arbitrary (not necessarily real) numbers, prove that the set of all vectors $\mathbf{z}$ forms a subspace, and give a spanning set for this subspace, when $\mathbf{z}$ is

$$\text{(a)} \begin{Bmatrix}z_1\\z_2\\z_1+az_2\end{Bmatrix},\quad \text{(b)} \begin{Bmatrix}z_1+z_2\\z_1-z_2\\0\end{Bmatrix},\quad \text{(c)} \begin{Bmatrix}az_1-bz_2\\0\\cz_2\end{Bmatrix}.$$

2.7. If $z_1, \ldots, z_n$ are such that

$$a_{11}z_1 + \ldots + a_{1n}z_n = 0$$
$$\ldots \quad \ldots \quad \ldots \quad .$$
$$a_{p1}z_1 + \ldots + a_{pn}z_n = 0$$

where $a_{11}, \ldots, a_{pn}$ are constants, show that the set of all vectors $\begin{Bmatrix}z_1\\ \cdot\\ \cdot\\ \cdot\\ z_n\end{Bmatrix}$ forms a subspace.

2.8. If z_1 and z_2 are arbitrary numbers, determine the constant a so that the set of all vectors $\mathbf{z}$ is a subspace, and give a spanning set for this subspace, when $\mathbf{z}$ is

$$\text{(a)} \begin{Bmatrix}a\\z_1\\z_2\\z_1+z_2\end{Bmatrix},\quad \text{(b)} \begin{Bmatrix}z_1\\z_1-z_2\\z_1+z_2\\az_1z_2\end{Bmatrix},\quad \text{(c)} \begin{Bmatrix}az_1^2+2z_2\\bz_2\\c(z_1-z_2)\\d(z_1+z_2)\end{Bmatrix}.$$

2.9. Let $\mathbf{a}_1, \ldots, \mathbf{a}_p$ and $\mathbf{b}_1, \ldots, \mathbf{b}_q$ span the same subspace. Show that each **a** is a linear combination of the **b**'s and that each **b** is a linear combination of the **a**'s.

2.10. If $\mathbf{b}_1, \ldots, \mathbf{b}_k$ are linear combinations of $\mathbf{a}_1, \ldots, \mathbf{a}_r$ prove that the two sets of vectors $\mathbf{a}_1, \ldots, \mathbf{a}_r$ and $\mathbf{a}_1, \ldots, \mathbf{a}_r, \mathbf{b}_1, \ldots, \mathbf{b}_k$ span the same subspace.

2.11. Let the + and · operations denote the ordinary sum and product, that is $(f+g)(x) = f(x) + g(x)$, $(cf)(x) = cf(x)$. Prove that

(a) The set of all functions $f(x)$ integrable on $a \leqq x \leqq b$ forms a vector space.

(b) The set of all functions $f(x)$ such that the value of $f(x)$ is rational or irrational when x is a rational or irrational number, respectively, does not form a vector space.

2.12. Let the points A and B in E_3 be represented by the vectors **a** and **b** of V_3, respectively. Show that the line segment AB is parallel to the vector $\mathbf{a} - \mathbf{b}$.

2.13. If k is any real number and $\alpha = 2$ or 3, show that

(i) All points $\mathbf{x} = k\mathbf{a} + \mathbf{b}$, where **a** and **b** are given elements of V_α, lie on a straight line (l) in E_α. The line (l) passes through the origin if **b** is parallel to **a** (or $\mathbf{b} = \mathbf{0}$).

(ii) For every line (l) in E_α vectors $\mathbf{a}, \mathbf{b} \in \mathsf{V}_\alpha$ can be determined such that each point of (l) can be represented by the vector $\mathbf{x} = k\mathbf{a} + \mathbf{b}$ for appropriate value of k. If (l) passes through the origin, **b** can be chosen to be $= \mathbf{0}$.

The equation $\mathbf{x} = k\mathbf{a} + \mathbf{b}$ is the **vector equation of the straight line** (l). [Prove the theorem for a line (l) through the origin and then shift the line parallel to itself.]

2.14. Show that the coordinates of the generic point **x** of the line $\mathbf{x} = k\mathbf{a} + \mathbf{b}$ are $x_i = ka_i + b_i$, $i = 1, 2, 3$. These are the **parametric equations of a straight line.**

2.15. Show that the vectors **a** and **b** in problem 2.13 are not uniquely determined when the line (l) is given.

2.16. Show that the line with equation $\mathbf{x} = k\mathbf{a} + \mathbf{b}$ passes through the point **b** and is parallel to the vectors $m\mathbf{a}$ for any real m.

2.17. Let the points A and B be represented by the vectors **a** and **b**, respectively. Show that the vector equation of the line AB is $\mathbf{x} = k(\mathbf{a} - \mathbf{b}) + \mathbf{b}$.

2.18. Give the vector equation of all lines parallel to a given vector **a**.

2.19. Write the vector and parametric equations of the line AB if the points A and B are, respectively,

$$\text{(a)}\ \begin{Bmatrix}0\\0\\0\end{Bmatrix}, \begin{Bmatrix}1\\2\\3\end{Bmatrix}; \quad \text{(b)}\ \begin{Bmatrix}2\\-6\\8\end{Bmatrix}, \begin{Bmatrix}-1\\3\\-4\end{Bmatrix}; \quad \text{(c)}\ \begin{Bmatrix}2\\-3\\4\end{Bmatrix}, \begin{Bmatrix}-2\\3\\-4\end{Bmatrix};$$

$$\text{(d)}\ \begin{Bmatrix}5\\6\\-8\end{Bmatrix}, \begin{Bmatrix}3\\2\\-1\end{Bmatrix}; \quad \text{(e)}\ \begin{Bmatrix}8\\3\\-9\end{Bmatrix}, \begin{Bmatrix}-16\\-6\\18\end{Bmatrix}; \quad \text{(f)}\ \begin{Bmatrix}5\\6\\-3\end{Bmatrix}, \begin{Bmatrix}2\\-1\\7\end{Bmatrix}.$$

Which of the above lines passes through the origin?

2.20. If m, n are real numbers, show that

(i) All points $\mathbf{x} = m\mathbf{a} + n\mathbf{b} + \mathbf{c}$, where $\mathbf{b}$ is not parallel to $\mathbf{a}$ and $\mathbf{a}$, $\mathbf{b}$ and $\mathbf{c}$ are given elements of V_3, lie on a plane (p) in E_3. The plane (p) passes through the origin if $\mathbf{c} = \mathbf{0}$.

(ii) For every plane (p) in E_3 vectors $\mathbf{a}$, $\mathbf{b}$, $\mathbf{c} \in \mathsf{V}_3$ can be determined such that each point of (p) is represented by the vector $\mathbf{x} = m\mathbf{a} + n\mathbf{b} + \mathbf{c}$ for appropriate values of m, n. If (p) passes through the origin, $\mathbf{c}$ can be chosen to be $= \mathbf{0}$.

The equation $\mathbf{x} = m\mathbf{a} + n\mathbf{b} + \mathbf{c}$, where $\mathbf{b}$ is not parallel to $\mathbf{a}$, is the **vector equation of the plane** (p). [Prove the theorem for a plane (p) through the origin and then shift the plane parallel to itself.]

2.21. Show that the vectors $\mathbf{a}$, $\mathbf{b}$, and $\mathbf{c}$ in problem 2.20 are not uniquely determined by the plane (p).

2.22. Show that the plane with equation $\mathbf{x} = m\mathbf{a} + n\mathbf{b} + \mathbf{c}$ passes through the point $\mathbf{c}$ and is parallel to the vectors $\mathbf{a}$, $\mathbf{b}$, and $k(\mathbf{a} - \mathbf{b})$ for any k.

2.23. Let the points A, B, C be represented by the vectors $\mathbf{a}$, $\mathbf{b}$, $\mathbf{c}$, respectively. Show that the vector equation of the plane ABC is

$$\mathbf{x} = m(\mathbf{c} - \mathbf{a}) + n(\mathbf{c} - \mathbf{b}) + \mathbf{c}.$$

2.24. Show that

$$\mathbf{x} = m\mathbf{a} + n\mathbf{b} + p\mathbf{c} + \mathbf{d}, \qquad m + n + p = 0,$$

is the vector equation of a plane through the point $\mathbf{d}$.

2.25. Show that the coordinates of the generic point $\mathbf{x}$ of the plane $\mathbf{x} = m\mathbf{a} + n\mathbf{b} + \mathbf{c}$ are $x_i = ma_i + nb_i + c_i$, $i = 1, 2, 3$. These are the **parametric equations of the plane.**

2.26. Write the vector and parametric equations of the plane ABC if the points A, B, C are given respectively by

$$\text{(a)}\ \begin{Bmatrix}0\\0\\0\end{Bmatrix}, \begin{Bmatrix}1\\-2\\4\end{Bmatrix}, \begin{Bmatrix}3\\-4\\0\end{Bmatrix}; \quad \text{(b)}\ \begin{Bmatrix}0\\0\\0\end{Bmatrix}, \begin{Bmatrix}-3\\6\\-2\end{Bmatrix}, \begin{Bmatrix}6\\-12\\4\end{Bmatrix};$$

$$\text{(c)}\ \begin{Bmatrix}1\\2\\-3\end{Bmatrix}, \begin{Bmatrix}-2\\-4\\6\end{Bmatrix}, \begin{Bmatrix}3\\0\\-5\end{Bmatrix}; \quad \text{(d)}\ \begin{Bmatrix}3\\1\\-2\end{Bmatrix}, \begin{Bmatrix}2\\-1\\3\end{Bmatrix}, \begin{Bmatrix}2\\4\\-10\end{Bmatrix};$$

$$\text{(e)}\ \begin{Bmatrix}3\\6\\8\end{Bmatrix}, \begin{Bmatrix}0\\1\\-1\end{Bmatrix}, \begin{Bmatrix}2\\-1\\3\end{Bmatrix}; \quad \text{(f)}\ \begin{Bmatrix}0\\1\\-1\end{Bmatrix}, \begin{Bmatrix}6\\7\\3\end{Bmatrix}, \begin{Bmatrix}1\\1\\1\end{Bmatrix}.$$

In which cases is the plane ABC not fully determined?

LECTURE 3

Inner Products and Norms of Vectors

The inner product of two elements of V_n • Properties of the inner product • The norm of an element of V_n • Properties of the norm • Unit vectors • Inequalities • The cosine of the angle between two vectors • Orthogonality • Orthogonality and linear homogeneous systems of equations • Subspace properties of solutions to linear homogeneous systems • Geometric interpretations • Problems

The operations of addition and multiplication by real numbers that were introduced in the last lecture in order to obtain the structure $(V_n;\ +,\ \cdot)$ have the property that they always yield elements that belong to V_n. This closure property of the operations $+$ and $\cdot$ is the essential ingredient of the structure $(V_n;\ +,\ \cdot)$. Another useful operation, known as the inner product, combines two elements of V_n in such a way that we obtain a real number rather than an element of V_n. Although this operation does not belong to the underlying structure $(V_n;\ +,\ \cdot)$, it is important for it gives a very natural way of defining subspaces by means of linear equations that the elements of the subspace must satisfy.

The inner product is defined in the following way. If **x** and **y** are any two elements of V_n, that is

$$\mathbf{x}=\begin{Bmatrix} x_1 \\ x_2 \\ \cdot \\ \cdot \\ \cdot \\ x_n \end{Bmatrix}, \qquad \mathbf{y}=\begin{Bmatrix} y_1 \\ y_2 \\ \cdot \\ \cdot \\ \cdot \\ y_n \end{Bmatrix},$$

then the **inner product** of **x** and **y** (denoted by $\mathbf{x}\circ\mathbf{y}$) is defined by

$$\mathbf{x}\circ\mathbf{y}=x_1\,y_1+x_2\,y_2+\ \ldots\ +x_n\,y_n. \tag{3.1}$$

The result of this operation is indeed a real number, for the right-hand side of Eq. (3.1) is just the sum of products of real numbers. We repeat again that the inner product does not belong to the structure $(V_n;\ +,\ \cdot)$ since this operation does not yield an element of V_n when it is used—it yields a single real number that is given by the definition (3.1). As an example of the inner product, if **a** and **b** belong to V_4 with

$$\mathbf{a}=\begin{Bmatrix} 1 \\ 0 \\ 2 \\ -2 \end{Bmatrix}, \quad \mathbf{b}=\begin{Bmatrix} -4 \\ 5 \\ 8 \\ 1 \end{Bmatrix},$$

then Eq. (3.1) gives us

$$\begin{aligned} \mathbf{a}\circ\mathbf{b} &= (1)(-4)+(0)(5)+(2)(8)+(-2)(1) \\ &= -4+0+16-2=10. \end{aligned}$$

As with any new operation, we have to obtain its properties and how it combines with the operations that we have already introduced, namely the operations $+$ and $\cdot$. Since multiplication of real numbers is a commutative operation, the definition (3.1) leads directly to the result

$$\mathbf{x}\circ\mathbf{y}=\mathbf{y}\circ\mathbf{x}. \tag{3.2}$$

Further, if we use Eq. (3.1) to write out the inner product $\mathbf{x}\circ\mathbf{x}$, we have

$$\mathbf{x}\circ\mathbf{x}=x_1x_1+x_2x_2+\ \ldots\ +x_nx_n=\sum_{i=1}^{n}(x_i)^2,$$

and hence

$$\mathbf{x}\circ\mathbf{x}\geq 0, \tag{3.3}$$

since the value of $\mathbf{x}\circ\mathbf{x}$ is the sum of squares of real numbers. This fact leads directly to the property

$$\mathbf{x}\circ\mathbf{x}=0 \quad \text{if and only if} \quad \mathbf{x}=\mathbf{0}. \tag{3.4}$$

When we combine the definition of the inner product with the definitions of the operations $+$ and $\cdot$, we obtain the following results:

$$(a\,\mathbf{x})\circ\mathbf{y}=\mathbf{x}\circ(a\,\mathbf{y}), \tag{3.5}$$

$$(a\,\mathbf{x})\circ\mathbf{y}=a(\mathbf{x}\circ\mathbf{y}), \tag{3.6}$$

$$(\mathbf{x}+\mathbf{y})\circ\mathbf{z}=\mathbf{x}\circ\mathbf{z}+\mathbf{y}\circ\mathbf{z}. \tag{3.7}$$

The verification of these properties is left to the student as an exercise.

The properties (3.3) and (3.4) are of importance, for they allow us to define the **length** or **norm** of an element of V_n. The **norm** of an element **x** of V_n (denoted by $||\mathbf{x}||$) is defined by the relation

$$||\mathbf{x}||=(\mathbf{x}\circ\mathbf{x})^{1/2}. \tag{3.8}$$

When Eq. (3.1) is used, this gives us

$$||\mathbf{x}||=\{(x_1)^2+(x_2)^2+\ \ldots\ +(x_n)^2\}^{1/2}.$$

In V_2 we have

$$||\mathbf{x}|| = \{(x_1)^2 + (x_2)^2\}^{1/2}$$

and in V_3 we have

$$||\mathbf{x}|| = \{(x_1)^2 + (x_2)^2 + (x_3)^2\}^{1/2},$$

which are just statements of the Pythagorean theorem in two and three dimensions. The norm of a vector in V_n is thus just the extension of the Pythagorean theorem to n-dimensions. For example, if

$$\mathbf{a} = \begin{Bmatrix} 1 \\ 0 \\ 2 \\ -2 \end{Bmatrix},$$

then

$$||\mathbf{a}|| = (1^2 + 0^2 + 2^2 + (-2)^2)^{1/2} = 9^{1/2} = 3.$$

We also note that Eqs. (3.3), (3.4) and (3.8) imply

$$||\mathbf{x}|| \geq 0, \tag{3.9}$$

$$||\mathbf{x}|| = 0 \quad \text{if and only if} \quad \mathbf{x} = \mathbf{0}, \tag{3.10}$$

$$||a\,\mathbf{x}|| = |a|\; ||\mathbf{x}||. \tag{3.11}$$

The last result is obtained by noting that the number a^2 will be a common factor in each product that occurs when we apply the definition (3.8) to $a\mathbf{x}$, and this can be taken outside of the square root to give the factor $|a|$.

If $\mathbf{x}$ is an element of V_n such that $||\mathbf{x}|| = 1$, then $\mathbf{x}$ is referred to as a **unit vector**. We can actually construct a unit vector starting with any vector in V_n other than the zero vector, $\mathbf{0}$. If $\mathbf{y}$ is a nonzero element of V_n, then

$$\mathbf{x} = \left(\frac{1}{||\mathbf{y}||}\right)\mathbf{y}$$

is a unit vector. In order to see this, we merely have to compute $||\mathbf{x}||$, and use the properties given by Eqs. (3.9) and (3.11):

$$||\mathbf{x}|| = \left|\left|\left(\frac{1}{||\mathbf{y}||}\right)\mathbf{y}\right|\right| = \left|\frac{1}{||\mathbf{y}||}\right|\; ||\mathbf{y}||$$
$$= \frac{1}{||\mathbf{y}||}\; ||\mathbf{y}|| = 1.$$

The result given by Eq. (3.11) tells us how the norm behaves when it is used in conjunction with the operation of multiplication of an element of V_n by a real number. We will now establish a number of results that obtain when the norm is used in conjunction with the operation of addition in V_n. A straightforward calculation gives us the results

$$||\mathbf{x} \pm \mathbf{y}||^2 = ||\mathbf{x}||^2 \pm 2\mathbf{x}\circ\mathbf{y} + ||\mathbf{y}||^2, \tag{3.12}$$

and hence we obtain

$$||\mathbf{x}+\mathbf{y}||^2 + ||\mathbf{x}-\mathbf{y}||^2 = 2||\mathbf{x}||^2 + 2||\mathbf{y}||^2, \tag{3.13}$$

$$||\mathbf{x}+\mathbf{y}||^2 - ||\mathbf{x}-\mathbf{y}||^2 = 4\mathbf{x}\circ\mathbf{y}. \tag{3.14}$$

The results (3.9) and (3.10) imply that

$$||\mathbf{x}+\mathbf{y}|| \geq 0, \tag{3.15}$$

$$||\mathbf{x}+\mathbf{y}|| = 0 \quad \text{if and only if} \quad \mathbf{x}+\mathbf{y} = \mathbf{0}. \tag{3.16}$$

We shall now establish the two inequalities

$$|\mathbf{x}\circ\mathbf{y}| \leq ||\mathbf{x}|| \quad ||\mathbf{y}|| \qquad \text{(Cauchy-Schwarz inequality)}, \tag{3.17}$$

$$||\mathbf{x}+\mathbf{y}|| \leq ||\mathbf{x}|| + ||\mathbf{y}|| \qquad \text{(triangle inequality)}. \tag{3.18}$$

If either $\mathbf{x} = \mathbf{0}$ or $\mathbf{y} = \mathbf{0}$, then Eqs. (3.17) and (3.18) are obviously true. We thus assume that $\mathbf{x} \neq \mathbf{0}$ and $\mathbf{y} \neq \mathbf{0}$ and start by computing $||\mathbf{x}-\alpha\mathbf{y}||^2$:

$$\begin{aligned} ||\mathbf{x}-\alpha\mathbf{y}||^2 &= (\mathbf{x}-\alpha\mathbf{y})\circ(\mathbf{x}-\alpha\mathbf{y}) \\ &= \mathbf{x}\circ\mathbf{x} - 2\alpha(\mathbf{x}\circ\mathbf{y}) + \alpha^2(\mathbf{y}\circ\mathbf{y}), \end{aligned}$$

where α is an arbitrary real number. When Eqs. (3.8) and (3.15) are used, we then have that

$$0 \leq ||\mathbf{x}||^2 - 2\alpha(\mathbf{x}\circ\mathbf{y}) + \alpha^2||\mathbf{y}||^2$$

must hold for all vectors $\mathbf{x}$ and $\mathbf{y}$ and all real numbers α. Thus, if we take α to be the real number

$$\alpha = \frac{\mathbf{x}\circ\mathbf{y}}{||\mathbf{y}||^2},$$

we then have the requirement that

$$\begin{aligned} 0 &\leq ||\mathbf{x}||^2 - 2\frac{\mathbf{x}\circ\mathbf{y}}{||\mathbf{y}||^2}(\mathbf{x}\circ\mathbf{y}) + \left(\frac{\mathbf{x}\circ\mathbf{y}}{||\mathbf{y}||^2}\right)^2 ||\mathbf{y}||^2 \\ &= ||\mathbf{x}||^2 - \frac{(\mathbf{x}\circ\mathbf{y})^2}{||\mathbf{y}||^2} = ||\mathbf{x}||^2\left(1 - \frac{(\mathbf{x}\circ\mathbf{y})^2}{||\mathbf{x}||^2||\mathbf{y}||^2}\right). \end{aligned}$$

This inequality can be satisfied for all $\mathbf{x}$ and $\mathbf{y}$ different from $\mathbf{0}$ if and only if we have

$$\frac{(\mathbf{x}\circ\mathbf{y})^2}{||\mathbf{x}||^2||\mathbf{y}||^2} \leq 1,$$

which is the same thing as Eq. (3.17). Now,

$$||\mathbf{x}+\mathbf{y}||^2 = ||\mathbf{x}||^2 + 2\mathbf{x}\circ\mathbf{y} + ||\mathbf{y}||^2 \leq ||\mathbf{x}||^2 + 2||\mathbf{x}|| \quad ||\mathbf{y}|| + ||\mathbf{y}||^2,$$

where the inequality $|\mathbf{x}\circ\mathbf{y}| < ||\mathbf{x}|| \quad ||\mathbf{y}||$ has been used. We therefore have $||\mathbf{x}+\mathbf{y}||^2 \leq (||\mathbf{x}|| + ||\mathbf{y}||)^2$ from which we obtain Eq. (3.18).

The inequality (3.17) tells us that

$$-1 \leq \frac{\mathbf{x}\circ\mathbf{y}}{||\mathbf{x}|| \ ||\mathbf{y}||} \leq 1.$$

It is thus consistent to define an angle θ $(0 \leq \theta \leq \pi)$ by the relation

$$\cos\theta = \frac{\mathbf{x}\circ\mathbf{y}}{||\mathbf{x}||\ ||\mathbf{y}||}.$$

When this is used in Eq. (3.12), we then have

$$||\mathbf{x}\pm\mathbf{y}||^2 = ||\mathbf{x}||^2 + ||\mathbf{y}||^2 \pm 2||\mathbf{x}||\ ||\mathbf{y}||\ \cos\theta,$$

namely, the law of cosines. These observations motivate the following definition: the **cosine of the angle between two nonzero vectors x** and **y** is given by

$$\cos\theta = \frac{\mathbf{x}\circ\mathbf{y}}{||\mathbf{x}||\ ||\mathbf{y}||}, \quad ||\mathbf{x}|| \neq 0,\ ||\mathbf{y}|| \neq 0. \tag{3.19}$$

This is not an unfamiliar formula, for it is exactly what is used in V_3 to define the direction cosines of vectors in your course in analytic geometry.

The definition (3.19) gives us the basis for the following statement: two elements **x** and **y** of V_n are **orthogonal** (or perpendicular) if and only if

$$\mathbf{x}\circ\mathbf{y} = 0. \tag{3.20}$$

This definition is more general than suggested by Eq. (3.19), for it allows us to conclude that *the zero vector is orthogonal to every vector.* Suppose that we are given a specific vector **a** and ask for all vectors in V_n that are orthogonal to **a**. The condition for this to be the case is simply

$$0 = \mathbf{a}\circ\mathbf{x} = a_1 x_1 + a_2 x_2 + \ . \ . \ . + a_n x_n; \tag{3.21}$$

that is, the numbers $x_1, \ . \ . \ . \ , x_n$ that define all such **x** must satisfy the homogeneous linear equation (3.21). We can now give one of the reasons for introducing the inner product, for we now prove that the collection of all vectors that are orthogonal to the given vector **a** forms a subspace of V_n. In order to prove this we must show that all solutions of Eq. (3.21) are closed under addition and multiplication by real numbers. If **u** is a solution of Eq. (3.21), that is $\mathbf{a}\circ\mathbf{u} = 0$, then

$$\mathbf{a}\circ(c\,\mathbf{u}) = c(\mathbf{a}\circ\mathbf{u}) = c(0) = 0,$$

for any real number c; the solutions of Eq. (3.21) are closed under multiplication by real numbers. If **u** and **v** are solutions of Eq. (3.21), then

$$\mathbf{a}\circ(\mathbf{u}+\mathbf{v}) = \mathbf{a}\circ\mathbf{u} + \mathbf{a}\circ\mathbf{v} = 0 + 0 = 0,$$

and hence the solutions of (3.21) are closed under addition, and the result is established.

Now, suppose that we are given a collection of p vectors $\mathbf{a}_1, \mathbf{a}_2, \ . \ . \ . \ , \mathbf{a}_p$

and we want all vectors in V_n that are simultaneously orthogonal to each of the given p vectors. We would then wish to solve the equations

$$\begin{aligned} 0 &= \mathbf{a}_1 \circ \mathbf{x} = a_{11} x_1 + a_{12} x_2 + \cdots + a_{1n} x_n, \\ 0 &= \mathbf{a}_2 \circ \mathbf{x} = a_{21} x_1 + a_{22} x_2 + \cdots + a_{2n} x_n, \\ &\ \ \vdots \\ 0 &= \mathbf{a}_p \circ \mathbf{x} = a_{p1} x_1 + a_{p2} x_2 + \cdots + a_{pn} x_n, \end{aligned} \tag{3.22}$$

namely, a system of p linear equations in n unknowns. If we repeat the argument given above for each of these p equations, we see that *the collections of all solutions of a system of homogeneous linear equations in n unknowns is always a subspace of* V_n.

The question that now presents itself is how to find the whole subspace of solutions of a given system of linear homogeneous equations. One way of describing a subspace is by specifying a spanning set for it. We could thus try to obtain a spanning set for the subspace of solutions of the system (3.22), but at this point, we have no systematic method of finding a spanning set starting just with the system (3.22). For instance, we could find a large number of solutions of Eq. (3.22) by trial and error and then hope that they form a spanning set, but we could not be sure of that fact at this point. A systematic procedure is available, however, and it hinges around finding a smallest spanning set for the subspace spanned by the vectors $\mathbf{a}_1, \ldots, \mathbf{a}_p$. This follows from the simple observation that if $\mathbf{x}$ satisfies the system (3.22) then $\mathbf{x}$ is not only orthogonal to each of the given vectors $\mathbf{a}_1, \ldots, \mathbf{a}_p$, it is also orthogonal to the entire subspace that is spanned by the vectors $\mathbf{a}_1, \ldots, \mathbf{a}_p$; that is, Eq. (3.22) implies that $\mathbf{x}$ also satisfies the equation

$$0 = (c_1 \mathbf{a}_1 + c_2 \mathbf{a}_2 + \cdots + c_p \mathbf{a}_p) \circ \mathbf{x},$$

for every collection of real numbers $c_1, \ldots, c_p$. Hence all vectors $\mathbf{x}$ that satisfy Eq. (3.22) are also orthogonal to the smallest collection of vectors that spans the subspace that is spanned by $\mathbf{a}_1, \ldots, \mathbf{a}_p$. Further, if $\mathbf{x}$ is orthogonal to this smallest spanning set then it is also orthogonal to $\mathbf{a}_1, \ldots, \mathbf{a}_p$ because $\mathbf{a}_1, \ldots, \mathbf{a}_p$ belong to the subspace that is spanned by the smaller spanning set.

The search for a smallest spanning set of a subspace is done in the most efficient fashion by use of another algebraic structure known as matrix algebra, which we shall develop in the next lecture.

Problems

3.1. If $\mathbf{z}$ and $\mathbf{w}$ are two complex vectors, their **inner product** is defined by $\mathbf{z} \circ \mathbf{w} = \bar{z}_1 w_1 + \ldots + \bar{z}_n w_n$. The **length** or **norm** of a complex vector $\mathbf{z}$ is the number $||\mathbf{z}|| = (\mathbf{z} \circ \mathbf{z})^{\frac{1}{2}}$. If $\mathbf{z}$ and $\mathbf{w}$ are real, these definitions agree with the definitions given by Eqs. (3.1) and (3.8). Two complex vectors $\mathbf{z}$ and $\mathbf{w}$ are **orthogonal** if and only if $\mathbf{z} \circ \mathbf{w} = 0$.

Calculate $\mathbf{x} \circ \mathbf{y}$, $||\mathbf{x}||$, and $||\mathbf{y}||$ when $\mathbf{x}$ and $\mathbf{y}$ are given respectively by

$$\text{(a)} \begin{Bmatrix} 1 \\ 2 \\ -3 \end{Bmatrix}, \begin{Bmatrix} 0 \\ -3 \\ -2 \end{Bmatrix}; \quad \text{(b)} \begin{Bmatrix} 3 \\ -7 \\ 8 \end{Bmatrix}, \begin{Bmatrix} -1 \\ 1 \\ 0 \end{Bmatrix}; \quad \text{(c)} \begin{Bmatrix} 3 \\ -2 \\ 0 \end{Bmatrix}, \begin{Bmatrix} 0 \\ 2 \\ -4 \end{Bmatrix};$$

$$\text{(d)} \begin{Bmatrix} -1 \\ 2 \\ -1 \end{Bmatrix}, \begin{Bmatrix} 3 \\ 6 \\ 9 \end{Bmatrix}; \quad \text{(e)} \begin{Bmatrix} 1+i \\ 0 \\ 3i \end{Bmatrix}, \begin{Bmatrix} i \\ 2+3i \\ 5 \end{Bmatrix}; \quad \text{(f)} \begin{Bmatrix} 1+2i \\ 0 \\ 6-3i \end{Bmatrix}, \begin{Bmatrix} 3i \\ 3 \\ -1 \end{Bmatrix}.$$

3.2. Find the unit vectors parallel to the vectors in problem 3.1.

3.3. Calculate the cosine of the angle between the two vectors $\mathbf{x}$ and $\mathbf{y}$ in example 3.1, (a) through (d). Which pair(s) of vectors are orthogonal?

3.4. Prove the formulae (3.5) through (3.7).

3.5. Prove that the formulae (3.2), (3.5), and (3.6) do not apply for complex vectors. Give the corresponding valid statements.

3.6. Prove that the formulae (3.3), (3.4), (3.7) through (3.11), (3.17) and (3.18) are valid for complex vectors.

3.7. Prove that the set of all solutions of (3.22) is a subspace of V_n. Is the set of all solutions of

$$\mathbf{a}_1 \circ \mathbf{x} = b_1; \quad \ldots \quad ; \mathbf{a}_p \circ \mathbf{x} = b_p$$

a subspace of V_n?

3.8. Let $\mathbf{y} \in \mathsf{B}$ where B is a subspace spanned by $\mathbf{a}_1, \ldots, \mathbf{a}_p$. If $\mathbf{x}$ is orthogonal to $\mathbf{a}_1, \ldots, \mathbf{a}_p$ then $\mathbf{x}$ is orthogonal to $\mathbf{y}$.

3.9. Show that for any two complex vectors $\mathbf{z}$ and $\mathbf{w}$ of the same order

$$||\mathbf{z} + \mathbf{w}||^2 + ||\mathbf{z} - \mathbf{w}||^2 = 2||\mathbf{z}||^2 + 2||\mathbf{w}||^2.$$

3.10. Let $\mathbf{z}_1, \ldots, \mathbf{z}_n$ be a set of mutually orthogonal complex vectors. Show that

$$||\mathbf{z}_1 + \ldots + \mathbf{z}_n||^2 = ||\mathbf{z}_1||^2 + \ldots + ||\mathbf{z}_n||^2.$$

Give a geometrical interpretation of this equality if $\mathbf{z}_1, \ldots, \mathbf{z}_n$ are real vectors of order 3.

3.11. Let $\mathbf{z}_1, \ldots, \mathbf{z}_p$ be a set of mutually orthogonal unit complex vectors. Show that for any vector $\mathbf{z}$

$$|\mathbf{z} \circ \mathbf{z}_1|^2 + \ldots + |\mathbf{z} \circ \mathbf{z}_p|^2 \leq ||\mathbf{z}||^2$$

where the equality sign is valid if and only if $\mathbf{z}$ is a linear combination of

$\mathbf{z}_1, \ldots, \mathbf{z}_p$. [Consider the length of the vector $\mathbf{k} = \mathbf{z} - (\overline{\mathbf{z} \circ \mathbf{z}_1})\mathbf{z}_1 - \ldots - (\overline{\mathbf{z} \circ \mathbf{z}_p})\mathbf{z}_p$.]

3.12. If $\mathbf{x}, \mathbf{y} \in \mathsf{V}_3$, give a geometrical interpretation to the triangle inequality (3.18).

3.13. If $\mathbf{x}$, $\mathbf{c}$, and $\mathbf{p}$ are elements of V_3, show that

$$(\mathbf{x} - \mathbf{c}) \circ \mathbf{p} = \mathbf{0}, \ \mathbf{p} \neq \mathbf{0},$$

is the vector equation of a plane in E_3 through the point $\mathbf{c}$ perpendicular to the vector $\mathbf{p}$.

3.14. If $x_1p_1 + x_2p_2 + x_3p_3 + k = 0$, $p_1^2 + p_2^2 + p_3^2 \neq 0$, show that the points $\mathbf{x}$ lie in a plane perpendicular to the vector $\mathbf{p}$ and deduce that a linear equation in x_1, x_2, x_3 always represents a plane in E_3.

3.15. If $\mathbf{a}, \mathbf{b} \in \mathsf{V}_3$ show that the vector $\mathbf{v} \in \mathsf{V}_3$ with entries

$$a_2b_3 - a_3b_2, \ a_3b_1 - a_1b_3, \ a_1b_2 - a_2b_1$$

is orthogonal to both $\mathbf{a}$ and $\mathbf{b}$. The vector $\mathbf{v}$ is called the **cross product of the vectors a** and **b** and it will be denoted by $\mathbf{v} = \mathbf{a} \times \mathbf{b}$.

3.16. Let (p) be the plane in E_3 through the point $\mathbf{c}$ parallel to the vectors $\mathbf{a}$ and $\mathbf{b}$. Derive an equation for (p) of the form $(\mathbf{x} - \mathbf{c}) \circ \mathbf{p} = 0$.

3.17. Give the vector and parametric equations of a straight line in E_3 perpendicular to the plane with equation

$$Ax_1 + Bx_2 + Cx_3 + D = 0, \ A^2 + B^2 + C^2 \neq 0.$$

3.18. If $\mathbf{a}, \mathbf{b} \in \mathsf{V}_3$, show that $(\mathbf{a} - \mathbf{b}) \circ (\mathbf{a} - \mathbf{b}) = (\mathbf{a} - \mathbf{b})^2$ represents in E_3 the square of the distance of the point $\mathbf{a}$ from the point $\mathbf{b}$.

3.19. Derive the equation $(x_1 - a_1)^2 + (x_2 - a_2)^2 + (x_3 - a_3)^2 = r^2$ of a sphere in E_3 with center at the point $\mathbf{a}$ and radius r.

LECTURE 4

Matrices

m-by-*n* matrices • Notation for matrices • Row matrices, column matrices • Equality of matrices • Addition of matrices • Properties of addition • Multiplication of matrices by real numbers • Properties of multiplication by real numbers • Isomorphism of $(\mathsf{V}_n; +, \cdot)$ and $(\mathsf{M}_{n,1}; +, \cdot)$ • Matrix multiplication • Representation of linear inhomogeneous systems of equations by means of matrices • The order of the factors in a matrix product • Commutivity and noncommutivity of matrix multiplication • Properties of matrix multiplication • The identity matrix • Diagonal matrices • Scalar matrices • The transpose of a matrix • The relation between matrix multiplication and the inner product of V_n • Properties of the transpose • Problems

We now introduce a new algebraic structure that will significantly simplify and systematize calculations that deal with systems of linear equations with many unknowns. This algebraic structure is known as **matrix algebra**. The basic reason why a new algebraic structure is needed is because the scalar product, $\circ$, that is used in constructing systems of linear equations in the form

$$\mathbf{a}_i \circ \mathbf{x} = b_i, \quad i = 1, \ . \ . \ . \ , m,$$

does not belong to $(\mathsf{V}_n; +, \cdot)$. Thus, we can not solve such linear systems using only the operations $+$ and $\cdot$ that belong to $(\mathsf{V}_n; +, \cdot)$. A larger structure which contains the additional operations that we need in order to solve linear systems of equations is thus required.

A **matrix** is a rectangular array of real numbers. The real numbers that comprise a matrix are called the **entries** of the matrix. In general, we write a matrix **A**, with m rows n columns and entries a_{ij}, in the form

$$\mathbf{A} = \begin{pmatrix} a_{11} & a_{12} & a_{13} & . \ . \ . & a_{1n} \\ a_{21} & a_{22} & a_{23} & . \ . \ . & a_{2n} \\ \cdot & \cdot & \cdot & & \cdot \\ \cdot & \cdot & \cdot & & \cdot \\ \cdot & \cdot & \cdot & & \cdot \\ a_{m1} & a_{m2} & a_{m3} & . \ . \ . & a_{mn} \end{pmatrix} = (a_{ij}).$$

Such a matrix **A** is called an m-by-n matrix. This same notation will be used throughout these lectures: $\mathbf{B}=(b_{ij})$, $\mathbf{C}=(c_{ij})$, and so forth. This notation is interpreted as follows. If we write $\mathbf{A}=(a_{ij})$ then we will mean the entire array of real numbers that is the matrix **A**. If we write a_{ij} then we will mean the entry of the matrix **A** that is found in the ith row and the jth column of the array that comprises **A**. Thus, it is natural to refer to the array

$$[a_{i1}\ a_{i2}\ a_{i3}\ \ . \ . \ . \ \ a_{in}]$$

as the *ith row* of the matrix **A** and to refer to the array

$$\begin{Bmatrix} a_{1j} \\ a_{2j} \\ \cdot \\ \cdot \\ \cdot \\ a_{mj} \end{Bmatrix}$$

as the *jth column* of the matrix **A**. If $m=n$, that is, there are as many rows of **A** as there are columns of **A**, then we say that **A** is a **square** matrix. A matrix with only one row is called a **row matrix** and a matrix with only one column is called a **column matrix**.

The notation introduced above for column matrices is reminiscent of the notation we have used for a vector. This is not by accident, for we shall see that vectors can be identified with column matrices. In order to make this identification, however, we have to introduce the operations that define the algebra of matrices and then compare this algebra with that which we already have for the structure $(\mathsf{V}_n;\ +,\ \cdot)$.

It is convenient to have a label for all m-by-n matrices, just as it was convenient to have the symbol V_n for all ordered n-tuples of real numbers. We therefore define $\mathsf{M}_{m,n}$ to be the collection of *all* m-by-n matrices. Thus, if we write $\mathbf{A}\in\mathsf{M}_{m,n}$ (which is to be read as "**A** belongs to the collection $\mathsf{M}_{m,n}$"), then **A** is an m-by-n matrix.

The first thing we have to do in constructing the matrix algebra is to say what we mean by the equality of two matrices. Let $\mathbf{A}\in\mathsf{M}_{m,n}$ and $\mathbf{B}\in\mathsf{M}_{p,q}$. The matrix **A** is **equal** to the matrix **B** if and only if

$$m=p,\ \ n=q, \tag{4.1}$$

and

$$a_{ij}=b_{ij},\ \ i=1,\ .\ .\ .\ ,\ m,\ \ j=1,\ .\ .\ .\ ,\ n, \tag{4.2}$$

in which case we write

$$\mathbf{A}=\mathbf{B}. \tag{4.3}$$

Thus, two matrices are equal if and only if they have the same number of rows, the same number of columns, and each entry of **A** is equal to the corresponding entry of **B**. Since there are mn entries in a matrix $\mathbf{A} \in \mathsf{M}_{m,n}$, the matrix equality (4.3) stands for mn equalities of real numbers.

We now have to define the basic operations that comprise the structure of matrix algebra. The first of these operations is matrix addition.

Let $\mathbf{A} \in \mathsf{M}_{m,n}$ and $\mathbf{B} \in \mathsf{M}_{p,q}$. The **sum** of **A** and **B** is defined if and only if $m=p$ and $n=q$. If these conditions are satisfied, then the matrix **C** with entries

$$c_{ij}=a_{ij}+b_{ij}, \quad i=1, \ldots, m, \; j=1, \ldots, n, \tag{4.4}$$

defines an element of $\mathsf{M}_{m,n}$, called the **sum** of **A** and **B**, and we write

$$\mathbf{C}=\mathbf{A}+\mathbf{B}. \tag{4.5}$$

We repeat, the sum of two matrices is only defined when both matrices belong to the same $\mathsf{M}_{m,n}$. Matrix addition of two matrices belonging to $\mathsf{M}_{m,n}$ is thus the same thing as mn additions of real numbers, as is stated by Eqs. (4.4). We can thus establish the following properties of matrix addition in exactly the same way as they were established for addition of two elements of V_n:

(1) $\mathsf{M}_{m,n}$ is *closed* under addition.

(2) Addition is commutative: $\mathbf{A}+\mathbf{B}=\mathbf{B}+\mathbf{A}$.

(3) Addition is associative: $\mathbf{A}+(\mathbf{B}+\mathbf{C})=(\mathbf{A}+\mathbf{B})+\mathbf{C}$.

(4) There exists an m-by-n matrix $\mathbf{0} \in \mathsf{M}_{m,n}$ such that $\mathbf{A}+\mathbf{0}=\mathbf{A}$. The matrix $\mathbf{0}$ has all of its entries equal to zero.

(5) For every $\mathbf{A} \in \mathsf{M}_{m,n}$, there exists a unique matrix denoted by $(-\mathbf{A})$ such that $\mathbf{A}+(-\mathbf{A})=\mathbf{0}$. If $\mathbf{A}=(a_{ij})$, then $(-\mathbf{A})=(-a_{ij})$.

The next thing we do is to define multiplication by real numbers. If $\mathbf{A} \in \mathsf{M}_{m,n}$ and if c is any real number, then the matrix $\mathbf{B} \in \mathsf{M}_{m,n}$ with entries

$$b_{ij}=c\,a_{ij}, \quad i=1, \ldots, m, \; j=1, \ldots, n, \tag{4.6}$$

is defined to be the matrix that results from **multiplication of A by the real number** c. This operation is denoted by

$$\mathbf{B}=c\,\mathbf{A}, \tag{4.7}$$

and signifies that we have multiplied each of the mn entries of the matrix **A** by the real number c in obtaining the matrix **B**. The properties of multiplication of real numbers can then be used to establish the following properties of the operation $\cdot$ [$\cdot$ denotes the operation of multiplication of a matrix by a real number].

(1) $\mathsf{M}_{m,n}$ is *closed* under multiplication by real numbers.

(2) $c(\mathbf{A}+\mathbf{B})=c\,\mathbf{A}+c\,\mathbf{B}$.

(3) $(a+b)\mathbf{A}=a\,\mathbf{A}+b\,\mathbf{A}$.
(4) $(ab)\mathbf{A}=a(b\,\mathbf{A})$.
(5) $1\,\mathbf{A}=\mathbf{A}$, $0\,\mathbf{A}=\mathbf{0}$.

For each given pair of numbers m and n, we therefore have the structure $(\mathsf{M}_{m,n};\ +,\ \cdot)$. This structure is closed under the operations $+$ and $\cdot$ and the operations have the properties that we have listed above. If we look at the structure $(\mathsf{M}_{n,1};\ +,\ \cdot)$ we are dealing with the structure of all column matrices with n entries. Each such column matrix can also be considered as an element of V_n since V_n is the collection of all n-tuples of real numbers and we have chosen to represent this ordered collection of n real numbers as a column (recall the notation from lecture 2). Now, the operations of $+$ and $\cdot$ when applied to elements of $\mathsf{M}_{n,1}$ are exactly the same as the operations of $+$ and $\cdot$ that we defined in lecture 2 for V_n. Thus, not only does an element of $\mathsf{M}_{n,1}$ look the same as an element of V_n, but also the operations $+$ and $\cdot$ of $(\mathsf{M}_{n,1};\ +,\ \cdot)$ are exactly the same as the operations $+$ and $\cdot$ of $(\mathsf{V}_n;\ +,\ \cdot)$. Stated another way, each element

$$\mathbf{A}=\begin{Bmatrix} a_{11} \\ a_{21} \\ \cdot \\ \cdot \\ \cdot \\ a_{n1} \end{Bmatrix}$$

belonging to $\mathsf{M}_{n,1}$ can be placed in a one-to-one correspondence with an element

$$\mathbf{a}=\begin{Bmatrix} a_{1} \\ a_{2} \\ \cdot \\ \cdot \\ \cdot \\ a_{n} \end{Bmatrix}$$

belonging to V_n by defining the n numbers a_i by the relations

$$a_1=a_{11},\quad a_2=a_{21},\quad \ldots,\quad a_n=a_{n1}.$$

We denote this correspondence by $\mathbf{A}\equiv\mathbf{a}$. Since the operations $+$ and $\cdot$ of $(\mathsf{M}_{n,1};\ +,\ \cdot)$ are identical with the operations $+$ and $\cdot$ of $(\mathsf{V}_n;\ +,\ \cdot)$ when this one-to-one correspondence of $\mathsf{M}_{n,1}$ and V_n is made, we say that the structures $(\mathsf{M}_{n,1};\ +,\ \cdot)$ and $(\mathsf{V}_n;\ +,\ \cdot)$ are **isomorphic** structures. Loosely speaking, structures are isomorphic if and only if their entries can be placed in a one-to-one correspondence and this correspondence also makes the operations of the two structures the same. There is thus nothing that is in any way different between $(\mathsf{M}_{n,1};\ +,\ \cdot)$ and $(\mathsf{V}_n;\ +,\ \cdot)$. [In fact, the student who really understands what we have been doing will realize that $(\mathsf{M}_{m,n};\ +,\ \cdot)$ is isomorphic to $(\mathsf{V}_{m,n};\ +,\ \cdot)$. Hence, if matrix algebra consisted only of structures such as $(\mathsf{M}_{m,n};\ +,\ \cdot)$ for given numbers m and n, then we would have just been grinding wheels, for $(\mathsf{V}_{mn};\ +,\ \cdot)$ allows us to do everything that we can do with $(\mathsf{M}_{m,n};\ +,\ \cdot)$.] Matrix algebra contains two additional operations besides the operations $+$ and $\cdot$, however, and it is for this reason that we go to the trouble to construct the matrix algebra. These two additional operations are what provide the basis whereby we will be able to solve important classes of problems. The fact to be noted at this point, however, is that $(\mathsf{V}_n;\ +,\ \cdot)$ is *isomorphic* to $(\mathsf{M}_{n,1};\ +,\ \cdot)$, and hence we can use the matrix algebra to solve problems that require us to find elements $\mathbf{x}$ of V_n that satisfy

$$\mathbf{a}_i \circ \mathbf{x} = b_i,\quad i = 1,\ \ldots,\ m,$$

by solving the corresponding matrix algebra problem that asks us to find elements $\mathbf{X}$ of $\mathsf{M}_{n,1}$ that satisfy a system of matrix equations. We will make this notion more precise after we have introduced the additional operations that comprise the matrix algebra.

The next operation we define is that of matrix multiplication. We could, perchance, motivate the definition of this operation, but such motivations almost invariably depend upon knowing what the definition of matrix multiplication is. Rather than attempt such a motivation, we shall simply define matrix multiplication and ask the student to accept for the moment that it is just what we want.

Let $\mathbf{A} \in \mathsf{M}_{m,n}$ and $\mathbf{B} \in \mathsf{M}_{n,p}$. The **product**

$$\mathbf{C} = \mathbf{AB} \tag{4.8}$$

of the matrices $\mathbf{A}$ and $\mathbf{B}$ is an element of $\mathsf{M}_{m,p}$ whose entries c_{ij} are given by

$$\begin{aligned} c_{ij} &= a_{i1}\, b_{1j} + a_{i2}\, b_{2j} + a_{i3}\, b_{3j} + \ldots + a_{in}\, b_{nj} \\ &= \sum_{k=1}^{n} a_{ik}\, b_{kj} \end{aligned} \tag{4.9}$$

for $i = 1,\ \ldots,\ m,\ j = 1,\ \ldots,\ p$. The student should carefully note that *the product of* $\mathbf{A}$ *and* $\mathbf{B}$ *is only defined when the number of columns of the left factor* $\mathbf{A}$ *is equal to the number of rows of the right factor* $\mathbf{B}$. An easy way of remembering this is $\mathbf{A} \in \mathsf{M}_{m,n}$, $\mathbf{B} \in \mathsf{M}_{n,p}$ then $\mathbf{C} = \mathbf{AB} \in \mathsf{M}_{m,p}$ so that we can write

$$\mathsf{M}_{m,n} \times \mathsf{M}_{n,p} \rightarrow \mathsf{M}_{m,p}.$$

The formula (4.9) may appear somewhat complicated on first sight, but it is really very simple to use in practice. Suppose we wish to calculate c_{ij},

$$
\begin{array}{c}
\quad j \\
\quad \downarrow
\end{array}
$$

$$
i \rightarrow \begin{pmatrix}
\circ & \circ & \circ & \circ & \circ \\
\circ & \circ & \circ & \circ & \circ \\
\circ & \circ & \circ & \circ & \circ \\
\circ & \circ & c_{ij} & \circ & \circ \\
\circ & \circ & \circ & \circ & \circ \\
\circ & \circ & \circ & \circ & \circ \\
\circ & \circ & \circ & \circ & \circ \\
\circ & \circ & \circ & \circ & \circ
\end{pmatrix}
$$

where **A** and **B** are given, respectively, by

$$
i \rightarrow \begin{pmatrix}
\circ & \circ & \circ & \circ & \circ \\
\circ & \circ & \circ & \circ & \circ \\
\circ & \circ & \circ & \circ & \circ \\
a_{i1} & a_{i2} & \circ & \circ & a_{in} \\
\circ & \circ & \circ & \circ & \circ \\
\circ & \circ & \circ & \circ & \circ \\
\circ & \circ & \circ & \circ & \circ \\
\circ & \circ & \circ & \circ & \circ
\end{pmatrix}
$$

and

$$
\begin{array}{c}
j \\
\downarrow
\end{array}
$$

$$
\begin{pmatrix}
\circ & \circ & b_{1j} & \circ & \circ & \circ \\
\circ & \circ & b_{2j} & \circ & \circ & \circ \\
\circ & \circ & \circ & \circ & \circ & \circ \\
\circ & \circ & \circ & \circ & \circ & \circ \\
\circ & \circ & \circ & \circ & \circ & \circ \\
\circ & \circ & \circ & \circ & \circ & \circ \\
\circ & \circ & b_{nj} & \circ & \circ & \circ
\end{pmatrix}
$$

Equations (4.9) then say that we simply multiply the entries in the ith row of **A** by the corresponding entries in the jth column of **B** and add them all up to obtain c_{ij}. Thus, if

$$
\mathbf{A} \equiv \begin{pmatrix} 1 & 3 \\ 0 & -1 \\ 5 & 1 \end{pmatrix} \in \mathsf{M}_{3,2}, \qquad \mathbf{B} \equiv \begin{pmatrix} 3 & -6 \\ & \\ 5 & 3 \end{pmatrix} \in \mathsf{M}_{2,2}
$$

then

$$\mathbf{C}=\mathbf{AB}\equiv\begin{pmatrix}(1)(3)+(3)(5) & (1)(-6)+(3)(3)\\ (0)(3)+(-1)(5) & (0)(-6)+(-1)(3)\\ (5)(3)+(1)(5) & (5)(-6)+(1)(3)\end{pmatrix}$$

$$=\begin{pmatrix}18 & 3\\ -5 & -3\\ 20 & -27\end{pmatrix}$$

and $\mathbf{C}$ belongs to $\mathsf{M}_{3,2}$, as indeed it should since $\mathbf{A}$ belongs to $\mathsf{M}_{3,2}$ and $\mathbf{B}$ belongs to $\mathsf{M}_{2,2}$. If we take $\mathbf{B}$ as the column matrix $\begin{Bmatrix}2\\4\end{Bmatrix}$, then

$$\mathbf{C}=\mathbf{AB}=\begin{pmatrix}1 & 3\\ 0 & -1\\ 5 & -1\end{pmatrix}\begin{Bmatrix}2\\4\end{Bmatrix}=\begin{Bmatrix}(1)(2)+(3)(4)\\ (0)(2)+(-1)(4)\\ (5)(2)+(1)(4)\end{Bmatrix}=\begin{Bmatrix}14\\-4\\14\end{Bmatrix}$$

belongs to $\mathsf{M}_{3,1}$ since $\mathbf{A}$ belongs to $\mathsf{M}_{3,2}$ and $\mathbf{B}$ belongs to $\mathsf{M}_{2,1}$. If $\mathbf{A}$ belongs to $\mathsf{M}_{p,n}$ and $\mathbf{B}$ belongs to $\mathsf{M}_{n,1}$, then their product is defined. Since

$$\mathbf{B}=\begin{Bmatrix}f_1\\ \cdot\\ \cdot\\ \cdot\\ \cdot\\ \cdot\\ f_n\end{Bmatrix}\in\mathsf{M}_{n,1},$$

we may identify $\mathbf{B}$ with an element of V_n,

$$\mathbf{B}=\{f\}\equiv\mathbf{f}$$

and we then have

$$\mathbf{AB}=\mathbf{A}\{f\}.$$

If we write out $\mathbf{A}\{f\}$, with

$$\mathbf{A}=\begin{pmatrix}a_{11} & a_{12} & \cdots & a_{1n}\\ a_{21} & a_{22} & \cdots & a_{2n}\\ \cdot & \cdot & & \\ \cdot & \cdot & & \\ \cdot & \cdot & & \\ a_{p1} & a_{p2} & \cdots & a_{pn}\end{pmatrix}$$

we have

$$\mathbf{A}\{f\}=\begin{Bmatrix}a_{11}f_1+a_{12}f_2+\ldots+a_{1n}f_n\\ a_{21}f_1+a_{22}f_2+\ldots+a_{2n}f_n\\ \cdot\\ \cdot\\ \cdot\\ a_{p1}f_1+a_{p2}f_2+\ldots+a_{pn}f_n\end{Bmatrix}\in\mathsf{M}_{p,1}.$$

If we now set $f_1=x_1$, $f_2=x_2$, . . . , $f_n=x_n$, that is

$$\{f\}=\{x\}\equiv\mathbf{x},$$

then the system of p linear equations given by (3.22) is now written in the compact form of a single matrix equation

$$\mathbf{A}\{x\}=\{0\}\in\mathsf{M}_{p,1}.$$

The economy and efficiency of matrix multiplication is now evident, for it allows us to represent the system of p linear equations (3.22) for the determination of the element $\mathbf{x}$ of V_n in terms of a single matrix equation for the determination of $\{x\}\equiv\mathbf{x}$, and this matrix equation involves only operations that are included in the matrix algebra. On the other hand, the system of equations (3.22) could not be handled within the structure $(\mathsf{V}_n;\ +,\ \cdot)$. The added operation of matrix multiplication that is defined in matrix algebra thus presents the possibility of solving the system of equations $\mathbf{A}\{x\}=\{0\}$ by use of matrix algebra operations since the equation $\mathbf{A}\{x\}=\{0\}$ only involves operations that belong to the matrix algebra. We shall obviously return to this important observation several times in these lectures.

Let $\mathbf{A}\in\mathsf{M}_{m,n}$ and $\mathbf{B}\in\mathsf{M}_{n,p}$, then $\mathbf{AB}\in\mathsf{M}_{m,p}$ is defined. The question naturally arises as to when is $\mathbf{BA}$ defined. Since $\mathbf{B}\in\mathsf{M}_{n,p}$ and $\mathbf{A}\in\mathsf{M}_{m,n}$, $\mathbf{BA}$ is only defined when the number of columns of $\mathbf{B}$ is equal to the number of rows of $\mathbf{A}$, that is, when $p=m$. Thus, $\mathbf{AB}$ and $\mathbf{BA}$ *are both defined only when* $\mathbf{A}\in\mathsf{M}_{m,n}$ and $\mathbf{B}\in\mathsf{M}_{n,m}$. This is probably the first time you have encountered a product which is defined for one order of the factors but which is not necessarily defined for the factors in the opposite order. A special case of our results is that *both* $\mathbf{AB}$ *and* $\mathbf{BA}$ *are defined when* $\mathbf{A}$ *and* $\mathbf{B}$ *are both square matrices with the same number of rows or columns.*

If $\mathbf{A}$ and $\mathbf{B}$ both belong to $\mathsf{M}_{n,n}$, it is not necessarily true that $\mathbf{AB}$ is equal to $\mathbf{BA}$, as the following simple example shows:

$$\mathbf{A}=\begin{pmatrix}1 & 2\\ 3 & 1\end{pmatrix},\qquad \mathbf{B}=\begin{pmatrix}1 & -1\\ 2 & 0\end{pmatrix},$$

$$\mathbf{AB}=\begin{pmatrix}5 & -1\\ 5 & -3\end{pmatrix},\qquad \mathbf{BA}=\begin{pmatrix}-2 & 1\\ 2 & 4\end{pmatrix}.$$

Thus, *matrix multiplication is, in general, not* **commutative**: there are pairs of square matrices $\mathbf{A}$, $\mathbf{B}$, for which $\mathbf{AB}\neq\mathbf{BA}$. Square matrices such that $\mathbf{AB}=\mathbf{BA}$ are said to **commute**. An example of commuting matrices is given by

$$\mathsf{A}=\begin{pmatrix}0 & 1 & 0\\ 0 & 0 & 1\\ 0 & 0 & 0\end{pmatrix},\qquad \mathsf{B}=\begin{pmatrix}0 & 2 & 0\\ 0 & 0 & 2\\ 0 & 0 & 0\end{pmatrix}.$$

We note here, for the record, the following properties:

$$\mathbf{A}(\mathbf{B}+\mathbf{C})=\mathbf{AB}+\mathbf{AC}, \tag{4.10}$$

$$\mathbf{A}(\mathbf{BC})=(\mathbf{AB})\mathbf{C}, \tag{4.11}$$

$$\mathbf{A}(a\mathbf{B})=a(\mathbf{AB}). \tag{4.12}$$

These results are easily established from the definitions and are left to the student as exercises.

Matrix multiplication yields some surprising results. If we start with the matrix

$$\mathbf{A}=\begin{pmatrix} 0 & 1 & 0 \\ 0 & 0 & 1 \\ 0 & 0 & 0 \end{pmatrix},$$

then

$$\mathbf{AA}=\mathbf{A}^2=\begin{pmatrix} 0 & 0 & 1 \\ 0 & 0 & 0 \\ 0 & 0 & 0 \end{pmatrix},$$

and

$$\mathbf{A}(\mathbf{A}^2)=\mathbf{A}^3=\begin{pmatrix} 0 & 0 & 0 \\ 0 & 0 & 0 \\ 0 & 0 & 0 \end{pmatrix}=\mathbf{0};$$

there are 3-by-3 matrices $\mathbf{A}$ such that $\mathbf{A}\neq\mathbf{0}$, $\mathbf{A}^2\neq\mathbf{0}$, but $\mathbf{A}^3=\mathbf{0}$. In fact, there are n-by-n matrices such that their first $(n-1)$ powers are not the zero matrix, but their nth power is the zero matrix.

The n-by-n matrix

$$\mathbf{E}=\begin{pmatrix} 1 & 0 & 0 & . & . & . & 0 \\ 0 & 1 & 0 & . & . & . & 0 \\ 0 & 0 & 1 & . & . & . & 0 \\ . & . & . & . & . & . & . \\ . & . & . & . & . & . & . \\ . & . & . & . & . & . & . \\ 0 & 0 & 0 & . & . & . & 1 \end{pmatrix} \tag{4.13}$$

is referred to as the **identity** matrix of $\mathsf{M}_{n,n}$ since we have

$$\mathbf{AE}=\mathbf{EA}=\mathbf{A},$$

for every $\mathbf{A}$ belonging to $\mathsf{M}_{n,n}$. $\mathbf{E}$ thus plays the same role in matrix multiplication as is played by 1 in the multiplication of real numbers. A matrix that has all of its nondiagonal elements equal to zero, such as $\mathbf{E}$, is called a **diagonal** matrix. A diagonal matrix with diagonal entries $\alpha_1, \alpha_2, \ldots, \alpha_n$ is denoted by $\mathbf{D}(\alpha_1, \alpha_2, \ldots, \alpha_n)$. The diagonal matrices that are obtained by multiplying **E** by a real number (i.e., $a\mathbf{E}$) are called **scalar** matrices.

We can now show another surprising property of matrix multiplication. If we form the square of the matrix

$$\mathbf{I}=\begin{pmatrix} 0 & 1 \\ -1 & 0 \end{pmatrix},$$

we have

$$\mathbf{I}^2=\mathbf{II}=\begin{pmatrix} 0 & 1 \\ -1 & 0 \end{pmatrix}\begin{pmatrix} 0 & 1 \\ -1 & 0 \end{pmatrix}=\begin{pmatrix} -1 & 0 \\ 0 & -1 \end{pmatrix}=(-1)\begin{pmatrix} 1 & 0 \\ 0 & 1 \end{pmatrix},$$

$$\mathbf{I}^2=-\mathbf{E}.$$

In arithmetic, there is no real number whose square is -1. In fact, the special symbol $i=(-1)^{1/2}$ is introduced in order to get complex numbers so that $x^2=-1$ can be solved. In matrix algebra, on the other hand, we have demonstrated a real matrix whose square is the negative of the identity matrix. A number of other interesting properties of matrices under the operation of multiplication are given in the problems.

There is another operation that can be performed on matrices which we shall require. If **A** belongs to $\mathsf{M}_{m,n}$, we define the **transpose** of **A** (written $\mathbf{A}^T$) as the matrix that is obtained from **A** by making the columns of **A** into rows of $\mathbf{A}^T$ and the rows of **A** into the columns of $\mathbf{A}^T$. In symbols, if

$$\mathbf{A}=\begin{pmatrix} a_{11} & \cdots & a_{1n} \\ \vdots & & \\ a_{m1} & \cdots & a_{mn} \end{pmatrix},$$

then

$$\mathbf{A}^T=\begin{pmatrix} b_{11} & \cdots & b_{1m} \\ \vdots & & \\ b_{n1} & & b_{nm} \end{pmatrix},$$

where b_{ij} is given by

$$b_{ij}=a_{ji}. \tag{4.14}$$

If

$$\mathbf{A}=\begin{pmatrix} 1 & 3 & 5 \\ 2 & 4 & 6 \end{pmatrix}, \quad \text{then } \mathbf{A}^T=\begin{pmatrix} 1 & 2 \\ 3 & 4 \\ 5 & 6 \end{pmatrix}.$$

In order to show why transposition is a useful operation, we return to the problem of determining all $\mathbf{x}$ belonging to V_n such that

$$\mathbf{a}\circ\mathbf{x}=0, \tag{4.15}$$

where $\mathbf{a}$ is a given element of V_n. We have seen that the elements of V_n can be identified with the elements of $M_{n,1}$, and hence we now view both $\mathbf{a}$ and $\mathbf{x}$ as column matrices $\{a\}$ and $\{x\}$. Since

$$\{a\}=\begin{Bmatrix} a_1 \\ \cdot \\ \cdot \\ \cdot \\ a_n \end{Bmatrix},$$

we have

$$\{a\}^T=[a_1\ a_2\ .\ .\ .\ a_n].$$

Thus, if we form the matrix product $\{a\}^T\{x\}$, the result is

$$\{a\}^T\{x\}=a_1\,x_1+a_2\,x_2+\ .\ .\ .\ +a_n\,x_n. \tag{4.16}$$

The right-hand side of Eq. (4.16) is, however, just exactly $\mathbf{a}\circ\mathbf{x}$. We have thus established the result that

$$\mathbf{a}\equiv\{a\},\ \ \mathbf{x}\equiv\{x\};\ \ \mathbf{a}\circ\mathbf{x}=\{a\}^T\{x\}. \tag{4.17}$$

This allows us to write the system of p linear equations

$$\mathbf{a}_k\circ\mathbf{x}=0,\ k=1,\ .\ .\ .,\ p, \tag{4.18}$$

in V_n as the corresponding system of matrix equations

$$\{a_k\}^T\{x\}=0,\ k=1,\ .\ .\ .,\ p. \tag{4.19}$$

Thus, if we form the matrix $\mathbf{A}$ by the prescription

$$\mathbf{A}=\begin{Bmatrix} \{a_1\}^T \\ \{a_2\}^T \\ \cdot \\ \cdot \\ \cdot \\ \{a_p\}^T \end{Bmatrix}=\begin{pmatrix} a_{11} & a_{12} & . . . & a_{1n} \\ a_{21} & a_{22} & . . . & a_{2n} \\ \cdot & & & \\ \cdot & & & \\ \cdot & & & \\ a_{p1} & a_{p2} & . . . & a_{pn} \end{pmatrix},\ \{a_k\}=\begin{Bmatrix} a_{k1} \\ a_{k2} \\ \cdot \\ \cdot \\ \cdot \\ a_{kn} \end{Bmatrix}, \tag{4.20}$$

$$\{a_k\}^T=[a_{k1}\ a_{k2}\ .\ .\ .\ a_{kn}],$$

the system of equations (4.19) becomes the single matrix equation

$$\mathbf{A}\{x\}=\{0\}\in M_{p,1}. \tag{4.21}$$

We note that $\mathbf{A}$ belongs to $M_{p,n}$ and that $\{0\}$ is the zero element of $M_{p,1}$ in Eq. (4.21).

The following properties of the transpose operation are easily verified and are thus left to the student as exercises:

$$(\mathbf{A}^T)^T = \mathbf{A}, \tag{4.22}$$

$$(\mathbf{A}+\mathbf{B})^T = \mathbf{A}^T + \mathbf{B}^T, \tag{4.23}$$

$$(\mathbf{AB})^T = \mathbf{B}^T\mathbf{A}^T. \tag{4.24}$$

Please note the positions of $\mathbf{A}^T$ and $\mathbf{B}^T$ in the last property.

The result (4.17) can now be used to write the norm of $\mathbf{x}$ in terms of matrix multiplication. Since $\|\mathbf{x}\| = (\mathbf{x} \circ \mathbf{x})^{1/2}$, we have

$$\|\{x\}\| = (\{x\}^T\{x\})^{1/2}, \quad \{x\} \equiv \mathbf{x}. \tag{4.25}$$

If $\{x\}$ is defined by

$$\{x\} = \mathbf{A}\{y\}, \tag{4.26}$$

where $\mathbf{A}$ belongs to $\mathsf{M}_{n,n}$, and $\{y\}$ belongs to $\mathsf{M}_{n,1}$, then

$$\|\{x\}\| = (\{y\}^T\mathbf{A}^T\mathbf{A}\{y\})^{1/2}. \tag{4.27}$$

Since we know that we can always multiply elements of $\mathsf{M}_{n,n}$ together, the student may expect that he can also divide. In certain instances this is indeed the case, but it is by no means the rule. In order to see that it is not the case in general, we first observe that

$$\begin{pmatrix} 0 & 1 \\ 0 & 0 \end{pmatrix}\begin{pmatrix} 0 & \pi \\ 0 & 0 \end{pmatrix} = \begin{pmatrix} 0 & 0 \\ 0 & 0 \end{pmatrix};$$

there is, however, no way that we can divide by $\begin{pmatrix} 0 & 1 \\ 0 & 0 \end{pmatrix}$ so as to come up with $\begin{pmatrix} 0 & \pi \\ 0 & 0 \end{pmatrix}$. Stated in general, if we are given the matrix equation

$$\mathbf{AB} = \mathbf{C}$$

and we are also given the matrices $\mathbf{A}$ and $\mathbf{C}$ explicitly, we can "divide" by $\mathbf{A}$ and recover $\mathbf{B}$ explicitly only when we can find a matrix $\mathbf{W}$ such that

$$\mathbf{WA} = \mathbf{E};$$

that is,

$$\mathbf{WAB} = \mathbf{WC} \;\Rightarrow\; (\mathbf{WA})\mathbf{B} = \mathbf{WC} \;\Rightarrow\; \mathbf{EB} = \mathbf{WC} \;\Rightarrow\; \mathbf{B} = \mathbf{WC}.$$

This is, after all, what you do when you divide by a real number b, for $c \equiv 1/b$ is defined by the relation $cb = 1$. We shall return to the problem of finding $\mathbf{W}$, when it exists, after we use the algebraic structure developed in this lecture to answer the questions we have posed concerning homogeneous linear systems.

For each pair of positive numbers n and m, the structure $(\mathsf{M}_{n,m};\ +,\ \cdot)$ is closed under the two operations + and · . Matrix multiplication, on the other hand, takes an element from $\mathsf{M}_{m,n}$ and from $\mathsf{M}_{n,p}$ and gives an element of $\mathsf{M}_{m,p}$, while the transpose operation takes an element of $\mathsf{M}_{m,n}$ and gives an element of $\mathsf{M}_{n,m}$. Hence matrix algebra is indeed a "larger" algebra than the algebra $(\mathsf{V}_n;\ +,\ \cdot)$. It is sometimes useful to have a symbolic representation for matrix algebra such as the symbolic representation $(\mathsf{V}_n;\ +,\ \cdot)$ for the algebra that we developed for V_n. Let M denote the collection of all matrices. By this we mean that M stands for what we obtain when we combine the $\mathsf{M}_{m,n}$'s for all values of m and n. Let $\times$ denote the operation of matrix multiplication and let T denote the operation of transposition. We can then represent matrix algebra by the symbol

$$(\mathsf{M};\ +,\ \cdot,\ \times,\ T)$$

The collection M is then **closed** under the four operations $+,\ \cdot,\ \times,\ T$ whenever these operations are defined for elements of M. Matrix algebra thus has the closure property that was so important in the algebra of $(\mathsf{V}_n;\ +,\ \cdot)$, but we now have the exception that the operations + and $\times$ are only defined for certain pairs of elements from M (recall that you can only add two elements of $\mathsf{M}_{m,n}$ together and that you can only multiply an element of $\mathsf{M}_{m,n}$ by an element of $\mathsf{M}_{n,p}$). If N denotes the collection of all square matrices with n rows and n columns, then $(\mathsf{N};\ +,\ \cdot,\ \times,\ T)$ is the algebra of square matrices. This algebra has the property that it is also closed and that all four of the operations are defined for all elements of N.

Problems

4.1. Calculate the matrix $2\mathbf{A} - \mathbf{B}$ when the matrices $\mathbf{A}$ and $\mathbf{B}$ are, respectively,

(a) $\begin{pmatrix} 1 & 0 & 2 \\ -1 & 3 & 0 \end{pmatrix}, \begin{pmatrix} 0 & 3 & 4 \\ -2 & 0 & -8 \end{pmatrix}$; (b) $\begin{pmatrix} 0 & -13 \\ 8 & 4 \end{pmatrix}, \begin{pmatrix} 7 & -6 \\ 9 & 6 \end{pmatrix}$;

(c) $\begin{pmatrix} 1 & 2 & 3 \\ 0 & 1 & 2 \\ 3 & 0 & -4 \end{pmatrix}, \begin{pmatrix} 17 & 0 & 13 \\ 0 & -8 & 4 \\ 7 & 6 & -5 \end{pmatrix}$; (d) $\begin{pmatrix} 3 & 13 \\ 6 & 8 \\ 7 & -6 \end{pmatrix}, \begin{pmatrix} 6 & 7 \\ 8 & 9 \\ 12 & 11 \end{pmatrix}$;

(e) $\begin{pmatrix} 2 \\ 0 \\ 4 \end{pmatrix}, \begin{pmatrix} 6 \\ 15 \\ 9 \end{pmatrix}$; (f) $\begin{pmatrix} 1 & 2 & 3 & 4 \\ 5 & 0 & 2 & 3 \\ 6 & 17 & 8 & 0 \end{pmatrix}, \begin{pmatrix} 0 & 3 & 0 & 5 \\ 8 & 0 & 6 & 0 \\ 4 & 13 & 7 & 1 \end{pmatrix}$.

4.2. Calculate the product $\mathbf{AB}$ where the matrices $\mathbf{A}$ and $\mathbf{B}$ are given, respectively, by

(a) $(1\ \ 0\ \ 3), \begin{pmatrix} 1 & 3 \\ 8 & -4 \\ 6 & 7 \end{pmatrix}$; (b) $\begin{pmatrix} 0 & 1 & 3 \\ 2 & 4 & 0 \end{pmatrix}, \begin{pmatrix} 1 \\ 8 \\ -7 \end{pmatrix}$;

(c) $\begin{pmatrix} 1 & 0 & 1 \\ 0 & 1 & 0 \\ 3 & 0 & 4 \end{pmatrix}, \begin{pmatrix} 2 \\ -3 \\ 6 \end{pmatrix}$; (d) $\begin{pmatrix} 1 & 2 & 0 \\ 2 & 0 & 4 \\ 1 & 0 & 1 \end{pmatrix}, \begin{pmatrix} 0 & 2 & -3 \\ -4 & 0 & 2 \\ 4 & 13 & 0 \end{pmatrix}$;

(e) $\begin{pmatrix} 2 & 1 & 0 \\ 3 & 2 & 1 \\ 0 & -4 & 2 \end{pmatrix}, \begin{pmatrix} 1 & 0 \\ 0 & 2 \\ 2 & 3 \end{pmatrix}$; (f) $\begin{pmatrix} 3 & 0 \\ -6 & 3 \\ 2 & 4 \end{pmatrix}, \begin{pmatrix} 2 & 0 & 1 \\ 1 & 0 & 3 \end{pmatrix}$;

(g) $(1 \quad 0 \quad 3), \begin{pmatrix} 4 \\ 5 \\ 6 \end{pmatrix}$; (h) $\begin{pmatrix} 7 \\ -5 \\ 3 \end{pmatrix}, (-8, 5, 7)$.

Is the product **BA** defined? If it is, calculate **BA**.

4.3. Calculate the matrix polynomial $\mathbf{A}^2 + b\mathbf{A} + c\mathbf{E}$ where **E** is the 2-by-2 identity matrix $\begin{pmatrix} 1 & 0 \\ 0 & 1 \end{pmatrix}$ and

(a) $\mathbf{A} = \begin{pmatrix} 1 & 2 \\ 3 & 4 \end{pmatrix}, b = -5, c = -2$; (b) $\mathbf{A} = \begin{pmatrix} 0 & 3 \\ 1 & -4 \end{pmatrix}, b = 4, c = -3$;

(c) $\mathbf{A} = \begin{pmatrix} 1 & 3 \\ -4 & 6 \end{pmatrix}, b = -7, c = 18$; (d) $\mathbf{A} = \begin{pmatrix} 2 & -3 \\ 4 & -2 \end{pmatrix}, b = 0, c = 8$;

(e) $\mathbf{A} = \begin{pmatrix} 3 & 0 \\ -2 & 1 \end{pmatrix}, b = -4, c = 3$;

(f) $\mathbf{A} = \begin{pmatrix} -1 & 3 \\ 0 & 4 \end{pmatrix}, b = -3, c = -4$.

4.4. Write the following systems of equations in the matrix form $\mathbf{A}\{x\} = \{b\}$:

(a) $\begin{aligned} x_2 + 3x_3 &= 1 \\ x_1 + 3x_2 &= 0 \\ 4x_3 &= 2 \end{aligned}$ (b) $\begin{aligned} x_1 + 2x_3 &= 1 \\ 2x_1 + 3x_2 + x_3 &= 2 \\ 4x_2 + x_3 &= 8 \end{aligned}$

(c) $\begin{aligned} x_1 + x_3 &= 1 \\ 7x_1 + 2x_2 &= 0 \\ 6x_1 + x_3 &= 2 \end{aligned}$ (d) $\begin{aligned} 6x_1 + 2x_2 &= 0 \\ 3x_1 - x_2 - 2x_3 &= 1 \end{aligned}$

(e) $\begin{aligned} x_1 + 2x_2 + x_3 &= 0 \\ 7x_1 - x_2 + x_3 &= 0 \\ 2x_1 - 13x_2 - x_3 &= 0 \end{aligned}$ (f) $\begin{aligned} x_1 + x_2 &= 3 \\ 2x_1 - x_2 &= 7 \\ 6x_1 + 3x_2 &= 8 \end{aligned}$

4.5. Prove the properties 1 through 5 described in pp. 38 and 39.

4.6. Prove that the following sets are isomorphic:

(a) All real numbers and all scalar n-by-n matrices.
(b) V_n and all diagonal n-by-n matrices.
(c) All complex numbers and V_2.
(d) V_{mn} and $\mathsf{M}_{m,n}$.

4.7. Prove the properties (4.10) through (4.12).

4.8. Prove the properties (4.22) through (4.24).

4.9. Show that the products $\mathbf{A}^T\mathbf{A}$ and $\mathbf{A}\mathbf{A}^T$ are always defined.

4.10. Show that both **A** and **B** are square matrices $\in \mathsf{M}_{p,p}$ if either of the following properties is valid:

(a) $\mathbf{A} + \mathbf{B}$, $\mathbf{A} + \mathbf{B}^T$ are defined,
(b) $\mathbf{AB} = \mathbf{BA}$.

4.11. Prove that a scalar n-by-n matrix commutes with all n-by-n matrices.

4.12. Show that two n-by-n diagonal matrices always commute.

4.13. Find the necessary and sufficient condition for the diagonal matrix $\mathbf{D}(\lambda_1, \ldots, \lambda_n)$ to commute with all n-by-n matrices.

4.14. Let $\mathbf{D}$ be a diagonal matrix with distinct diagonal entries. Show that if the matrix $\mathbf{A}$ commutes with $\mathbf{D}$, then $\mathbf{A}$ is a diagonal matrix.

4.15. Show that the matrices $\mathbf{A}$ and $\mathbf{B}$ commute if and only if $\mathbf{A}^T$ and $\mathbf{B}^T$ commute.

4.16. Let $\mathbf{A}$ be a p-by-n matrix

$$\mathbf{A} = \begin{Bmatrix} \{a_1\}^T \\ \cdot \\ \cdot \\ \cdot \\ \{a_p\}^T \end{Bmatrix}.$$

If $\{b\}_j$ denotes the jth column of the n-by-n matrix $\mathbf{B}$ then we can write $\mathbf{B} = [\{b\}_1, \ldots, \{b\}_n]$. Show that

$$\mathbf{AB} = [\mathbf{A}\{b\}_1, \ldots, \mathbf{A}\{b\}_n] = \begin{Bmatrix} \{a_1\}^T\mathbf{B} \\ \cdot \\ \cdot \\ \cdot \\ \{a_p\}^T\mathbf{B} \end{Bmatrix}.$$

4.17. Show that

(a) $[\{u\}_1, \ldots, \{u\}_n]\,\mathbf{D}(\lambda_1, \ldots, \lambda_n) = [\lambda_1\{u\}_1, \ldots, \lambda_n\{u\}_n]$,

(b) $$\mathbf{D}(\lambda_1, \ldots, \lambda_n) \begin{Bmatrix} \{u_1\}^T \\ \cdot \\ \cdot \\ \cdot \\ \{u_n\}^T \end{Bmatrix} = \begin{Bmatrix} \lambda_1\{u_1\}^T \\ \\ \\ \lambda_n\{u_n\}^T \end{Bmatrix}.$$

4.18. Prove that $[\{u\}_1, \ldots, \{u\}_n]\{k\} = k_1\{u\}_1 + \ldots + k_n\{u\}_n$.

4.19. Let $\{e\}_i \in \mathsf{M}_{n,1}$ denote the column matrix with all entries zero except the ith which is equal to 1. If $\mathbf{A} = (a_{ij})$ is an n-by-n matrix, show that

(i) $\{e\}_i^T\mathbf{A} = [a_{i1}, a_{i2}, \ldots, a_{in}]$

(ii) $\mathbf{A}\{e_i\} = [a_{1i}, a_{2i}, \ldots, a_{ni}]^T$

(iii) $\{e\}_i^T\mathbf{A}\{e\}_j = a_{ij}$.

4.20. The square matrix $\mathbf{A} = (a_{ij})$ is called **upper triangular** if $a_{ij} = 0$ for $i > j$ and **lower triangular** if $a_{ij} = 0$ for $i < j$. Prove that the product of two m-by-m upper (lower) triangular matrices is an upper (lower) triangular matrix.

4.21. Show that the set of all matrices which commute with a given square matrix is closed under addition and multiplication.

4.22. If $\mathbf{A}$ is a square matrix and n any positive integer, we write

$$\mathbf{A}^0 = \mathbf{E}, \quad \mathbf{A}^{n+1} = \mathbf{AA}^n, \; n = 1, 2, \ldots,$$

which defines recursively all **positive integer powers** of a square matrix. Show that, if p and q are positive integers or zero,

$$\mathbf{A}^p\mathbf{A}^q = \mathbf{A}^q\mathbf{A}^p = \mathbf{A}^{p+q};$$

i.e., *the powers of a square matrix commute.*

4.23. If $\mathbf{A}$ is a square matrix and p is an integer or zero, prove that

$$(\mathbf{A}^p)^T = (\mathbf{A}^T)^p.$$

4.24. Let $\mathbf{A}$ and $\mathbf{B}$ be two n-by-n matrices and p, q positive integers or zero. Show that if $\mathbf{A}$ and $\mathbf{B}$ commute, so do $\mathbf{A}^p$ and $\mathbf{B}^q$.

4.25. Show that if the matrices $\mathbf{B}$ and $\mathbf{C}$ both commute with $\mathbf{A}$ then $\mathbf{B}^p\mathbf{C}^q$, where p and q are positive integers or zero, commutes with $\mathbf{A}$.

4.26. Let $f(x)$ be the polynomial in x

$$f(x) = a_0 + a_1x + a_2x^2 + \ldots + a_px^p,$$

$\mathbf{A}$ be an n-by-n square matrix and $\mathbf{E}$ be the n-by-n unit matrix. The **matrix polynomial** $f(\mathbf{A})$ will denote the matrix

$$f(\mathbf{A}) = a_0\mathbf{E} + a_1\mathbf{A} + a_2\mathbf{A}^2 + \ldots + a_p\mathbf{A}^p.$$

Let $f(x)$, $g(x)$ and $h(x)$ be three polynomials in x and $\mathbf{A}$ a square matrix. If $f(x)g(x) = h(x)$, show that $f(\mathbf{A})g(\mathbf{A}) = h(\mathbf{A})$ and deduce that *matrix polynomials of the same square matrix commute.*

4.27. Show that two matrix polynomials of commuting matrices commute.

4.28. If $\mathbf{A}\in \mathsf{M}_{k,r}$, $\mathbf{B}\in \mathsf{M}_{k,n-r}$, $\mathbf{C}\in \mathsf{M}_{m-k,r}$, $\mathbf{D}\in \mathsf{M}_{m-k,n-r}$ are matrices with elements a_{ij}, b_{ij}, c_{ij}, and d_{ij}, respectively, the **partition matrix**

$$\begin{pmatrix} \mathbf{A}_{k,\,r} & \mathbf{B}_{k,\,n-r} \\ \mathbf{C}_{m-k,\,r} & \mathbf{D}_{m-k,\,n-r} \end{pmatrix}$$

will denote the matrix

$$\begin{pmatrix} a_{11} & \ldots & a_{1r} & b_{11} & \ldots & b_{1(n-r)} \\ \cdot & \cdots\cdot & & \cdot & \cdots\cdot & \\ a_{k1} & \ldots & a_{rk} & b_{k1} & \ldots & b_{k(n-r)} \\ c_{11} & \ldots & c_{1r} & d_{11} & \ldots & d_{1(n-r)} \\ \cdot & \cdots\cdot & & \cdot & \cdots\cdot & \\ c_{(m-k)1} & \ldots & c_{(m-k)r} & d_{(m-k)1} & \ldots & d_{(m-k)(n-r)} \end{pmatrix}.$$

In the above notation, show that

$$(\mathbf{F}_{p,\,k}\ \mathbf{Q}_{p,\,(m-k)})\begin{pmatrix} \mathbf{A}_{k,\,r} & \mathbf{B}_{k,\,n-r} \\ \mathbf{C}_{m-k,\,r} & \mathbf{D}_{m-k,\,n-r} \end{pmatrix} = ((\mathbf{FA}+\mathbf{QC})_{p,\,r}\ (\mathbf{FB}+\mathbf{QD})_{p,\,n-r}).$$

Generalize this result.

LECTURE 5

Minimal Spanning Sets and Linear Independence

Systems of linear homogeneous equations and matrix formulations • Spanning sets for a subspace • Minimal spanning sets for a subspace • Conditions for minimality of a spanning set • Linear independence • Linear independence of a minimal spanning set • Dimension of a subspace • Inequalities which the dimension of a subspace satisfies • Row equivalence of matrices • Elementary row operations • The row space of a matrix • Row equivalence in terms of equality of row spaces • Problems

We have stressed several times the need for efficient methods of solving problems. In fact, if mathematics is to be really useful to you, it should do more than just allow you to solve problems—it should allow you to solve the problems in an efficient manner. This lecture will use the results that we have already obtained in the previous lectures to set the requirements that will give an efficient method for solving general linear homogeneous problems of the form

$$\mathbf{A}\{x\}=\{0\}.$$

As it turns out, efficiency is the keynote, for once we have obtained the conditions for a method to be efficient, the problem of obtaining the method itself is fairly simple and routine.

We start by recalling how we came by the matrix equation $\mathbf{A}\{x\}=\{0\}$. We have seen that any element of V_n, say

$$\mathbf{x}=\begin{Bmatrix} x_1 \\ x_2 \\ \cdot \\ \cdot \\ \cdot \\ x_n \end{Bmatrix} \tag{5.1}$$

can be identified with a unique element of $\mathsf{M}_{n,1}$ defined by the relation $\{x\}\equiv\mathbf{x}$. In fact, we showed that $(\mathsf{V}_n;\ +,\ \cdot)$ and $(\mathsf{M}_{n,1};\ +,\ \cdot)$ are algebraically isomorphic. If we are given p explicit elements of V_n,

$$\mathbf{a}_1 = \begin{Bmatrix} a_{11} \\ a_{12} \\ \cdot \\ \cdot \\ \cdot \\ a_{1n} \end{Bmatrix}, \quad \mathbf{a}_2 = \begin{Bmatrix} a_{21} \\ a_{22} \\ \cdot \\ \cdot \\ \cdot \\ a_{2n} \end{Bmatrix}, \quad . \; . \; . \; , \quad \mathbf{a}_p = \begin{Bmatrix} a_{p1} \\ a_{p2} \\ \cdot \\ \cdot \\ \cdot \\ a_{pn} \end{Bmatrix},$$

then we can also identify these p elements of V_n with p elements of $\mathsf{M}_{n,1}$ by the identification

$$\{a_1\} \equiv \mathbf{a}_1, \; \{a_2\} \equiv \mathbf{a}_2, \; . \; . \; . \; , \; \{a_p\} \equiv \mathbf{a}_p.$$

Thus, if we wish to determine all $\mathbf{x} \in \mathsf{V}_n$ such that

$$\mathbf{a}_i \circ \mathbf{x} = 0, \quad i = 1, \; . \; . \; . \; , \; p \tag{5.2}$$

(to find all $\mathbf{x}$ that are perpendicular to the $\mathbf{a}_1, \; . \; . \; . \; , \; \mathbf{a}_p$), this problem is equivalent to finding all $\{x\} \in \mathsf{M}_{n,1}$ such that

$$\{a_i\}^T \{x\} = 0, \quad i = 1, \; . \; . \; . \; , \; p. \tag{5.3}$$

The equivalence of these two problems follows from the identity

$$\mathbf{y} \circ \mathbf{x} = \{y\}^T \{x\}, \quad \{x\} \equiv \mathbf{x}, \quad \{y\} \equiv \mathbf{y}, \tag{5.4}$$

that we established in the last lecture. Further if we define the matrix $\mathbf{A} \in \mathsf{M}_{p,n}$ by the relations

$$\mathbf{A} \equiv \begin{Bmatrix} \{a_1\}^T \\ \{a_2\}^T \\ \cdot \\ \cdot \\ \cdot \\ \{a_p\}^T \end{Bmatrix} = \begin{pmatrix} a_{11} & a_{12} & a_{13} & \cdots & a_{1n} \\ a_{21} & a_{22} & a_{23} & \cdots & a_{2n} \\ \cdot & \cdot & \cdot & & \\ \cdot & \cdot & \cdot & & \\ \cdot & \cdot & \cdot & & \\ a_{p1} & a_{p2} & a_{p3} & \cdots & a_{pn} \end{pmatrix}, \tag{5.5}$$

the system of p equations (5.3) becomes the single matrix equation

$$\mathbf{A}\{x\} = \{0\}, \tag{5.6}$$

where $\{0\}$ is the zero element of $\mathsf{M}_{p,1}$. The operation T of the matrix algebra thus allows us to formulate the system of equations (5.3) in terms of an equivalent matrix equation (5.6) and this equivalent equation involves only operations that belong to the matrix algebra. We may thus expect that the problem of solving (5.6) is a problem that is handled by the operations of matrix algebra, as is indeed the case.

Before we formulate the basic question that must be answered in order to solve the matrix equation $\mathbf{A}\{x\} = \{0\}$, it is perhaps useful to become a little more accustomed to viewing a system of p linear equations in n unknowns as a single matrix equation. We therefore take this opportunity to prove that *the collection of all solutions of Eq.* (5.6) *forms a subspace of*

$\mathsf{M}_{n,1}$ (forms a subspace of V_n since $\mathsf{M}_{n,1}$ is identical with V_n). If $\{x\}$ satisfies Eq. (5.6), then

$$\mathbf{A}(a\{x\})=a(\mathbf{A}\{x\})=a\{0\}=\{0\},$$

and hence we have that $a\{x\}$ also satisfies Eq. (5.6). If $\{x\}$ and $\{y\}$ satisfy Eq. (5.6), then

$$\mathbf{A}(\{x\}+\{y\})=\mathbf{A}\{x\}+\mathbf{A}\{y\}=\{0\}+\{0\}=\{0\},$$

and hence $\{x\}+\{y\}$ satisfies Eq. (5.6). The collection of all solutions of (5.6) is thus closed under addition and multiplication by a real number, and hence it forms a subspace. Our problem is to find an efficient method for finding the subspace that constitutes the solution of Eq. (5.6).

If we go back to the formulation of the problem in terms of inner products given in Eqs. (5.2), what we require is the set of all elements $\mathbf{x}$ that are simultaneously orthogonal to each of the given vectors $\mathbf{a}_i$, $i=1, \ldots, p$. This in turn implies that $\mathbf{x}$ must be orthogonal to every linear combination of the vectors $\mathbf{a}_i$,

$$(c_1\,\mathbf{a}_1+c_2\,\mathbf{a}_2+\;\ldots\;+c_p\,\mathbf{a}_p)\circ\mathbf{x}=0 \tag{5.7}$$

for every choice of the real numbers $c_1, c_2, \ldots, c_p$. Now, the collection of all linear combinations of a given set of vectors forms a subspace, the *subspace that is spanned by the given vectors.* Thus, all solutions of the system of given equations must be orthogonal to the subspace spanned by the given vectors $\mathbf{a}_1, \mathbf{a}_2, \ldots, \mathbf{a}_p$. A spanning set of vectors of a subspace may be "redundant," however. For example, the vectors

$$\begin{Bmatrix}1\\0\\0\end{Bmatrix},\quad \begin{Bmatrix}0\\1\\0\end{Bmatrix},\quad \begin{Bmatrix}1\\1\\0\end{Bmatrix},\quad \begin{Bmatrix}1\\2\\0\end{Bmatrix},\quad \begin{Bmatrix}3\\-5\\0\end{Bmatrix},$$

span a subspace of V_3, but this same subspace is also spanned by the collection

$$\begin{Bmatrix}1\\0\\0\end{Bmatrix},\quad \begin{Bmatrix}0\\1\\0\end{Bmatrix}.$$

We certainly must get rid of any redundant vectors in the collection $\mathbf{a}_1, \ldots, \mathbf{a}_p$ if we are to have an efficient method of finding all $\mathbf{x}$ such that $\mathbf{a}_i\circ\mathbf{x}=0$, for this system actually requires us to find all $\mathbf{x}$ that are orthogonal to the subspace that is spanned by the vectors $\mathbf{a}_1, \ldots, \mathbf{a}_p$. If the number of spanning vectors of the subspace can be reduced (that is, the spanning set is redundant) then the original system of equations (5.3) contains at least one equation that is a linear combination of the other equations, and hence this equation contains no new information.

If we start with a set of vectors that spans a subspace, we are led to the idea of a minimal spanning subset of a spanning set. A **minimal spanning subset,**

$$\mathbf{u}_1, \mathbf{u}_2, \ldots, \mathbf{u}_r,$$

of a given spanning set,

$$\mathbf{a}_1, \mathbf{a}_2, \ldots, \mathbf{a}_p,$$

is a subset of this collection with the following two properties:

(1) The vectors $\mathbf{u}_1, \ldots, \mathbf{u}_r$ span the subspace spanned by the given vectors $\mathbf{a}_1, \ldots, \mathbf{a}_p$;

(2) no proper subset of the vectors $\mathbf{u}_1, \ldots, \mathbf{u}_r$ spans the subspace spanned by the given vectors $\mathbf{a}_1, \ldots, \mathbf{a}_p$.

We shall first establish necessary and sufficient conditions that a subset of a given set of vectors shall be a minimal spanning subset, and then obtain the algorithm for finding such a minimal set. Let $\mathbf{a}_1, \ldots, \mathbf{a}_p$ be the given set of vectors. We assume that none of the vectors $\mathbf{a}_k$ is the zero vector, for such a vector can be thrown out from the start since it is a member of all subspaces. If we can find real numbers $c_1, \ldots, c_p$, not all of which are zero, such that

$$c_1 \mathbf{a}_1 + c_2 \mathbf{a}_2 + \ldots + c_p \mathbf{a}_p = \mathbf{0} \tag{5.8}$$

then we can write at least one of the $\mathbf{a}_k$ in terms of the remaining ones. For instance, if $c_1 \neq 0$, then we have

$$\mathbf{a}_1 = \frac{-1}{c_1}(c_2 \mathbf{a}_2 + \ldots + c_p \mathbf{a}_p). \tag{5.9}$$

Since $\mathbf{a}_1$ is not the zero vector by assumption, at least one of the numbers $c_2, \ldots, c_p$ is also nonzero. The subspace that is spanned by $\mathbf{a}_1, \mathbf{a}_2, \ldots, \mathbf{a}_p$ would then be spanned by

$$\frac{-1}{c_1}(c_2 \mathbf{a}_2 + \ldots + c_p \mathbf{a}_p), \mathbf{a}_2, \mathbf{a}_3, \ldots, \mathbf{a}_p,$$

and hence it would also be spanned by the collection

$$\mathbf{a}_2, \mathbf{a}_3, \ldots, \mathbf{a}_p.$$

Thus, if Eq. (5.8) *can be satisfied where not all of the numbers* $c_1, \ldots, c_p$ *are zero, then the subspace that is spanned by the p vectors* $\mathbf{a}_1, \ldots, \mathbf{a}_p$ *is also spanned by at most* $p-1$ *of these vectors.* Continuing on in this manner, after a *finite* number of operations we will come to a point where we can no longer reduce the system further. We thus arrive at a subset of the given vectors, which we label

$$\mathbf{u}_1, \mathbf{u}_2, \ldots, \mathbf{u}_r,$$

with the following properties: (1) the equation

$$c_1\,\mathbf{u}_1+c_2\,\mathbf{u}_2+\;.\;.\;.\;+c_r\,\mathbf{u}_r=\mathbf{0} \tag{5.10}$$

will be satisfied if and only if we have

$$c_1=0,\, c_2=0,\;.\;.\;.\;,\, c_r=0, \tag{5.11}$$

and (2) $\mathbf{u}_1, \ldots, \mathbf{u}_r$ span the subspace that is spanned by $\mathbf{a}_1, \ldots, \mathbf{a}_p$. The first property follows since we can reduce the system further only if not all of the c's are zero. The second property follows from the fact that each new subset we obtain by the above procedure spans the subspace spanned by $\mathbf{a}_1, \ldots, \mathbf{a}_p$.

We now claim that *the subset* $\mathbf{u}_1, \ldots, \mathbf{u}_r$ with the above two properties constitutes a *minimal spanning subset* of the collection $\mathbf{a}_1, \ldots, \mathbf{a}_p$. Condition one in the definition of a minimal spanning subset is already established by property two of the subset $\mathbf{u}_1, \ldots, \mathbf{u}_r$. It thus remains only to show that no proper subset of $\mathbf{u}_1, \ldots, \mathbf{u}_r$ spans the subspace that is spanned by $\mathbf{a}_1, \ldots, \mathbf{a}_p$. Suppose, therefore, that we could delete the j member of the subset $\mathbf{u}_1, \ldots, \mathbf{u}_r$ and that the resulting set of $r-1$ vectors also spans the same subspace A that is spanned by $\mathbf{a}_1, \ldots, \mathbf{a}_p$. Since u_j belongs to the subspace A, we would then have

$$\mathbf{u}_j=c_1\,\mathbf{u}_1+\;.\;.\;.\;+c_{j-1}\,\mathbf{u}_{j-1}+c_{j+1}\,\mathbf{u}_{j+1}+\;.\;.\;.\;+c_r\,\mathbf{u}_r, \tag{5.12}$$

because $\mathbf{u}_1, \ldots, \mathbf{u}_{j-1}, \mathbf{u}_{j+1}, \ldots, \mathbf{u}_r$ would be a spanning set for the subspace A. The system of equations (5.12) states, however, that Eq. (5.10) can be satisfied without all of the c's being zero. We thus have a contradiction. Hence, the assumption that we can reduce the system $\mathbf{u}_1, \ldots, \mathbf{u}_r$ further is false.

A collection of vectors that satisfy Eq. (5.10) only when Eqs. (5.11) hold is of obvious importance in view of our results thus far. In fact, the importance of such systems of vectors is such that they have been given a specific name: they are called **linearly independent**. Stated in this terminology, our above results read as follows: *A subset of r vectors* $\mathbf{u}_1, \mathbf{u}_2, \ldots, \mathbf{u}_r$ *of a given set of vectors* $\mathbf{a}_1, \ldots, \mathbf{a}_p$ *is a minimal spanning subset if and only if* (1) *the vectors* $\mathbf{u}_1, \mathbf{u}_2, \ldots, \mathbf{u}_r$ *are linearly independent, and* (2) $\mathbf{u}_1, \ldots, \mathbf{u}_r$ *span the subspace that is spanned by the given set of vectors* $\mathbf{a}_1, \ldots, \mathbf{a}_p$. The student must carefully note that both conditions must be satisfied in oder to have a minimal spanning subset. It is not enough just to find a linearly independent subset of the given set $\mathbf{a}_1, \ldots, \mathbf{a}_p$, for you do not know that such a linearly independent set necessarily spans the subspace spanned by $\mathbf{a}_1, \ldots, \mathbf{a}_p$. Clearly *if* $\mathbf{u}_1, \ldots, \mathbf{u}_r$ *are linearly independent, then any subset of* $\mathbf{u}_1, \ldots, \mathbf{u}_r$ *is also linearly independent.* [We leave the proof of this fact to the student as an exercise.] We know, however, that if $\mathbf{u}_1, \ldots, \mathbf{u}_r$ is a minimal spanning subset, then no proper subset of $\mathbf{u}_1, \ldots, \mathbf{u}_r$ will span the subspace that is spanned by $\mathbf{a}_1, \ldots, \mathbf{a}_p$. Thus, a proper subset of a minimal spanning subset is a linearly independent set, but it is not a spanning set for the subspace that is spanned by the original set.

It is natural to use the number of vectors in a minimal spanning subset of a subspace as the **dimension** of a subspace. If A is used to designate the subspace spanned by the given spanning set $\mathbf{a}_1, \ldots, \mathbf{a}_p$, then we write

$$\dim(\mathsf{A}) = \text{number of vectors in a minimal spanning subset for } \mathsf{A}. \tag{5.13}$$

Thus, if A is the subspace spanned by the given system of p vectors $\mathbf{a}_1, \mathbf{a}_2, \ldots, \mathbf{a}_p$, then

$$\dim(\mathsf{A}) \leq p.$$

Further, since the elements that comprise A belong to V_n and the system of n vectors $\mathbf{e}_1, \mathbf{e}_2, \ldots, \mathbf{e}_n$ introduced in lecture two is a maximal system of linearly independent vectors in V_n, we also have

$$\dim(\mathsf{A}) \leq n.$$

Thus, *if* A *is a subspace of* V_n *that is spanned by a given system of p vectors, then*

$$\dim(\mathsf{A}) \leq \min(n, p). \tag{5.14}$$

At this point, $\dim(\mathsf{A})$ could depend on the given spanning set and the way in which we select a minimal spanning subset. The proof that $\dim(\mathsf{A})$ *is a unique number that is determined by the subspace* A will be given in a later lecture. This question does not really concern us here, since we are trying to solve the system (5.2) with the *given* vectors $\mathbf{a}_1, \ldots, \mathbf{a}_p$.

What we now have to do is to find an efficient algorithm for finding a minimal spanning subset for a subspace when we are given a spanning set. This brings us around full circle, for the desired algorithm is obtained by the three elementary operations discussed in the first lecture. This same algorithm will allow us to solve the system of equations (5.6) in a direct manner. In fact, the reason why the algorithm works is exactly the fact that the rows of the matrix (5.6) are identified with the transposes of a given set of vectors that spans the subspace in question, while the system (5.6) is also a system of p equations in n unknowns to which we may apply the three rules that were given in lecture 1. When the matrix equation $\mathbf{A}\{x\} = \{0\}$ is written out, we obtain the system of p equations

$$\begin{array}{l}
a_{11}x_1 + a_{12}x_2 + \cdots + a_{1n}x_n = 0 \\
a_{21}x_1 + a_{22}x_2 + \cdots + a_{2n}x_n = 0 \\
\quad \vdots \qquad \vdots \qquad\qquad \vdots \quad \vdots \\
a_{p1}x_1 + a_{p2}x_2 + \cdots + a_{pn}x_n = 0.
\end{array}$$

The three rules given in lecture 1, when applied to the above system of equations, are seen to be the same thing as operating on the rows of the coefficient matrix **A** of the matrix equation $\mathbf{A}\{x\}=\{0\}$ by the three **elementary row operations**

(1) interchange any two rows,
(2) multiply any row by a nonzero number,
(3) replace any row by itself plus a multiple of any other row.

If **B** is a matrix that is obtained from a matrix **A** by performing a sequence of elementary row operations, then the matrix **B** is said to be **row equivalent** to the matrix **A**. The important thing to note here is the following fact: *if* **B** *is row equivalent to* **A**, *then* $\mathbf{A}\{x\}=\{0\}$ *and* $\mathbf{B}\{x\}=\{0\}$ *have exactly the same solutions.* This follows from the fact that the two systems of p equations that we obtain from writing out the matrix equations $\mathbf{A}\{x\}=\{0\}$ and $\mathbf{B}\{x\}=\{0\}$ are equivalent systems of equations since the second system came from the first system by applying the three rules given in lecture 1. It is thus natural to say that *two matrix equations* $\mathbf{A}\{x\}=\{0\}$ *and* $\mathbf{B}\{x\}=\{0\}$ *are* **equivalent** *if their coefficient matrices* **A** *and* **B** *are row equivalent.*

If **B** is known to be row equivalent to a matrix **A** by row operations then **B** can actually be obtained from **A** by multiplying **A** from the left by a suitable matrix. We leave this matrix formulation of the elementary row operations to a later lecture.

What concerns us here is that we can replace the given matrix equation $\mathbf{A}\{x\}=\{0\}$ by an equivalent matrix equation $\mathbf{B}\{x\}=\{0\}$. Now, the rows of the matrix **A** are the transposes of the given elements $\{a_k\}\equiv\mathbf{a}_k$ of $\mathsf{M}_{n,1}$,

$$\mathbf{A}=\begin{Bmatrix}\{a_1\}^T\\ \{a_2\}^T\\ \cdot\\ \cdot\\ \cdot\\ \{a_p\}^T\end{Bmatrix}=\begin{pmatrix}a_{11} & a_{12} & \cdots & a_{1n}\\ a_{21} & a_{22} & \cdots & a_{2n}\\ \cdot & \cdot & & \cdot\\ \cdot & \cdot & & \cdot\\ \cdot & \cdot & & \cdot\\ a_{p1} & a_{p2} & \cdots & a_{pn}\end{pmatrix}, \tag{5.15}$$

while, if **B** is row equivalent to **A**, the rows of the matrix **B** are the transposes of a collection of elements $\{b_1\}, \ldots, \{b_p\}$ of $\mathsf{M}_{n,1}$ that are obtained from the transposes of the given elements $\{a_1\}, \ldots, \{a_p\}$ by elementary row operations:

$$\mathbf{B}=\begin{Bmatrix}\{b_1\}^T\\ \{b_2\}^T\\ \cdot\\ \cdot\\ \cdot\\ \{b_p\}^T\end{Bmatrix}=\begin{pmatrix}b_{11} & b_{12} & \cdots & b_{1n}\\ b_{21} & b_{22} & \cdots & b_{2n}\\ \cdot & \cdot & & \\ \cdot & \cdot & & \\ \cdot & \cdot & & \\ b_{p1} & b_{p2} & \cdots & b_{pn}\end{pmatrix}. \tag{5.16}$$

We know that $\{a_1\}, \ldots, \{a_p\}$ span a subspace of $\mathsf{V}_n \equiv \mathsf{M}_{n,1}$ and hence their transposes span a subspace of $\mathsf{M}_{1,n}$. Since the transposes of $\{a_1\}, \ldots, \{a_p\}$ are what actually occur in the matrix **A**, it is more convenient to work with the transposes of $\{a_1\}, \ldots, \{a_p\}$. We refer to the subspace of $\mathsf{M}_{1,n}$ that is spanned by the row vectors $\{a_1\}^T, \ldots, \{a_p\}^T$, as the **row space** of the matrix **A** given by Eq. (5.15). Thus, the row space of **B** is the subspace of $\mathsf{M}_{1,n}$ that is spanned by the row matrices $\{b_1\}^T, \ldots, \{b_p\}^T$. We now note that *the row space of* **A** *is identical with the row space of* **B** *if* **B** *is obtained by row operations applied to* **A**. This follows from the fact that every row of **B** is obtained from elementary row operations on the rows of **A** and *that every row of* **A** *is obtained from elementary row operations on* **B**. Thus, *every* linear combination of the rows of **A** can be obtained from appropriate linear combinations of the rows of **B** since the elementary row operations are nothing more than means for forming linear combinations. Hence the rows of **B** span the same subspace of $\mathsf{M}_{1,n}$ as is spanned by the rows of **A**.

We have thus reduced the search for the algorithm for finding a minimal spanning subset for the row space of **A** to that of finding a minimal spanning subset for the row space of a matrix **B** that is obtained from **A** by elementary row operations. The reason for this reduction, which is obtained by use of the elementary row operations, is that we can make the matrix **B** simpler than the matrix **A**. In fact, we shall construct the actual algorithm in the next lecture, where we will show that we can always replace **A** by a row equivalent matrix **B** such that **B** will allow us to *read off a minimal spanning subset by inspection.* At the same time, we will be able to read off all solutions to the matrix equation $\mathbf{A}\{x\}=\{0\}$ by inspection. The algorithm that accomplishes this is known as **row echelon reduction** of a matrix, and the solution of $\mathbf{A}\{x\}=\{0\}$ by this algorithm is known as **Gauss reduction** or **Gauss elimination.**

Problems

5.1. Let $c_1\mathbf{u}_1 + \cdots + c_p\mathbf{u}_p = \mathbf{0}$. Write the conditions that $c_1, \ldots, c_p$ must satisfy if $\mathbf{u}_1, \ldots, \mathbf{u}_p$ are given respectively by:

(a) $\begin{Bmatrix}2\\3\end{Bmatrix}, \begin{Bmatrix}3\\-1\end{Bmatrix}, \begin{Bmatrix}6\\8\end{Bmatrix}$; (b) $\begin{Bmatrix}1\\-2\end{Bmatrix}, \begin{Bmatrix}6\\7\end{Bmatrix}$; (c) $\begin{Bmatrix}0\\3\end{Bmatrix}, \begin{Bmatrix}14\\7\end{Bmatrix}, \begin{Bmatrix}-3\\10\end{Bmatrix}$;

(d) $\begin{Bmatrix}1\\2\\3\end{Bmatrix}, \begin{Bmatrix}1\\0\\3\end{Bmatrix}$; (e) $\begin{Bmatrix}6\\0\\0\end{Bmatrix}, \begin{Bmatrix}0\\8\\3\end{Bmatrix}, \begin{Bmatrix}0\\0\\4\end{Bmatrix}, \begin{Bmatrix}1\\1\\7\end{Bmatrix}$; (f) $\begin{Bmatrix}8\\13\\5\end{Bmatrix}, \begin{Bmatrix}14\\0\\6\end{Bmatrix}$.

5.2. Determine whether the following sets of vectors $\mathbf{u}_1, \ldots, \mathbf{u}_p$ are linearly dependent. If they are, calculate a set at numbers $c_1, \ldots, c_p$, not all zero, such that $c_1\mathbf{u}_1 + \ldots + c_p\mathbf{u}_p = \mathbf{0}$.

(a) $\begin{Bmatrix}1\\2\end{Bmatrix}, \begin{Bmatrix}2\\5\end{Bmatrix}$; (b) $\begin{Bmatrix}1\\-1\end{Bmatrix}, \begin{Bmatrix}2\\-4\end{Bmatrix}, \begin{Bmatrix}3\\-4\end{Bmatrix}$; (c) $\begin{Bmatrix}6\\4\end{Bmatrix}, \begin{Bmatrix}-2\\4\end{Bmatrix}, \begin{Bmatrix}1\\6\end{Bmatrix}$;

(d) $\begin{Bmatrix}6\\3\\5\end{Bmatrix}, \begin{Bmatrix}2\\13\\8\end{Bmatrix}$; (e) $\begin{Bmatrix}0\\1\\2\end{Bmatrix}, \begin{Bmatrix}3\\-1\\4\end{Bmatrix}, \begin{Bmatrix}-3\\3\\0\end{Bmatrix}$; (f) $\begin{Bmatrix}3\\5\\7\end{Bmatrix}, \begin{Bmatrix}0\\0\\1\end{Bmatrix}, \begin{Bmatrix}2\\0\\0\end{Bmatrix}$.

5.3. Show that the following sets of vectors are linearly independent: [Use problem 5.10]

(a) $\begin{Bmatrix}1\\1\end{Bmatrix}, \begin{Bmatrix}1\\-1\end{Bmatrix}$; (b) $\begin{Bmatrix}2\\3\end{Bmatrix}, \begin{Bmatrix}3\\-2\end{Bmatrix}$; (c) $\begin{Bmatrix}1\\1\\1\end{Bmatrix}, \begin{Bmatrix}1\\1\\-2\end{Bmatrix}, \begin{Bmatrix}1\\-1\\0\end{Bmatrix}$;

(d) $\begin{Bmatrix}1\\1\\2\end{Bmatrix}, \begin{Bmatrix}4\\2\\-3\end{Bmatrix}, \begin{Bmatrix}-7\\11\\-2\end{Bmatrix}$; (e) $\begin{Bmatrix}2\\3\\4\end{Bmatrix}, \begin{Bmatrix}2\\4\\-4\end{Bmatrix}, \begin{Bmatrix}-28\\16\\2\end{Bmatrix}$.

5.4. If $\mathbf{u}_1, \ldots, \mathbf{u}_n$ is a set of linearly independent vectors, then any subset of $\mathbf{u}_1, \ldots, \mathbf{u}_n$ is linearly independent.

5.5. If $\mathbf{u}_1, \ldots, \mathbf{u}_m$ are linearly dependent then $\mathbf{u}_1, \ldots, \mathbf{u}_m, \mathbf{u}_{m+1}, \ldots, \mathbf{u}_{m+n}$ are linearly dependent.

5.6. Let $\mathbf{u}_1, \ldots, \mathbf{u}_p, \mathbf{u}$ be linearly dependent. Show, by way of example, that $\mathbf{u}$ need not be equal to a linear combination of $\mathbf{u}_1, \ldots, \mathbf{u}_p$.

5.7. Let $\mathbf{u}_1, \ldots, \mathbf{u}_m$ be linearly independent and $\mathbf{u}_1, \ldots, \mathbf{u}_m, \mathbf{u}$ linearly dependent. Prove that $\mathbf{u}$ is a linear combination of $\mathbf{u}_1, \ldots, \mathbf{u}_m$.

5.8. Let $\mathbf{u}_1, \ldots, \mathbf{u}_p$ be linearly independent. If $\mathbf{u}$ cannot be expressed linearly in terms of $\mathbf{u}_1, \ldots, \mathbf{u}_p$, show that $\mathbf{u}_1, \ldots, \mathbf{u}_p, \mathbf{u}$ are linearly independent.

5.9. Let μ be the maximum number of linearly independent vectors in the set $\mathbf{u}_1, \ldots, \mathbf{u}_m$ and ν be the maximum number of linearly independent vectors in the set $\mathbf{w}_1, \ldots, \mathbf{w}_n$ where $\mathbf{u}_i, \mathbf{w}_j$ are vectors of the same order. Show that the maximum number of linearly independent vectors in the set $\mathbf{u}_1, \ldots, \mathbf{u}_m, \mathbf{w}_1, \ldots, \mathbf{w}_n$ is $\leqq \mu + \nu$.

5.10. If $\mathbf{u}_1, \ldots, \mathbf{u}_n$ is a set of mutually orthogonal nonzero vectors, i.e. $\mathbf{u}_i \circ \mathbf{u}_j = 0$ for $i \neq j$ *and* $\mathbf{u}_i \circ \mathbf{u}_i \neq 0$, then these vectors are linearly independent.

5.11. Give n vectors in V_n such that

(a) $\mathbf{u}_1, \ldots, \mathbf{u}_n$ are linearly dependent.
(b) for each j, $1 \leq j \leq n$, $\mathbf{u}_j$ is a linear combination of $\mathbf{u}_1, \ldots, \mathbf{u}_{j-1}, \mathbf{u}_{j+1}, \ldots, \mathbf{u}_n$.

5.12. Prove, by way of example, that a minimal spanning subset of a given set of vectors is not, in general, uniquely determined.

5.13. Show that the set $\mathbf{u}_1, \ldots, \mathbf{u}_p$ is a minimal spanning subset of a subspace S if and only if every element $\mathbf{u} \in$ S is expressed as a unique linear combination of $\mathbf{u}_1, \ldots, \mathbf{u}_p$ [i.e., if and only if from $\mathbf{u} = \alpha_1\mathbf{u}_1 + \ldots + \alpha_p\mathbf{u}_p$ and $\mathbf{u} = \beta_1\mathbf{u}_1 + \ldots + \beta_p\mathbf{u}_p$ it follows that $\alpha_1 = \beta_1, \ldots, \alpha_p = \beta_p$].

5.14. Show that if a matrix **B** is obtained from a matrix **A** by a sequence of row operations, then **A** can be obtained by applying row operations to **B**.

5.15. Let **a** and **b** be two nonzero elements of V_3. In E_3, **a** and **b** are parallel if and only if they are linearly dependent.

5.16. Let **a** and **b** be two given nonzero elements of V_3. If **r** is any vector such that **a** and **r** are linearly dependent, show that

(i) The points **r** in E_3 lie on a straight line through the origin.

(ii) The points $\mathbf{r} + \mathbf{b}$ in E_3 lie on a straight line through the point **b**. This line passes through the origin if and only if **a** and **b** are linearly dependent.

5.17. Let **a** and **b** be two given nonzero linearly independent elements of V_3. If **r** is any vector such that **a**, **b**, **r** are linearly dependent, show that

(i) The points **r** in E_3 lie on a plane through the origin.

(ii) The points $\mathbf{r} + \mathbf{c}$, where **c** is a given vector, lie on a plane through the point **c**. This plane passes through the origin if and only if **a**, **b** and **c** are linearly dependent.

5.18. Let $\mathbf{a} \equiv \{a\}$ and $\mathbf{b} \equiv \{b\}$, where $\mathbf{a} \neq \mathbf{0}$, be two elements of V_3. Show that $\{a\}^T\{x\} = \{b\}$ is the equation of a plane in E_3 perpendicular to the vector **a**. This plane passes through the origin if and only if $\mathbf{b} = \mathbf{0}$.

LECTURE 6

The Row Echelon Algorithm and Linear Homogeneous Systems

The row echelon algorithm • Columns with a corner entry • The row reduced form of a matrix • Minimal spanning subsets for the row space of a matrix in terms of the nonzero rows of the row reduced form of the matrix • Linear independence of rows with corner entries of the row reduced matrix • Basis for a subspace • Rank • Solution space of a system of linear homogeneous equations • Rank(**A**) + dim (solution space of $\mathbf{A}\{x\} = \{0\}$) $= n$ • Basis for the solution space • Solution by inspection of the row reduced form of the coefficient matrix • Problems

We shall now construct the basic algorithm of these lectures, the **row echelon algorithm.** The use of this algorithm, is commonly referred to as Gauss elimination.

We start with a given *nonzero* matrix **A** belonging to $\mathsf{M}_{m,n}$. Since **A** is nonzero, we can perform

STEP 1. *Find the first column of* **A**, *counting from the left, that is not a zero column.*

Suppose that this column is the i_1th column, so that **A** will, in general, look like

$$\mathbf{A}=\left(\begin{array}{cccc|c|ccc} & & & & \overset{i_1\text{th column}}{\downarrow} & & & \\ 0 & 0 & \ldots & 0 & X & X & \ldots & X \\ 0 & 0 & \ldots & 0 & X & X & \ldots & X \\ \cdot & \cdot & & \cdot & \cdot & \cdot & & \cdot \\ \cdot & \cdot & & \cdot & \cdot & \cdot & & \cdot \\ \cdot & \cdot & & \cdot & \cdot & \cdot & & \cdot \\ 0 & 0 & \ldots & 0 & X & X & \ldots & X \end{array}\right).$$

The symbols X in the above array stand for given real numbers. Since at least one of the entries in the i_1th column of **A** is nonzero, we can use the first row operation to perform

STEP 2. *Bring the first nonzero entry in the column found in step 1 (the i_1th column) into the first position in that column.*

The second row operation is used to perform

STEP 3. *Divide the first row of the matrix by the entry that now sits in the first row of the column found in step 1.*

After these three steps, the matrix will look as follows:

$$\begin{array}{c} \qquad\qquad\qquad i_1\text{th column} \\ \qquad\qquad\qquad\downarrow \\ \left(\begin{array}{cccc|c|ccc} 0 & 0 & \ldots & 0 & 1 & X & \ldots & X \\ 0 & 0 & \ldots & 0 & X & X & \ldots & X \\ \cdot & \cdot & & \cdot & \cdot & \cdot & & \cdot \\ \cdot & \cdot & & \cdot & \cdot & \cdot & & \cdot \\ \cdot & \cdot & & \cdot & \cdot & \cdot & & \cdot \\ 0 & 0 & \ldots & 0 & X & X & \ldots & X \end{array}\right). \end{array}$$

We now use the third row operation successively to perform

STEP 4A. *Reduce to zero every entry but the first in the column found in step 1 by subtracting an appropriate multiple of the first row from each of the other rows in turn.*

The above sequence of steps results in the following form for the matrix:

$$\begin{array}{c} \qquad\qquad\qquad i_1\text{th column} \\ \qquad\qquad\qquad\downarrow \\ \left(\begin{array}{cccc||c|ccc} 0 & 0 & \ldots & 0 & 1 & X & \ldots & X \\ \hline 0 & 0 & \ldots & 0 & 0 & X & \ldots & X \\ \cdot & \cdot & & \cdot & \cdot & \cdot & & \cdot \\ \cdot & \cdot & & \cdot & \cdot & \cdot & & \cdot \\ \cdot & \cdot & & \cdot & \cdot & \cdot & & \cdot \\ 0 & 0 & \ldots & 0 & 0 & X & \ldots & X \end{array}\right). \end{array}$$

The i_1th column is now referred to as a **column with a corner entry.** The **corner entry** in the i_1th column is the entry that we have enclosed in the illustration with double lines to the left.

The $(m-1)$-by-$(n-i_1)$ matrix that is enclosed in the lower right-hand box in the above illustration is a new matrix to which we can apply the above sequence of steps. We refer to this new matrix as the **step 4 subordinate matrix**. We can thus perform

STEP 5. *Apply step 1 through 4 to the step 4 subordinate matrix.*

Thus, if the i_2th column of the original matrix contains the first nonzero column of the step 4 subordinate matrix, we would then have

$$\begin{array}{c} \quad\quad i_1 \quad\quad\quad\quad\quad i_2 \\ \quad\quad \downarrow \quad\quad\quad\quad\quad \downarrow \\ \begin{pmatrix} 0 & 0 & \ldots & 0 & 1 & X & \ldots & X & X & X & \ldots & X \\ 0 & 0 & \ldots & 0 & 0 & 0 & \ldots & 0 & 1 & X & \ldots & X \\ 0 & 0 & \ldots & 0 & 0 & 0 & \ldots & 0 & 0 & X & \ldots & X \\ \cdot & \cdot & & \cdot & \cdot & \cdot & & \cdot & \cdot & \cdot & & \cdot \\ \cdot & \cdot & & \cdot & \cdot & \cdot & & \cdot & \cdot & \cdot & & \cdot \\ \cdot & \cdot & & \cdot & \cdot & \cdot & & \cdot & \cdot & \cdot & & \cdot \\ 0 & 0 & \ldots & 0 & 0 & 0 & \ldots & 0 & 0 & X & \ldots & X \end{pmatrix} \end{array}$$

new step 4
subordinate
matrix

There is another operation that we now need to perform before applying step 5 again to the new step 4 subordinate matrix. We accordingly designate this new step as step 4B and perform it by the third elementary row operation. (The inclusion of this step after step 4A in the original sequence of steps will not change anything since there is no row above the first row to which the original sequence was applied.)

STEP 4B. *Reduce to zero all but the corner entry of the column of the complete matrix with the corner entry found in step 4A. This is to be done by using the row of the complete matrix with the corner entry that was found in step 4A.*

The matrix now looks as follows:

$$\begin{array}{c} \quad\quad i_1 \quad\quad\quad\quad\quad i_2 \\ \quad\quad \downarrow \quad\quad\quad\quad\quad \downarrow \\ \begin{pmatrix} 0 & 0 & \ldots & 0 & 1 & X & \ldots & X & 0 & X & \ldots & X \\ 0 & 0 & \ldots & 0 & 0 & 0 & \ldots & 0 & 1 & X & \ldots & X \\ 0 & 0 & \ldots & 0 & 0 & 0 & \ldots & 0 & 0 & X & \ldots & X \\ \cdot & \cdot & & \cdot & \cdot & \cdot & & \cdot & \cdot & \cdot & & \cdot \\ \cdot & \cdot & & \cdot & \cdot & \cdot & & \cdot & \cdot & \cdot & & \cdot \\ \cdot & \cdot & & \cdot & \cdot & \cdot & & \cdot & \cdot & \cdot & & \cdot \\ 0 & 0 & \ldots & 0 & 0 & 0 & \ldots & 0 & 0 & X & \ldots & X \end{pmatrix} \end{array}.$$

This process is obviously a cycle since step 5 simply calls for repeating the process again. We must thus provide a stop statement. After at most n cycles of these operations we will have exhausted the entries of the matrix or we will arrive at a zero step 4 subordinate matrix. (Recall that $A \in M_{m,n}$ and hence there can be no more than n columns with corner elements since there are only n columns of A.) We thus have

STEP 6. *Stop when the step 4 subordinate matrix is either the zero matrix, or no matrix at all.*

When this algorithm is completed, the matrix will have a definite form, the **row echelon form**

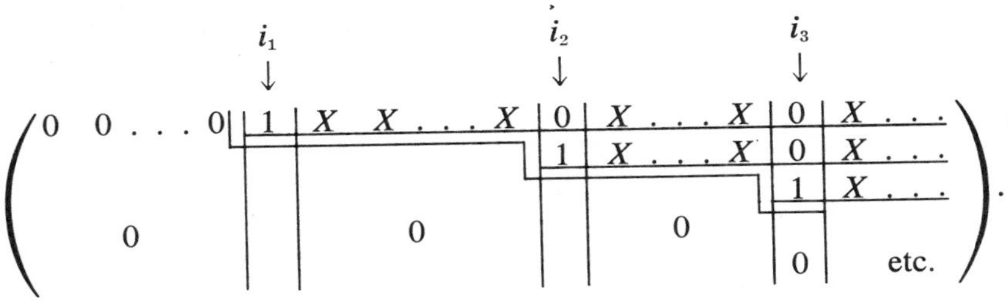

The algorithm used in the construction of the row echelon form of a given matrix **A** consists of a finite sequence of steps and each step is uniquely determined by the entries of the matrix **A**. The row echelon algorithm thus gives a *unique* row reduced form for each given matrix **A**. It can actually be proved that *the row reduced form of a given matrix* **A** *is always the same,* even if we use a different algorithm for constructing the row reduced form; that is, *the row reduced form of a given matrix* **A** *is a unique matrix.*

When we apply the elementary row operations to a given matrix, the resulting matrix is row equivalent to the given matrix, but it is *not equal* to the given matrix, as even the simplest example shows. It is convenient, however, to have a notation for the fact that two matrices are row equivalent. We accordingly write

$$\mathbf{A}\,\Omega\,\mathbf{B}$$

if **A** and **B** are row equivalent. Thus, in the example used in constructing the row echelon algorithm, we would write

$\mathbf{A}\,\Omega$

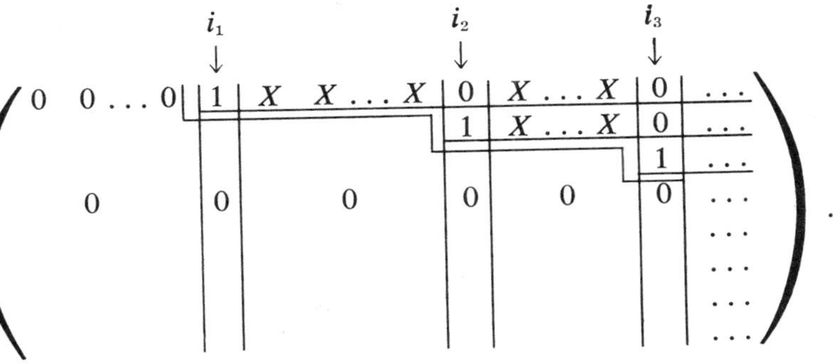

The following example should serve to illustrate the algorithm of row echelon reduction. The matrix **A** belongs to $\mathsf{M}_{3,4}$ with

$$\mathbf{A}=\begin{pmatrix} 0 & 0 & 3 & -1 \\ 0 & -1 & 4 & 7 \\ 0 & -1 & 7 & 6 \end{pmatrix};$$

Steps 1 and 2 ($i_1=2$ since the first nonzero column of $\mathbf{A}$ is the second)

$$\mathbf{A}\ \Omega\begin{pmatrix} 0 & -1 & 4 & 7 \\ 0 & 0 & 3 & -1 \\ 0 & -1 & 7 & 6 \end{pmatrix};$$

Step 3

$$\mathbf{A}\ \Omega\begin{pmatrix} 0 & 1 & -4 & -7 \\ 0 & 0 & 3 & -1 \\ 0 & -1 & 7 & 6 \end{pmatrix};$$

Step 4A

$$\mathbf{A}\ \Omega\begin{pmatrix} 0 & 1 & -4 & -7 \\ 0 & 0 & 3 & -1 \\ 0 & 0 & 3 & -1 \end{pmatrix};$$

and the step 4 subordinate matrix is

$$\begin{pmatrix} 3 & -1 \\ 3 & -1 \end{pmatrix};$$

Step 5

$$\mathbf{A}\ \Omega\begin{pmatrix} 0 & 1 & -4 & -7 \\ 0 & 0 & 1 & -1/3 \\ 0 & 0 & 3 & -1 \end{pmatrix}\Omega\begin{pmatrix} 0 & 1 & -4 & -7 \\ 0 & 0 & 1 & -1/3 \\ 0 & 0 & 0 & 0 \end{pmatrix};$$

Step 4B

$$\mathbf{A}\ \Omega\begin{pmatrix} 0 & 1 & 0 & -25/3 \\ 0 & 0 & 1 & -1/3 \\ 0 & 0 & 0 & 0 \end{pmatrix};$$

step 4 subordinate matrix is the zero matrix and hence

Step 6, STOP.

We now claim that *the nonzero rows of the row echelon form of any matrix* $\mathbf{A}$ *constitute a minimal spanning subset for the row space of* $\mathbf{A}$. If we use $\mathbf{A}_R$ to denote the **row echelon form of A,** then in the general case we have

$$\mathbf{A}_R=\left(\begin{array}{c|c|c|c|c|c|c}
0\ \ldots\ 0 & 1 & X \ldots X & 0 & X \ldots X & 0 & X \ldots \\
 & & & 1 & X \ldots X & 0 & X \ldots \\
 & & & & & 1 & X \ldots \\
0 & & 0 & & 0 & & \ldots \\
 & & & & & & \ldots \\
 & & & & & & \ldots
\end{array}\right).$$

Thus, each *nonzero* row of $\mathbf{A}_R$ will have a one in a column where all of the other *nonzero* rows of $\mathbf{A}_R$ will have zeros in that column. If we denote the *nonzero* rows of $\mathbf{A}_R$ by row matrices $\{u_1\}^T, \ldots, \{u_r\}^T$, which are referred to as the **rows with a corner entry**, then the r vectors $\{u_1\}, \ldots, \{u_r\}$ are easily seen to be *linearly independent*. For example if $\mathbf{A} \in \mathsf{M}_{4,7}$ and

$$\mathbf{A}_R=\begin{pmatrix} 0 & 1 & 2 & 4 & 0 & -1 & 0 \\ 0 & 0 & 0 & 0 & 1 & 6 & 0 \\ 0 & 0 & 0 & 0 & 0 & 0 & 1 \\ 0 & 0 & 0 & 0 & 0 & 0 & 0 \end{pmatrix},$$

then the second, fifth, and seventh columns are columns with a corner entry; the first, second, and third rows are rows with a corner entry,

$$\{u_1\}^T=[0, 1, 2, 4, 0, -1, 0],$$
$$\{u_2\}^T=[0, 0, 0, 0, 1, 6, 0],$$
$$\{u_3\}^T=[0, 0, 0, 0, 0, 0, 1],$$

$$\{u_1\}=\begin{Bmatrix} 0 \\ 1 \\ 2 \\ 4 \\ 0 \\ -1 \\ 0 \end{Bmatrix}, \quad \{u_2\}=\begin{Bmatrix} 0 \\ 0 \\ 0 \\ 0 \\ 1 \\ 6 \\ 0 \end{Bmatrix}, \quad \{u_3\}=\begin{Bmatrix} 0 \\ 0 \\ 0 \\ 0 \\ 0 \\ 0 \\ 1 \end{Bmatrix}.$$

Thus,

$$c_1\{u_1\}+c_2\{u_2\}+c_3\{u_3\}=\begin{Bmatrix} 0 \\ c_1 \\ 2c_1 \\ 4c_1 \\ c_2 \\ -c_1+6c_2 \\ c_3 \end{Bmatrix}$$

is the zero column matrix belonging to $\mathsf{M}_{7,1}$ only when $c_1=c_2=c_3=0$. This shows that $\{u_1\}\equiv\mathbf{u}_1$, $\{u_2\}\equiv\mathbf{u}_2$, $\{u_3\}\equiv\mathbf{u}_3$ are linearly independent elements of V_7.

We know that the row space of $\mathbf{A}$ is identical with the row space of $\mathbf{A}_R$ since $\mathbf{A}\ \Omega\ \mathbf{A}_R$. The rows of $\mathbf{A}_R$ thus span the row space of $\mathbf{A}$. The non-zero rows of $\mathbf{A}_R$ also span the row space of $\mathbf{A}_R$ (of $\mathbf{A}$) since the zero rows may always be discarded from a spanning set. We have just established, however, that the *nonzero* rows of $\mathbf{A}_R$ are *linearly independent*. The non-zero rows of $\mathbf{A}_R$ thus satisfy both of the requirements established in the previous lecture in order that a collection of vectors be a minimal spanning subset of a subspace (the subspace being the row space of $\mathbf{A}$).

A minimal spanning set of a subspace is called a **basis** for the subspace. We may thus summarize our findings as follows. *The nonzero rows of the row echelon form of any matrix* $\mathbf{A}$ *is a basis for the row space of* $\mathbf{A}$. The definition of the dimension of a subspace given in the last lecture then gives us the fact that *the number of nonzero rows in the row echelon form of any matrix* $\mathbf{A}$ *is equal to the dimension of the row space of* $\mathbf{A}$. The dimension of the row space of a matrix $\mathbf{A}$ has had another name given to it in the literature. The **rank** of a matrix $\mathbf{A}$, denoted by rank($\mathbf{A}$), is equal to the dimension of the row space of $\mathbf{A}$. Thus, rank($\mathbf{A}$) = (*number of nonzero rows of* $\mathbf{A}_R$). In the numerical example given above, the number of nonzero rows of $\mathbf{A}_R$ is 3, and hence rank($\mathbf{A}$) = 3 for the matrix $\mathbf{A}$ used in the example.

The row echelon algorithm has a very important use: it provides the basis upon which all solutions of the matrix equation

$$\mathbf{A}\{x\}=\{0\} \tag{6.1}$$

can be found *by inspection*. We know, by the row echelon algorithm, that $\mathbf{A}$ and $\mathbf{A}_R$ are row equivalent matrices. Thus, the matrix equation (6.1) is equivalent to the matrix equation

$$\mathbf{A}_R\{x\}=\{0\}. \tag{6.2}$$

Now, with $\mathbf{A}\in\mathsf{M}_{p,n}$, $\{x\}\in\mathsf{M}_{n,1}$, $\{0\}\in\mathsf{M}_{p,1}$ and rank($\mathbf{A}$) $=r$, so that $r\le\min(p,n)$, the matrix equation $\mathbf{A}_R\{x\}=\{0\}$ has the form

$$
\begin{array}{r}
1\rightarrow\\ 2\rightarrow\\ 3\rightarrow\\ \cdot\\ \cdot\\ \cdot\\ r\rightarrow\\ r+1\rightarrow\\ \\ \\
\end{array}
\left(\begin{array}{cccccccccccccccc}
 & & & i_1\downarrow & & & & i_2\downarrow & & & & i_3\downarrow & & & & i_r\downarrow \quad \\
0 & \cdots & 0 & 1 & X & \cdots & X & 0 & X & \cdots & X & 0 & X & \cdots & \cdots & 0 \;\; X \cdots\\
 & & & & & & & 1 & X & \cdots & X & 0 & X & \cdots & \cdots & 0 \;\; X \cdots\\
 & & & & & & & & & & & 1 & X & \cdots & \cdots & 0 \;\; X \cdots\\
 & & & & & & & & & & & & & & & \vdots \quad \vdots\\
 & & & & 0 & & & & & & & & & & & 1 \;\; X \cdots\\
 & & & & & & & & & & & & & & & 0 \;\; 0 \cdots\\
 & & & & & & & & & & & & & & & \vdots \quad \vdots\\
 & \cdots & & & & \cdots & & & & \cdots & & & & \cdots & & 0 \;\; 0 \cdots
\end{array}\right)
\left\{\begin{array}{c} x_1\\ x_2\\ x_3\\ \vdots\\ x_r\\ \vdots\\ x_n \end{array}\right\}
$$

$$
=\begin{array}{r}
1\rightarrow\\ 2\rightarrow\\ 3\rightarrow\\ \cdot\\ \cdot\\ \cdot\\ r\rightarrow\\ r+1\rightarrow\\ \cdot\\ \cdot\\ \cdot\\ p\rightarrow
\end{array}
\left\{\begin{array}{r}
x_{i_1}+Xx_{i_1+1}\cdots Xx_{i_2-1}+Xx_{i_2+1}+\cdots+Xx_{i_3-1}+Xx_{i_3+1}+\cdots+Xx_{i_r-1}+Xx_{i_r+1}+\cdots+Xx_n\\
x_{i_2}\;+Xx_{i_2+1}+\cdots+Xx_{i_3-1}+Xx_{i_3+1}+\cdots+Xx_{i_r-1}+Xx_{i_r+1}+\cdots+Xx_n\\
x_{i_3}\;+Xx_{i_3+1}+\cdots+Xx_{i_r-1}+Xx_{i_r+1}+\cdots+Xx_n\\
\vdots\qquad\qquad\qquad\\
x_{i_r}\;+Xx_{i_r+1}+\cdots+Xx_n\\
0\qquad\qquad\qquad\\
0\qquad\qquad\qquad\\
\vdots\qquad\qquad\qquad\\
0\qquad\qquad\qquad
\end{array}\right\}=\{0\},
$$

where the X's stand for numbers that occur in the matrix $\mathbf{A}_R$. The matrix equation (6.2) is thus seen to be equivalent to the following system of r simultaneous equations when we use the definition of equality of column matrices:

$$\begin{aligned}
0 &= x_{i_1} + Xx_{i_1+1} + \dots + Xx_{i_2-1} + Xx_{i_2+1} + \dots + Xx_{i_3-1} + Xx_{i_3+1} + \dots + Xx_{i_r-1} + Xx_{i_r+1} + \dots + Xx_n, \\
0 &= x_{i_2} + Xx_{i_2+1} + \dots + Xx_{i_3-1} + Xx_{i_3+1} + \dots + Xx_{i_r-1} + Xx_{i_r+1} + \dots + Xx_n, \\
0 &= x_{i_3} + Xx_{i_3+1} + \dots + Xx_{i_r-1} + Xx_{i_r+1} + \dots + Xx_n, \\
&\vdots \\
0 &= x_{i_r} + Xx_{i_r+1} + \dots + Xx_n.
\end{aligned} \tag{6.3}$$

This system of equations can be solved by inspection:

$$\begin{aligned}
x_{i_1} &= -(Xx_{i_r+1} + \dots + Xx_{i_2-1} + Xx_{i_2+1} + \dots + Xx_{i_3-1} + Xx_{i_3+1} + \dots + Xx_{i_r-1} + Xx_{i_r+1} + \dots + Xx_n), \\
x_{i_2} &= -(Xx_{i_2+1} + \dots + Xx_{i_3-1} + Xx_{i_3+1} + \dots + Xx_{i_r-1} + Xx_{i_r+1} + \dots + Xx_n), \\
x_{i_3} &= -(Xx_{i_3+1} + \dots + Xx_{i_r-1} + Xx_{i_r+1} + \dots + Xx_n), \\
&\vdots \\
x_{i_r} &= -(Xx_{i_r+1} + \dots + Xx_n).
\end{aligned} \tag{6.4}$$

Because of the form of $\mathbf{A}_R$, we have been able to solve for the r x's, corresponding to the r "corners" of the r nonzero rows of $\mathbf{A}_R$, in terms of the remaining $n-r=(n-\text{rank}(\mathbf{A}))$ x's [recall that we have assumed that $\text{rank}(\mathbf{A})=r$]. The $(n-\text{rank}(\mathbf{A}))$ x's that occur on the right-hand side of Eqs. (6.4) can be assigned any values we please and then Eqs. (6.4) give the r remaining x's such that all n of the x's that are determined in this way will constitute the entries of an element of $\mathsf{M}_{n,1}$ that will satisfy the matrix equation (6.1). Thus, when the $(n-\text{rank}(\mathbf{A}))$ x's that appear on the right hand side of Eqs. (6.4) are allowed to assume all possible values, and the r remaining x's have their values determined by Eqs. (6.4), we obtain the general solution of the matrix equation (6.1).

We know that the general solution of Eqs. (6.4) forms a subspace of $\mathsf{M}_{n,1}$ (i.e., forms a subspace of V_n under the identification $\mathbf{x}\equiv\{x\}$), while the ability to assign arbitrary values to $(n-\text{rank}(\mathbf{A}))$ of the x's and then to determine the remaining x's by Eqs. (6.4) suggests that the dimension of the **solution space** (subspace of solutions) of Eq. (6.1) would be $(n-\text{rank}(\mathbf{A}))$. We can actually establish this important fact. In the course of doing so, we will also establish a *basis* for the solution space; that is, a minimal spanning subset for the solution space.

The number of elements in any row of $\mathbf{A}$ is equal to the number of components of $\{x\}$, namely n, since $\{x\}\in\mathsf{M}_{n,1}$. When Eqs. (6.4) are used we can write

$$
\{x\}=\begin{Bmatrix} x_1\\ x_2\\ \cdot\\ \cdot\\ \cdot\\ x_{i_1}\\ \cdot\\ \cdot\\ \cdot\\ x_{i_2}\\ \cdot\\ \cdot\\ \cdot\\ x_{i_r}\\ \cdot\\ \cdot\\ \cdot\\ x_n \end{Bmatrix}
=
\begin{array}{r} \\ \\ \\ \\ \\ i_1\rightarrow \\ \\ \\ \\ i_2\rightarrow \\ \\ \\ \\ i_r\rightarrow \\ \\ \\ \\ \\ \end{array}
\begin{Bmatrix} x_1\\ \cdot\\ \cdot\\ \cdot\\ x_{i_1-1}\\ -Xx_{i_1+1}- \ . \ . \ . \ -Xx_{i_2-1}-Xx_{i_2+1}- \ . \ . \ . \ -Xx_{i_3-1}-Xx_{i_3+1}- \ . \ . \ . \ -Xx_{i_r-1}-Xx_{i_r+1}- \ . \ . \ . \ -Xx_n\\ x_{i_1+1}\\ \cdot\\ \cdot\\ \cdot\\ x_{i_2-1}\\ -Xx_{i_2+1}- \ . \ . \ . \ -Xx_{i_3-1}-Xx_{i_3+1}- \ . \ . \ . \ -Xx_{i_r-1}-Xx_{i_r+1}- \ . \ . \ . \ -Xx_n\\ \cdot\\ \cdot\\ \cdot\\ x_{i_r-1}\\ -Xx_{i_r+1}- \ . \ . \ . \ -Xx_n\\ x_{i_r+1}\\ \cdot\\ \cdot\\ \cdot\\ x_n \end{Bmatrix}, \qquad (6.5)
$$

where $i_1, i_2, \ldots, i_r$ list the r columns of $\mathbf{A}_R$ with a corner entry. Since the right-hand side of (6.5) contains the common factors $x_1, \ldots, x_{i_1-1}, x_{i_1+1}, \ldots, x_{i_2-1}, x_{i_2+1}, \ldots, x_{i_r-1}, x_{i_r+1}, \ldots, x_n$, we can write (6.5) in the equivalent form

$$
\{x\}=x_1\begin{Bmatrix} 1\\ 0\\ \cdot\\ \cdot\\ \cdot\\ 0 \end{Bmatrix}\begin{array}{l}\leftarrow 1\\ \\ \\ \\ \\ \\ \end{array}
+\ .\ .\ .\ +x_{i_1-1}\begin{Bmatrix} 0\\ \cdot\\ \cdot\\ \cdot\\ 0\\ 1\\ 0\\ \cdot\\ \cdot\\ \cdot\\ 0 \end{Bmatrix}\begin{array}{l} \\ \\ \\ \\ \\ \leftarrow(i_1-1)\\ \\ \\ \\ \\ \\ \end{array}
+x_{i_1+1}\begin{Bmatrix} 0\\ \cdot\\ \cdot\\ \cdot\\ 0\\ -X\\ 1\\ 0\\ \cdot\\ \cdot\\ \cdot\\ 0 \end{Bmatrix}\begin{array}{l} \\ \\ \\ \\ \\ \leftarrow i_1\\ \leftarrow(i_1+1)\\ \\ \\ \\ \\ \\ \end{array}
+\ .\ .\ .\ +x_{i_2-1}\begin{Bmatrix} 0\\ \cdot\\ \cdot\\ \cdot\\ 0\\ -X\\ 0\\ \cdot\\ \cdot\\ \cdot\\ 1\\ 0\\ \cdot\\ \cdot\\ \cdot\\ 0 \end{Bmatrix}\begin{array}{l} \\ \\ \\ \\ \\ \leftarrow i_1\\ \\ \\ \\ \\ \leftarrow(i_2-1)\\ \\ \\ \\ \\ \\ \end{array}
+\ .\ .\ .
$$

$$
+x_{i_3-1}\begin{Bmatrix} 0\\ \cdot\\ \cdot\\ \cdot\\ 0\\ -X\\ 0\\ \cdot\\ \cdot\\ \cdot\\ 0\\ -X\\ 0\\ \cdot\\ \cdot\\ \cdot\\ 0\\ 1\\ 0\\ \cdot\\ \cdot\\ \cdot\\ 0 \end{Bmatrix}\begin{array}{l} \\ \\ \\ \\ \\ \leftarrow i_1\\ \\ \\ \\ \\ \\ \leftarrow i_2\\ \\ \\ \\ \\ \\ \leftarrow(i_3-1)\\ \\ \\ \\ \\ \\ \end{array}
+x_{i_3+1}\begin{Bmatrix} 0\\ \cdot\\ \cdot\\ \cdot\\ 0\\ -X\\ 0\\ \cdot\\ \cdot\\ \cdot\\ 0\\ -X\\ 0\\ \cdot\\ \cdot\\ \cdot\\ -X\\ 1\\ 0\\ \cdot\\ \cdot\\ \cdot\\ 0 \end{Bmatrix}\begin{array}{l} \\ \\ \\ \\ \\ \leftarrow i_1\\ \\ \\ \\ \\ \\ \leftarrow i_2\\ \\ \\ \\ \\ \leftarrow i_3\\ \leftarrow(i_3+1)\\ \\ \\ \\ \\ \\ \end{array}
+\ .\ .\ .\ x_{n-1}\begin{Bmatrix} 0\\ \cdot\\ \cdot\\ \cdot\\ 0\\ -X\\ 0\\ \cdot\\ \cdot\\ \cdot\\ 0\\ -X\\ 0\\ \cdot\\ \cdot\\ \cdot\\ 0\\ -X\\ 0\\ \cdot\\ \cdot\\ \cdot\\ 1\\ 0 \end{Bmatrix}\begin{array}{l} \\ \\ \\ \\ \\ \leftarrow i_1\\ \\ \\ \\ \\ \\ \leftarrow i_2\\ \\ \\ \\ \\ \\ \leftarrow i_r\\ \\ \\ \\ \\ \leftarrow(n-1)\\ \\ \end{array}
+x_n\begin{Bmatrix} 0\\ \cdot\\ \cdot\\ \cdot\\ 0\\ -X\\ 0\\ \cdot\\ \cdot\\ \cdot\\ 0\\ -X\\ 0\\ \cdot\\ \cdot\\ \cdot\\ 0\\ -X\\ 0\\ \cdot\\ \cdot\\ \cdot\\ 0\\ 1 \end{Bmatrix}\begin{array}{l} \\ \\ \\ \\ \\ \leftarrow i_1\\ \\ \\ \\ \\ \\ \leftarrow i_2\\ \\ \\ \\ \\ \\ \leftarrow i_r\\ \\ \\ \\ \\ \leftarrow(n-1)\\ \leftarrow n \end{array}
. \qquad (6.6)
$$

That is, the general solution of Eq. (6.1) can be written as the linear combination of $(n-\text{rank}(\mathbf{A}))$ specific column matrices that are uniquely *determined from the row echelon form of* **A**. This system of $(n-\text{rank}(\mathbf{A}))$ column matrices given by Eq. (6.6) thus spans the solution space of the matrix equation $\mathbf{A}\{x\}=\{0\}$. Further, it is a minimal spanning set for the solution space of $\mathbf{A}\{x\}=\{0\}$ [i.e., a basis for the solution space of $\mathbf{A}\{x\}=\{0\}$ since the system of column matrices given by Eq. (6.6) is a linearly independent system]. This fact follows directly from the forms of the column matrices that occur in Eq. (6.6); that is, Eq. (6.6) shows that $\{x\}=\{0\}$ if and only if $x_1=x_2=\ldots=x_{i_1-1}=x_{i_1+1}=\ldots=x_{i_r-1}=x_{i_r+1}=x_{i_r+2}=\ldots=x_{n-1}=x_n=0$. Since the dimension of a subspace is equal to the number of column matrices that constitutes a minimal spanning set for the subspace, the dimensions of the solution space of $\mathbf{A}\{x\}=\{0\}$ is indeed equal to $(n-\text{rank}(\mathbf{A}))$. We summarize this finding with the formula

$$\text{rank}(\mathbf{A})+\dim(\text{solution space of } \mathbf{A}\{x\}=\{0\})=\dim(\mathsf{M}_{n,1})=n. \tag{6.7}$$

This is one of the most important results of linear algebra and it is the basis upon which many problems can be solved in a very simple fashion.

The calculations are admittedly lengthy in the general case, since generality always has its price. We thus give the solution of one of the example problems that we have already encountered: $n=4$,

$$\mathbf{A}=\begin{pmatrix} 0 & 0 & 3 & -1 \\ 0 & -1 & 4 & 7 \\ 0 & -1 & 7 & 6 \end{pmatrix},$$

$$\mathbf{A}_R=\begin{pmatrix} 0 & 1 & 0 & -25/3 \\ 0 & 0 & 1 & -1/3 \\ 0 & 0 & 0 & 0 \end{pmatrix}, \quad \text{rank}(\mathbf{A})=2,\ i_1=2,\ i_2=3,$$

$$\mathbf{A}_R\{x\}=\begin{Bmatrix} x_2-(25/3)x_4 \\ x_3-\ (1/3)x_4 \\ 0 \end{Bmatrix}=\{0\}$$

$$\Rightarrow x_2=\frac{25}{3}x_4,\quad x_3=\frac{1}{3}x_4,$$

$$\Rightarrow \{x\}=\begin{Bmatrix} x_1 \\ (25/3)x_4 \\ (1/3)x_4 \\ x_4 \end{Bmatrix}=x_1\begin{Bmatrix} 1 \\ 0 \\ 0 \\ 0 \end{Bmatrix}+x_4\begin{Bmatrix} 0 \\ 25/3 \\ 1/3 \\ 1 \end{Bmatrix}.$$

A basis for the row space of **A** is [0, 1, 0, −25/3], [0, 0, 1, −1/3], a basis for the solution space is

$$\{v\}_1=\begin{Bmatrix}1\\0\\0\\0\end{Bmatrix},\qquad \{v\}_2=\begin{Bmatrix}0\\25/3\\1/3\\1\end{Bmatrix}.$$

If we now take $\{v\}_1^T=[1,0,0,0]$, $\{v\}_2^T=[0,25/3,1/3,1]$ and adjoin them to the nonzero rows of $\mathbf{A}_R$ we have

$$\mathbf{W}=\begin{pmatrix}0 & 1 & 0 & -25/3\\ 0 & 0 & 1 & -1/3\\ 1 & 0 & 0 & 0\\ 0 & 25/3 & 1/3 & 1\end{pmatrix},$$

and rank$(\mathbf{W})=4=$dimension of V_4. In fact, a little thought will convince you that the basis for the row space of $\mathbf{A}$ together with the transposes of the basis for the solution space of $\mathbf{A}\{x\}=\{0\}$ always constitutes a basis for $\mathsf{M}_{1,n}$.

Problems

6.1. Use the row echelon algorithm to find (i) $\mathbf{A}_R$, (ii) a basis for the row space of $\mathbf{A}$, (iii) rank$(\mathbf{A})$, (iv) the general solution of $\mathbf{A}\{x\}=\{0\}$, (v) the dimension and a basis for the solution space of $\mathbf{A}\{x\}=\{0\}$ when the matrix $\mathbf{A}$ is

(a) $\begin{pmatrix}-2 & -6 & 12\\ 1 & 2 & -3\\ 3 & 8 & -12\end{pmatrix}$, (b) $\begin{pmatrix}12 & 18 & 6\\ 10 & 15 & 5\\ 34 & 51 & 17\\ 14 & 21 & 7\end{pmatrix}$,

(c) $\begin{pmatrix}24 & -7 & -14 & 21\\ -3 & 1 & 2 & -3\\ 6 & -2 & -4 & 6\end{pmatrix}$, (d) $\begin{pmatrix}3 & 0 & -1 & 2\\ 3 & 2 & 4 & -8\\ 9 & 6 & 10 & -20\end{pmatrix}$,

(e) $\begin{pmatrix}1 & 2 & 4 & -2\\ -1 & 4 & 8 & -4\\ 1 & -3 & -6 & 3\end{pmatrix}$.

6.2. Give a basis for each of the vector spaces spanned by the columns of the matrices in problem 6.1.

6.3. Determine α so that the system

$$\begin{aligned}5x_1-2x_2-4x_3+6x_4&=0\\ -x_1+x_2+2x_3-3x_4&=0\\ 7x_1-4x_2+(\alpha^2-\alpha-8)x_3+(-\alpha+13)x_4&=0\\ 6x_1-3x_2-6x_3+(4\alpha-1)x_4&=0\end{aligned}$$

has a two-dimensional solution space. For this value of α give the general solution and a basis for the solution space. For what value of α has the above system a three-dimensional row space?

6.4. Prove, by way of example, that a basis of a vector space is not uniquely determined.

6.5. Prove that, for any m-by-n matrix $\mathbf{A}$, the columns of $\mathbf{A}_R$ with a corner entry are linearly independent.

6.6. Prove that, for any m-by-n matrix $\mathbf{A}$, the nonzero rows of $\mathbf{A}_R$ form a minimal spanning set for the row space of $\mathbf{A}$.

6.7. Let $\mathbf{a}_\alpha \equiv \{a_\alpha\}$, $\alpha = 1, 2$, be two elements of V_n, where $\mathbf{a}_1 \neq \mathbf{0}$. Show that the vectors $\mathbf{a}_\alpha$ are linearly dependent if and only if

$$\operatorname{rank}\begin{pmatrix}\{a_1\}^T\\ \{a_2\}^T\end{pmatrix} = 1.$$

6.8. Give a geometric interpretation of problem 6.7 if $n = 3$.

6.9. Let $\{a_\alpha\}^T\{x\} = 0$, $\alpha = 1, 2$, be the equations of two planes in E_3. Show that

(i) The two planes have a line in common if

$$\operatorname{rank}\begin{pmatrix}\{a_1\}^T\\ \{a_2\}^T\end{pmatrix} = 2.$$

(ii) The two planes coincide if and only if

$$\operatorname{rank}\begin{pmatrix}\{a_1\}^T\\ \{a_2\}^T\end{pmatrix} = 1.$$

6.10. Let $\{a_i\}^T\{x\} = 0$, $i = 1, 2, 3$, be the equations of three planes in E_3. Show that these planes have

(i) only one point in common if

$$\operatorname{rank}\begin{pmatrix}\{a_1\}^T\\ \{a_2\}^T\\ \{a_3\}^T\end{pmatrix} = 3,$$

(ii) one common straight line if

$$\operatorname{rank}\begin{pmatrix}\{a_1\}^T\\ \{a_2\}^T\\ \{a_3\}^T\end{pmatrix} = 2,$$

(iii) they are identical if

$$\operatorname{rank}\begin{pmatrix}\{a_1\}^T\\ \{a_2\}^T\\ \{a_3\}^T\end{pmatrix} = 1.$$

LECTURE 7

Linear Systems and Their Solutions

Conditions for the existence of a nontrivial solution • Tests for linear independence using row echelon reduction • Elementary row matrices • Row reduction in terms of matrix multiplication • Computation of the row reducing matrix by row reduction of an augmented matrix • Consistency of linear inhomogeneous systems • Test for consistency by row reduction of the augmented matrix • Finding a particular solution by inspection from the row reduced form • General solution of a linear inhomogeneous system • Uniqueness and nonuniqueness of solutions • The homogeneous adjoint of a given system • Consistency test for inhomogeneous linear systems in terms of orthogonality of the inhomogeneous part with all solutions of the homogeneous adjoint system • Problems

Now that we know how to solve systems of homogeneous linear equations of the form

$$\mathbf{A}\{x\}=\{0\}, \quad \{0\}=\text{zero element of } \mathsf{M}_{n,1}, \tag{7.1}$$

there are several important results that we can obtain. It is clear that Eq. (7.1) always admits the **trivial solution**

$$\{x\}=\{0\}. \tag{7.2}$$

It is of obvious importance to know when Eq. (7.1) admits at least one nontrivial solution, for it will then also admit a solution space whose dimension is at least one. *If* $\{x\}$ *belongs to* $\mathsf{V}_n \equiv \mathsf{M}_{n,1}$, *if* $\mathbf{A}$ *belongs to* $\mathsf{M}_{p,n}$, *and if* $p<n$, *then* $\mathbf{A}\{x\}=\{0\}$ *has at least one nontrivial* (nonzero) *solution.* [*If we have p linear homogeneous equations in n unknowns with* $p<n$ *then there exists a nontrivial solution.*] This theorem is very easy to establish. We know that row echelon reduction of $\mathbf{A}$ gives us $\mathbf{A}_R$, and $\mathbf{A}_R$ gives us the number $\text{rank}(\mathbf{A})=$ (dimension of row space of $\mathbf{A}_R$). Now $\text{rank}(\mathbf{A})\leq p$ since $\mathbf{A}$ belongs to $\mathsf{M}_{p,n}$ and the dimension of the row space of $\mathbf{A}$ cannot exceed the number of rows of $\mathbf{A}$. We established in the last lecture that

$$\text{rank}(\mathbf{A})+\dim(\mathbf{A}\{x\}=\{0\})=n$$

and hence we have

$$\dim(\mathbf{A}\{x\}=\{0\})=n-\text{rank}(\mathbf{A}).$$

Since rank$(\mathbf{A}) \leq p$, we have

$$\dim(\mathbf{A}\{x\}=\{0\}) \geq n-p.$$

By hypothesis $n>p$, and hence we have the desired conclusion that

$$\dim(\mathbf{A}\{x\}=\{0\})>0;$$

that is, there is at least a one-dimensional space of solutions of $\mathbf{A}\{x\}=\{0\}$.

The exact same reasoning based on

$$\operatorname{rank}(\mathbf{A})+\dim(\mathbf{A}\{x\}=\{0\})=\dim(\mathsf{V}_n)=n$$

can be used to prove that *the system of equations* $\mathbf{A}\{x\}=\{0\}$, *for* $\{x\}$ *belonging to* $\mathsf{M}_{n,1}\equiv\mathsf{V}_n$ *and* $\mathbf{A}$ *belonging to* $\mathsf{M}_{p,n}$, *has only the trivial solution* $\{x\}=\{0\}$ *if and only if*

$$\operatorname{rank}(\mathbf{A})=n.$$

(Incidently, we have used the fact that *the dimension of a subspace which consists of the single entry* $\{0\}$ *is zero.*) We can also prove that this condition is sufficient directly from the given data and row echelon reduction. If $\mathbf{A}$ belongs to $\mathsf{M}_{p,n}$ and has rank n, then we must have $p\geq n$ and the row echelon form of $\mathbf{A}$ can only have the form

$$\mathbf{A}_R=\left(\begin{array}{ccccccc} & & & & & & n\\ & & & & & & \downarrow\\ 1&0&0&0&0&\cdots&0\\ &1&0&0&0&\cdots&0\\ & &1&0&0&\cdots&0\\ & & &1&0&\cdots&0\\ & & & &1&\cdots&0\\ & & & & &\cdots&0\\ & & & & & &1\\ \hline 0& &0& &0& &0\\ 0& &0& &0& &0\\ & & & & & &0 \end{array}\right)\begin{array}{l}\\ \\ \\ \\ \\ \\ \\ \\ \leftarrow n\\ \\ \\ \\ \end{array}=\left(\begin{array}{c} n\times n\\ \text{identity}\\ \text{matrix}\\ \\ \hline (p-n)\times n\ \text{zero}\\ \text{matrix}\end{array}\right)$$

Thus, $\mathbf{A}_R\{x\}=\{0\}$ gives $\left\{\begin{array}{c}\mathbf{E}\\ \mathbf{0}_1\end{array}\right\}\{x\}=\{0\}$ where $\mathbf{0}_1$ is the zero element of $\mathsf{M}_{p-n,n}$, and $\mathbf{E}$ is the identity element of $\mathsf{M}_{n,n}$. We thus have that $\mathbf{A}_R\{x\}=\{0\}$ is equivalent to $\mathbf{E}\{x\}=\{0\}\in\mathsf{M}_{n,1}$, that is, $\{x\}=\{0\}$.

When we defined the dimension of a subspace, we used the number of vectors in a minimal spanning subset of a given spanning set. It was thus not proved that the dimension of a subspace was a unique number. Suppose that we obtained two different minimal spanning subsets of a subspace T,

$$\{u\}_1, \ldots, \{u\}_r, \qquad \mathbf{u}_i \equiv \{u\}_i,$$

and

$$\{v\}_1, \ldots, \{v\}_s, \qquad \mathbf{v}_i \equiv \{v\}_i,$$

of T, with $s > r$. We want to show that this is impossible, that is, it is impossible to have a different number of vectors in a minimal spanning subset for a given subspace T. Since $\{u\}_1, \ldots, \{u\}_r$ are a spanning set for T, any element of T can be written as a linear combination of these elements. Since $\{v\}_1, \ldots,$ $\{v\}_s$ belong to T, there exist numbers w_{ji}, $i = 1, \ldots, s$, $j = 1, \ldots, r$ such that

$$\{v\}_1 = \sum_{j=1}^{r} w_{ji}\{u\}_j, \qquad i = 1, \ldots, s.$$

If we form a linear combination of the $\{v\}_i$, we have

$$\{w\} = \sum_{i=1}^{s} c_i\{v\}_i = \sum_{i=1}^{s} c_i \left(\sum_{j=1}^{r} w_{ji}\{u\}_j \right)$$

$$= \sum_{j=1}^{r} \left(\sum_{i=1}^{s} w_{ji}c_i \right) \{u\}_j$$

We can now test to see if the $\{v\}_i$ are linearly independent, for the definition of linear independence says that $\{w\} = \{0\}$ if and only if we have $c_1 = c_2 = \ldots = c_s = 0$. When we set $\{w\} = \{0\}$ and use the above calculation, we obtain

$$\{0\} = \sum_{j=1}^{r} \left(\sum_{i=1}^{s} w_{ji}c_i \right) \{u\}_j.$$

Since the $\{u\}_i$ are a minimal spanning subset of T, they are linearly independent, and hence the above equality can hold if and only if

$$\sum_{i=1}^{s} w_{ji}c_i = 0, \qquad j = 1, \ldots, r.$$

Since we have assumed that $s > r$, we have r equations in $s > r$ unknowns $c_1, \ldots, c_s$. We know that such a system always possesses a nontrivial solution; that is, we can find c's that satisfy

$$\sum_{i=1}^{s} w_{ji}c_i = 0, \qquad j = 1, \ldots, r,$$

where not all of the numbers $c_1, \ldots, c_s$ are equal to zero. We have therefore shown that

$$\{w\} = \sum_{i=1}^{s} c_i\{v\}_i = \{0\}$$

can be satisfied without all of the c's being equal to zero. This shows that the s vectors $\{v\}_1, \ldots, \{v\}_s$ are linearly dependent. The vectors $\{v\}_1, \ldots,$ $\{v\}_s$ thus do not form a minimal spanning set for T. The hypothesis that there can be different numbers of vectors in a minimal spanning set for a given subspace T is false; we must have $r = s$.

Now that we know that *the number of vectors in a minimal spanning set of a subspace is independent of how a spanning set of a subspace is specified,* there are several direct results that we can obtain. We know that the nonzero rows of $\mathbf{A}_R$ are a minimal spanning set for the row space of $\mathbf{A}$, and hence they are a linearly independent system of row matrices. This gives us a direct and simple means of deciding whether a given collection of vectors $\mathbf{w}_1, \mathbf{w}_2, \ldots, \mathbf{w}_p$ of V_n are linearly independent. We simply make the identification $\{w_i\} \equiv \mathbf{w}_i$, take the transposes of these elements of $\mathsf{M}_{n,1}$, form the matrix

$$\mathbf{A} = \begin{pmatrix} \{w_1\}^T \\ \cdot \\ \cdot \\ \cdot \\ \{w_p\}^T \end{pmatrix},$$

and then compute $\mathbf{A}_R$. Since $\{w_1\}^T, \ldots, \{w_p\}^T$ span the row space of $\mathbf{A}$, they are linearly independent if and only if the dimension of the row space of $\mathbf{A}$ is equal to p; that is, if and only if the number of nonzero rows of $\mathbf{A}_R$ is p. If $\operatorname{rank}(\mathbf{A}) = q < p$, then $\mathbf{w}_1, \ldots, \mathbf{w}_p$ are linearly dependent and span a subspace of V_n whose dimension is q.

Suppose that we are given a system of p elements $\mathbf{w}_1, \ldots, \mathbf{w}_p$ of V_n and we wish to know whether a given vector $\mathbf{u}$ belongs to the subspace spanned by the p given vectors $\mathbf{w}_1, \ldots, \mathbf{w}_p$. If $\mathbf{u}$ belongs to the subspace spanned by the given vectors $\mathbf{w}_1, \ldots, \mathbf{w}_p$, then the $p+1$ vectors $\mathbf{w}_1, \ldots, \mathbf{w}_p, \mathbf{u}$ span the same subspace of V_n as is spanned by the vectors $\mathbf{w}_1, \ldots, \mathbf{w}_p$. If we proceed as before and make use of what we know about $\mathbf{A}_R$, we see that *$\mathbf{u}$ belongs to the subspace spanned by $\mathbf{w}_1, \ldots, \mathbf{w}_p$ if and only if*

$$\operatorname{rank}\begin{pmatrix} \{w_1\}^T \\ \cdot \\ \cdot \\ \cdot \\ \{w_p\}^T \\ \{u\}^T \end{pmatrix} = \operatorname{rank}\begin{pmatrix} \{w_1\}^T \\ \cdot \\ \cdot \\ \cdot \\ \{w_p\}^T \end{pmatrix}$$

Starting with any nonzero matrix $\mathbf{A}$ we have a fixed procedure [i.e., the row-echelon algorithm] for obtaining a matrix $\mathbf{A}_R$ such that the systems $\mathbf{A}\{x\} = \{0\}$ and $\mathbf{A}_R\{x\} = \{0\}$ are equivalent and $\mathbf{A}_R$ has the row-echelon form. The proof that *the matrix $\mathbf{A}_R$ is uniquely determined when the matrix $\mathbf{A}$ is given* is left to the student as an exercise. The row-echelon algorithm uses only the three elementary row operations and at each step the row-operation that is used is uniquely dictated by the entries of the matrix $\mathbf{A}$.

It is useful at this point to introduce matrices which will perform the elementary row operations by means of matrix multiplication. Let $\mathbf{A}$ belong to $\mathsf{M}_{p,n}$. The **elementary row matrix** $\mathbf{E}_{\mathrm{I}}(r,s)$, that interchanges the rth and the sth rows of $\mathbf{A}$ by means of the matrix product $\mathbf{E}_1(r,s)\mathbf{A}$, belongs to $\mathsf{M}_{p,p}$ and is given by

$$\mathbf{E}_{\mathrm{I}}(r,s) = \left(\begin{array}{cc|c|ccc|c|cc}
1 & & & & & & & & \\
 & \ddots & & & & & & & 0 \\
 & 1 & 0 & 0 & \cdots & 0 & 0 & 0 & \\ \hline
 & 0 & 0 & 0 & \cdots & 0 & 1 & 0 & \\ \hline
 & 0 & 0 & 1 & & 0 & 0 & 0 & \\
0 & & \vdots & & \ddots & & \vdots & & 0 \\
 & 0 & 0 & 0 & & 1 & 0 & 0 & \\ \hline
 & 0 & 1 & 0 & \cdots & 0 & 0 & 0 & \\ \hline
 & 0 & 0 & 0 & \cdots & 0 & 0 & 1 & \\
0 & & & & 0 & & & & \ddots \\
 & & & & & & & & 1 \\
 & & \uparrow & & & & \uparrow & & \\
 & & r & & & & s & &
\end{array}\right) \begin{array}{l} \\ \\ \\ \leftarrow r \\ \\ \\ \\ \leftarrow s \\ \\ \\ \\ \\ \\ \end{array} . \quad (7.3)$$

The **elementary row matrix** $\mathbf{E}_{\mathrm{II}}(r;b)$ that multiplies the rth row of $\mathbf{A}$ by the number b belongs to $\mathsf{M}_{p,p}$ and is given by

$$\mathbf{E}_{\mathrm{II}}(r;b) = \left(\begin{array}{cc|c|cc}
1 & & & & \\
 & \ddots & 0 & & 0 \\
0 & 1 & 0 & 0 & \\ \hline
 & 0 & b & 0 & \\ \hline
 & 0 & 0 & 1 & \\
 & & & \ddots & 0 \\
0 & & & 0 & \ddots \\
 & & & & 1 \\
 & & \uparrow & & \\
 & & r & &
\end{array}\right) \begin{array}{l} \\ \\ \\ \leftarrow r. \\ \\ \\ \\ \\ \\ \\ \end{array} \quad (7.4)$$

The **elementary row matrix** $\mathbf{E}_{\text{III}}(r,s;c)$ that replaces the rth row by itself plus c times the sth row belongs to $\mathsf{M}_{p,p}$ and is given by

$$
{}_{\text{II}}(r,s;c)=\left(\begin{array}{ccccccccc}
1 \; 1 \; 1 \ddots & 0 & & & 0 & & & & 0\\
0 & 1 & 0 & 0 & & 0 & 0 & 0 & \\
 & 0 & 1 & 0 & & 0 & c & 0 & \\
 & 0 & 0 & 1 & & 0 & 0 & 0 & \\
0 & & & & \ddots \; 0 \; \ddots & & 0 & & 0\\
 & 0 & 0 & 0 & & 1 & 0 & 0 & \\
 & 0 & 0 & 0 & & 0 & 1 & 0 & \\
 & 0 & 0 & 0 & & 0 & 0 & 1 & \\
0 & & & & 0 & & 0 & & \ddots \; 1
\end{array}\right)
\begin{array}{c}
\\ \\ \leftarrow r \\ \\ \\ \\ \leftarrow s \\ \\ \\
\end{array}
\quad . \qquad (7.5)
$$

$$
\uparrow r \qquad\qquad \uparrow s
$$

Note that *we obtain any elementary row operation matrix by performing the corresponding operation on the identity matrix.*

Let S denote the collection of all p-by-p matrices that can be obtained by forming finitely many products of $\mathbf{E}_{\text{I}}$, $\mathbf{E}_{\text{II}}$, and $\mathbf{E}_{\text{III}}$. We know that for each given $\mathbf{A}$ belonging to $\mathsf{M}_{p,n}$, there exists an element $\mathbf{S}_A$ of S such that

$$\mathbf{S}_A\mathbf{A}=\mathbf{A}_R. \tag{7.6}$$

The matrix $\mathbf{S}_A$ is the unique ordered product of the specific matrices $\mathbf{E}_{\text{I}}$, $\mathbf{E}_{\text{II}}$, and $\mathbf{E}_{\text{III}}$ that accomplish the row reduction of $\mathbf{A}$ by the given row-echelon algorithm. Though $\mathbf{S}_A$ is uniquely determined when A is given, it is left to the student as an exercise to prove that there are matrices $\mathbf{A}$ such that $\mathbf{SA}=\mathbf{A}_R$, $\mathbf{S}\in$S, and $\mathbf{S}\neq\mathbf{S}_A$; that is a *matrix which row reduces a given matrix is not necessarily unique.*

Equation (7.6) is just another way of writing $\mathbf{A}\;\Omega\;\mathbf{A}_R$, since multiplying $\mathbf{A}$ by $\mathbf{S}_A$ on the left is what accomplishes row-echelon reduction by matrix multiplication. For example, if

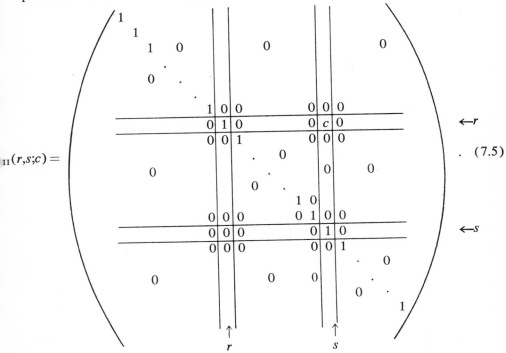

$$\mathbf{A}=\begin{pmatrix} 0 & 0 & 2 \\ 0 & 2 & 0 \\ 0 & 1 & 0 \end{pmatrix},$$

then

$$\mathbf{A}_R=\begin{pmatrix} 0 & 1 & 0 \\ 0 & 0 & 1 \\ 0 & 0 & 0 \end{pmatrix},$$

$$\mathbf{S}_A=\mathbf{E}_{II}(2;\tfrac{1}{2})\ \mathbf{E}_{III}(3,1;-1)\ \mathbf{E}_{II}(1;-\tfrac{1}{2})\ \mathbf{E}_I(1,2)$$

$$=\begin{pmatrix} 1 & 0 & 0 \\ 0 & \tfrac{1}{2} & 0 \\ 0 & 0 & 1 \end{pmatrix}\begin{pmatrix} 1 & 0 & 0 \\ 0 & 1 & 0 \\ -1 & 0 & 1 \end{pmatrix}\begin{pmatrix} \tfrac{1}{2} & 0 & 0 \\ 0 & 1 & 0 \\ 0 & 0 & 1 \end{pmatrix}\begin{pmatrix} 0 & 1 & 0 \\ 1 & 0 & 0 \\ 0 & 0 & 1 \end{pmatrix}$$

$$=\begin{pmatrix} 0 & \tfrac{1}{2} & 0 \\ \tfrac{1}{2} & 0 & 0 \\ 0 & -\tfrac{1}{2} & 1 \end{pmatrix},$$

and

$$\mathbf{S}_A\mathbf{A}=\begin{pmatrix} 0 & \tfrac{1}{2} & 0 \\ \tfrac{1}{2} & 0 & 0 \\ 0 & -\tfrac{1}{2} & 1 \end{pmatrix}\begin{pmatrix} 0 & 0 & 2 \\ 0 & 2 & 0 \\ 0 & 1 & 0 \end{pmatrix}=\mathbf{A}_R.$$

We can now use matrix multiplication based upon Eq. (7.6) to solve a number of problems.

The first thing we note is that if $\mathbf{A}$ belongs to $\mathsf{M}_{p,q}$, then $\mathbf{S}_A$ is defined. Next, if $\mathbf{A}$ belongs to $\mathsf{M}_{p,n}$ and $\mathbf{W}$ belongs to $\mathsf{M}_{p,q}$, we then can form a new matrix belonging to $\mathsf{M}_{p,(n+q)}$ by adjoining $\mathbf{W}$ to the right of $\mathbf{A}$. We denote this new **augmented** matrix by

$$[\mathbf{A}|\mathbf{W}].$$

Thus, if

$$\mathbf{A}=\begin{pmatrix} 1 & 0 & 1 & -1 \\ 0 & 1 & 1 & 1 \\ 0 & 1 & 5 & 0 \end{pmatrix}\in\mathsf{M}_{3,4}, \qquad \mathbf{W}=\begin{pmatrix} \alpha & \theta \\ \beta & \phi \\ \gamma & \psi \end{pmatrix}\in\mathsf{M}_{3,2},$$

then

$$[\mathbf{A}|\mathbf{W}]=\begin{pmatrix} 1 & 0 & 1 & -1 & \alpha & \theta \\ 0 & 1 & 1 & 1 & \beta & \phi \\ 0 & 1 & 5 & 0 & \gamma & \psi \end{pmatrix}\in\mathsf{M}_{3,6}.$$

An easy calculation shows that

$$\mathbf{B}[\mathbf{A}|\mathbf{W}]=[\mathbf{BA}|\mathbf{BW}] \tag{7.7}$$

for any matrix $\mathbf{B} \in \mathsf{M}_{q,p}$, since this is nothing more than a restatement of what we mean by matrix multiplication. From

$$\mathbf{S}_A \mathbf{A} = \mathbf{A}_R \tag{7.8}$$

and Eq. (7.7) with $\mathbf{B} = \mathbf{S}_A$, we then have

$$\mathbf{S}_A [\mathbf{A} | \mathbf{W}] = [\mathbf{A}_R | \mathbf{S}_A \mathbf{W}]. \tag{7.9}$$

Thus, if $\mathbf{W} = \mathbf{E}$, Eq. (7.9) gives us

$$\mathbf{S}_A [\mathbf{A} | \mathbf{E}] = [\mathbf{A}_R | \mathbf{S}_A]. \tag{7.10}$$

This formula tells us that if we apply the row echelon algorithm to

$$[\mathbf{A} | \mathbf{E}]$$

rather than to just $\mathbf{A}$ and *stop* when we have row reduced $\mathbf{A}$, we will obtain $[\mathbf{A}_R | \mathbf{S}_A]$:

$$\mathbf{S}_A [\mathbf{A} | \mathbf{E}] = [\mathbf{A}_R | \mathbf{S}_A]. \tag{7.11}$$

This is the obvious way to compute $\mathbf{S}_A$.

You could compute the matrix $\mathbf{S}_A$ by multiplying all of the required elementary row matrices together, but, this would be a foolish waste of time since the theory gives Eq. (7.11). Thus computing $\mathbf{S}_A$ is only a little more work than to compute $\mathbf{A}_R$ by the row echelon algorithm.

We now turn to the problem of solving a general system of linear, inhomogeneous equations. Let $\mathbf{A}$ be a given member of $\mathsf{M}_{p,n}$, and let $\{b\}$ be a given member of $\mathsf{M}_{p,1}$. We wish to find *all* $\{x\}$ belonging to $\mathsf{M}_{n,1}$ such that

$$\mathbf{A}\{x\} = \{b\}. \tag{7.12}$$

The three simple problems worked in lecture 1 showed that there may be no solution whatsoever to the system (7.12). For this reason, we say that a matrix equation $\mathbf{A}\{x\} = \{b\}$ is **consistent** if and only if it has at least one solution. If there exist no solutions of $\mathbf{A}\{x\} = \{b\}$, then $\mathbf{A}\{x\} = \{b\}$
inhomogeneous equations. Let $\mathbf{A}$ be a given member of $\mathsf{M}_{p,n}$, and let $\{b\}$
essary and sufficient conditions that the given matrix equation (7.12) is consistent.

We know that the row echelon algorithm gives us a matrix $\mathbf{S}_A$ such that

$$\mathbf{S}_A \mathbf{A} = \mathbf{A}_R. \tag{7.13}$$

If we multiply both sides of Eq. (7.12) from the left by this $\mathbf{S}_A$, we obtain

$$\mathbf{S}_A \mathbf{A}\{x\} = \mathbf{S}_A \{b\},$$

and hence Eq. (7.13) gives us

$$\mathbf{A}_R \{x\} = \mathbf{S}_A \{b\}.$$

This row echelon reduction applied to both sides of Eq. (7.12) is conveniently written as

$$\mathbf{S}_A[\mathbf{A}|\{b\}]=[\mathbf{S}_A\mathbf{A}|\mathbf{S}_A\{b\}]=[\mathbf{A}_R|\mathbf{S}_A\{b\}], \tag{7.14}$$

which is read to mean that the matrix equation

$$\mathbf{A}\{x\}=\{b\}$$

is equivalent to the matrix equation

$$\mathbf{A}_R\{x\}=\mathbf{S}_A\{b\}. \tag{7.15}$$

We know that the number of nonzero rows of $\mathbf{A}_R$ is given by rank($\mathbf{A}$). For definiteness, we write

$$\text{rank}(\mathbf{A})=r, \tag{7.16}$$

where r is a number such that

$$r\leq\min(p,n) \tag{7.17}$$

[i.e. the number of nonzero rows in the row echelon form of an element of $\mathsf{M}_{p,n}$ *can not* exceed $\min(p,n)$]. We thus know that the last $(p-r)$ rows of $\mathbf{A}_R$ are all zero. Equation (7.15) then tells us that we have a contradiction unless the last $(p-r)$ entries in $\mathbf{S}_A\{b\}$ are also zero. We thus have that $\mathbf{A}\{x\}=\{b\}$ is inconsistent unless the last $(p-r)$ rows of

$$[\mathbf{A}_R|\mathbf{S}_A\{b\}]$$

are zero. This, however, is nothing more than the requirement that

$$\text{rank}(\mathbf{A})=\text{rank}([\mathbf{A}|\{b\}]).$$

We thus have inconsistency unless

$$\text{rank}(\mathbf{A})=\text{rank}([\mathbf{A}|\{b\}]). \tag{7.18}$$

Another way of stating this result is that we have inconsistency unless the row echelon reduction of $\mathbf{A}$ by $\mathbf{S}_A$ is also row echelon reduction of $[\mathbf{A}|\{b\}]$; that is, if

$$\mathbf{S}_A\mathbf{A}=\mathbf{A}_R, \tag{7.19}$$

then

$$\mathbf{S}_A[\mathbf{A}|\{b\}]=[\mathbf{A}|\{b\}]_R, \tag{7.20}$$

where $[\mathbf{A}|\{b\}]_R$ is the row echelon reduction of the whole **augmented matrix** $[\mathbf{A}|\{b\}]$ of the matrix equation $\mathbf{A}\{x\}=\{b\}$. If we combine Eqs. (7.19), (7.20), and (7.7), we have another equivalent statement of the condition (7.20), namely

$$[\mathbf{A}_R|\mathbf{S}_A\{b\}]=[\mathbf{A}|\{b\}]_R, \quad \mathbf{S}_A\mathbf{A}=\mathbf{A}_R. \tag{7.21}$$

All three statements (7.18), (7.20), and (7.21) say the same thing, so we leave it to each student to pick which is most suggestive for the calculations which must be performed. We prefer Eq. (7.18), and hence we shall use the statement

$$\text{rank}(\mathbf{A}) = \text{rank}[\mathbf{A}|\{b\}]$$

from now on.

At this point we know that we must satisfy

$$\text{rank}(\mathbf{A}) = \text{rank}[\mathbf{A}|\{b\}], \tag{7.22}$$

or else, the equation $\mathbf{A}\{x\} = \{b\}$ is inconsistent; that is Eq. (7.22) is necessary for consistency of $\mathbf{A}\{x\} = \{b\}$. We still have to show sufficiency; namely, if Eq. (7.22) is satisfied then there exists at least one solution of $\mathbf{A}\{x\} = \{b\}$.

Again, with $\text{rank}(\mathbf{A}) = r \leq \min(p,n)$, Eq. (7.22) gives $\text{rank}([\mathbf{A}|\{b\}]) = r$. Thus the equation

$$\mathbf{A}_R\{x\} = \mathbf{S}_A\{b\} \equiv \{\bar{b}\}, \tag{7.23}$$

which is equivalent to $\mathbf{A}\{x\} = \{b\}$, has the form

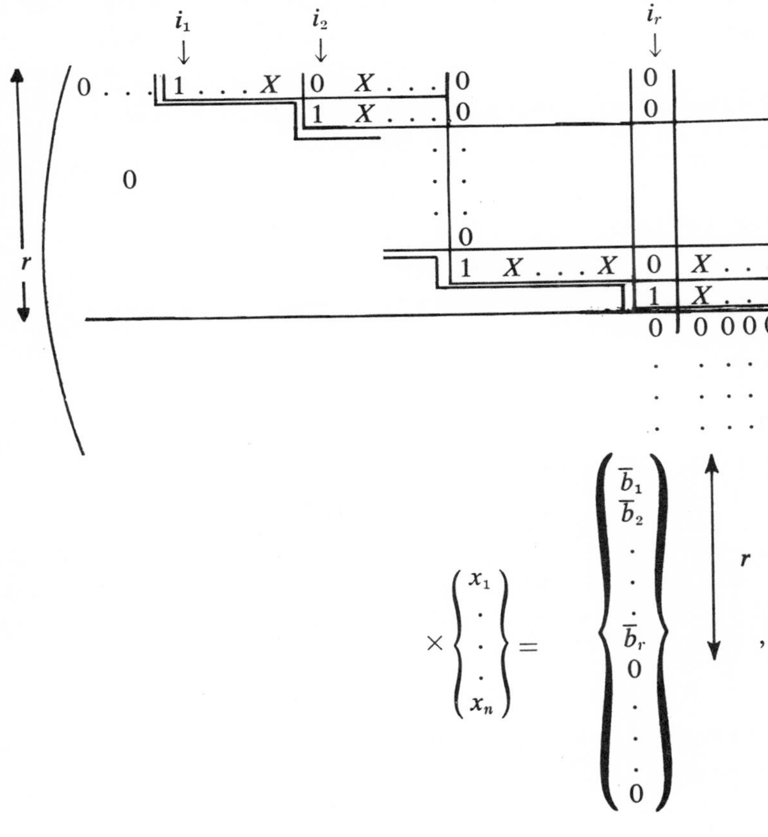

, (7.24)

where $i_1, i_2, \ldots, i_r$ are the columns with corner elements in $\mathbf{A}_R$. If we perform the indicated matrix multiplication in Eq. (7.24), it is clear that the system (7.23) [and hence the system $\mathbf{A}\{x\}=\{b\}$] has a solution given by

$$x_{i_1}=\bar{b}_1,\ x_{i_2}=\bar{b}_2,\ \ldots,\ x_{i_r}=\bar{b}_r,$$

and all other $x_i=0$. We have thus established that

$$\operatorname{rank}(\mathbf{A})=\operatorname{rank}([\mathbf{A}|\{b\}]),$$

is both necessary and sufficient for consistency of the matrix equation $\mathbf{A}\{x\}=\{b\}$. In addition, the row reduction of $[\mathbf{A}|\{b\}]$, which has to be made in order to compute $\operatorname{rank}[\mathbf{A}|\{b\}]$, allows us to read off an explicit solution of $\mathbf{A}\{x\}=\{b\}$ by *inspection*. This is another testament to the efficiency of the row echelon algorithm.

An explicit solution of the inhomogeneous matrix equation $\mathbf{A}\{x\}=\{b\}$, such as the one we have found by inspection from $\mathbf{A}_R\{x\}=\mathbf{S}_A\{b\}=\{\bar{b}\}$, is referred to as a **particular solution**. The following fact is worth noting at this point: *if* $\mathbf{A}\in \mathsf{M}_{p,n}$ *with* $p\leq n$, *and* $\operatorname{rank}(\mathbf{A})=p$, *then* $\mathbf{A}\{x\}=\{b\}$ *is always consistent*. We leave the proof of this statement to the student as an exercise. If $\operatorname{rank}(\mathbf{A})=\operatorname{rank}(\mathbf{A}|\{b\})=n$, $\mathbf{A}\in\mathsf{M}_{p,n}$, $p\geq n$, then $\mathbf{A}_R=\begin{Bmatrix}\mathbf{E}\\ \mathbf{0}\end{Bmatrix}$ where $\mathbf{E}$ is the n-by-n identity matrix. In this case Eq. (7.23) gives $x_i=\bar{b}_i$ for $i=1, \ldots, n$ and hence the solution is unique.

We now have to find the general solution of the matrix equation

$$\mathbf{A}\{x\}=\{b\}, \tag{7.25}$$

which we assume to be a consistent equation. The first thing we establish is that the solutions of Eq. (7.25) do *not* form a subspace of $\mathsf{V}_n\equiv\mathsf{M}_{n,1}$. If $\{x\}$ and $\{y\}$ are solutions of Eq. (7.25), then

$$\mathbf{A}(\{x\}+\{y\})=\mathbf{A}\{x\}+\mathbf{A}\{y\}=\{b\}+\{b\}=2\{b\},$$

and hence $(\{x\}+\{y\})$ satisfies

$$\mathbf{A}(\{x\}+\{y\})=2\{b\},$$

not $\mathbf{A}(\{x\}+\{y\})=\{b\}$. Thus, the sum of two solutions is not a solution and the solutions do not form a subspace. The question thus arises as to just what sort of "animals" are the solutions of Eq. (7.25). If $\{x\}$ and $\{y\}$ are solutions of Eq. (7.25), then

$$\mathbf{A}(\{x\}-\{y\})=\mathbf{A}\{x\}-\mathbf{A}\{y\}=\{b\}-\{b\}=\{0\}.$$

Thus, the difference of any two solutions of Eq. (7.25) satisfy the homogeneous equation

$$\mathbf{A}\{u\}=\{0\}, \qquad \{u\}=\{x\}-\{y\}.$$

From this we conclude that *if* $\{w\}$ *is a particular solution of Eq.* (7.25), *then every solution of Eq.* (7.25) *can be written as*

$$\{x\}=\{w\}+\{u\}, \tag{7.26}$$

where $\{u\}$ *is a solution of the associated homogeneous equation*

$$\mathbf{A}\{u\}=\{0\}. \tag{7.27}$$

We can now summarize our findings. *Let* $\mathbf{A}$ *be a given element of* $\mathsf{M}_{p,n}$ *and let* $\{b\}$ *be a given element of* $\mathsf{M}_{p,1}$. *Solutions of*

$$\mathbf{A}\{x\}=\{b\} \tag{7.28}$$

exist if and only if

$$\operatorname{rank}(\mathbf{A})=\operatorname{rank}[\mathbf{A}|\{b\}]. \tag{7.29}$$

If this condition is satisfied then the general solution of Eq. (7.28) *consists of all column matrices (vectors) of the form*

$$\{x\}=\{w\}+\{u\}, \tag{7.30}$$

where $\{w\}$ *is a particular solution of Eq.* (7.28) *and* $\{u\}$ *is a solution of the associated homogeneous equation*

$$\mathbf{A}\{u\}=\{0\}.$$

The solution of Eq. (7.28) *is* **unique** *if and only if* $\operatorname{rank}(\mathbf{A})=n$ [*i.e.*, $\mathbf{A}\{u\}=\{0\}$ *has only the trivial solution* $\{u\}=\{0\}$].

The following examples illustrate the method.

EXAMPLE 1.

$$\mathbf{A}=\begin{pmatrix} 0 & -2 & -4 & 0 & 6 & 0 \\ 0 & 1 & 2 & 3 & 15 & 0 \\ 0 & -3 & -6 & 1 & 15 & -5 \\ 0 & 3 & 6 & -2 & -21 & 6 \end{pmatrix}, \quad \{b\}=\begin{Bmatrix} -8 \\ 10 \\ 0 \\ 5 \end{Bmatrix};$$

$$[\mathbf{A}|\{b\}]=\left(\begin{array}{cccccc|c} 0 & -2 & -4 & 0 & 6 & 0 & -8 \\ 0 & 1 & 2 & 3 & 15 & 0 & 10 \\ 0 & -3 & -6 & 1 & 15 & -5 & 0 \\ 0 & 3 & 6 & -2 & -21 & 6 & 5 \end{array}\right);$$

$$\mathbf{S}_A[\mathbf{A}|\{b\}]=[\mathbf{A}_R|\mathbf{S}_A\{b\}]=\left(\begin{array}{cccccc|c} 0 & 1 & 2 & 0 & -3 & 0 & 4 \\ 0 & 0 & 0 & 1 & 6 & 0 & 2 \\ 0 & 0 & 0 & 0 & 0 & 1 & -2 \\ 0 & 0 & 0 & 0 & 0 & 0 & 9 \end{array}\right);$$

$\operatorname{rank}(\mathbf{A})=3$, $\operatorname{rank}[\mathbf{A}|\{b\}]=4$; the problem is inconsistent.

EXAMPLE 2. The matrix **A** is the same as in example 1,

$$\{b\}=\begin{Bmatrix}-8\\10\\0\\-2\end{Bmatrix};\ [\mathbf{A}|\{b\}]=\left(\begin{array}{cccccc|c}0&-2&-4&0&6&0&-8\\0&1&2&3&15&0&10\\0&-3&-6&1&15&-5&0\\0&3&6&-2&-21&6&-2\end{array}\right);$$

$$\mathbf{S}_A[\mathbf{A}|\{b\}]=[\mathbf{A}_R|\mathbf{S}_A\{b\}]=\left(\begin{array}{cccccc|c}0&1&2&0&-3&0&4\\0&0&0&1&6&0&2\\0&0&0&0&0&1&-2\\0&0&0&0&0&0&0\end{array}\right);$$

$$3=\text{rank}(\mathbf{A})=\text{rank}[\mathbf{A}|\{b\}];$$

the problem is consistent; the corner columns of **A** are the second, fourth, and sixth, $i_1=2$, $i_2=4$, $i_3=6$; a particular solution of $\mathbf{A}\{u\}=\{b\}$ is $u_2=4$, $u_4=2$, $u_6=-2$ and the other u's are zero, that is

$$\{u\}=\begin{Bmatrix}0\\4\\0\\2\\0\\-2\end{Bmatrix}.$$

The general solution of the associated homogeneous equation $\mathbf{A}\{v\}=\{0\}$ is given by $v_2=-2v_3+3v_5$, $v_4=-6_5v$, $v_6=0$, that is

$$\{v\}=v_1\begin{Bmatrix}1\\0\\0\\0\\0\\0\end{Bmatrix}+v_5\begin{Bmatrix}0\\-2\\1\\0\\0\\0\end{Bmatrix}+v_3\begin{Bmatrix}0\\3\\0\\-6\\1\\0\end{Bmatrix}.$$

The general solution of $\mathbf{A}\{x\}=\{b\}$ is therefore given by

$$\{x\}=\begin{Bmatrix}0\\4\\0\\2\\0\\-2\end{Bmatrix}+v_1\begin{Bmatrix}1\\0\\0\\0\\0\\0\end{Bmatrix}+v_3\begin{Bmatrix}0\\-2\\1\\0\\0\\0\end{Bmatrix}+v_5\begin{Bmatrix}0\\3\\0\\-6\\1\\0\end{Bmatrix}.$$

EXAMPLE 3.

$$\mathbf{A}=\begin{pmatrix}0&0&1&1\\0&0&1&-1\\1&-1&0&0\\1&1&0&0\end{pmatrix};\ \mathbf{b}=\begin{Bmatrix}2\\1\\1\\-2\end{Bmatrix};$$

$$[\mathbf{A}|\{b\}]=\left(\begin{array}{cccc|c} 0 & 0 & 1 & 1 & 2 \\ 0 & 0 & 1 & -1 & 1 \\ 1 & -1 & 0 & 0 & 1 \\ 1 & 1 & 0 & 0 & -2 \end{array}\right);$$

$$\mathbf{S}_A[\mathbf{A}|\{b\}]=[\mathbf{A}_R|\mathbf{S}_A\{b\}]=\left(\begin{array}{cccc|c} 1 & 0 & 0 & 0 & -1/2 \\ 0 & 1 & 0 & 0 & -3/2 \\ 0 & 0 & 1 & 0 & 3/2 \\ 0 & 0 & 0 & 1 & 1/2 \end{array}\right);$$

$$\text{rank}(\mathbf{A})=\text{rank}[\mathbf{A}|\{b\}]=4;$$

and the system is consistent; the only solution of the associated homogeneous equation $\mathbf{A}\{v\}=\{0\}$ is $\{v\}=\{0\}$ since $\mathbf{A}_R=\mathbf{E}$ [i.e., $\mathbf{A}\{v\}=\{0\}$ is equivalent to $\mathbf{A}_R\{v\}=\{0\}\Rightarrow\mathbf{E}\{v\}=\{v\}=\{0\}$]; the solution of $\mathbf{A}\{u\}=\{b\}$ is *unique* and is given by

$$\{u\}=\left\{\begin{array}{r} -1/2 \\ -3/2 \\ 3/2 \\ 1/2 \end{array}\right\}.$$

For actual numerical calculation, the consistency test $\text{rank}([\mathbf{A}|\{b\}]) = \text{rank}(\mathbf{A})$ is simple and straightforward to apply. There are a number of instances, however, in which an alternative consistency test for inhomogeneous linear systems is more useful. This is particularly true in theoretical investigations.

Let $\mathbf{A}$ be a given element of $\mathsf{M}_{p,n}$ and let $\{b\}$ be a given element of $\mathsf{M}_{p,1}$. We want to know when is there at least one $\{x\}\in\mathsf{M}_{n,1}$ which satisfies the linear inhomogeneous system

$$\mathbf{A}\{x\} = \{b\}. \tag{7.31}$$

Let $\{y\}$ be an arbitrary element of $\mathsf{M}_{p,1}$, then we can multiply Eq. (7.31) on the left by $\{y\}^T$ and obtain the scalar equation

$$\{y\}^T\mathbf{A}\{x\} = \{y\}^T\{b\}. \tag{7.32}$$

Now, $\{y\}^T\mathbf{A}\{x\} = (\{y\}^T\mathbf{A})\{x\} = (\mathbf{A}^T\{y\})^T\{x\}$, and hence Eq. (7.32) can be written in the equivalent form

$$(\mathbf{A}^T\{y\})^T\{x\} = \{y\}^T\{b\}. \tag{7.33}$$

Thus, *if Eq.* (7.31) *has at least one solution* $\{x\}$, *then Eq.* (7.33) *is true for all* $\{y\}\in\mathsf{M}_{p,1}$. Accordingly, Eq. (7.33) is also true for all $\{y\}$ that belong to a subspace of $\mathsf{M}_{p,1}$ if Eq. (7.31) has at least one solution. Since $\mathbf{A}^T\in\mathsf{M}_{n,p}$, the system of homogeneous linear equations,

$$\mathbf{A}^T\{y\} = \{0\}, \tag{7.34}$$

has a solution space Y that is a subspace of $\mathsf{M}_{p,1}$. The system (7.34) is usually referred to as the **homogeneous adjoint** of the linear inhomogeneous system (7.31). For each $\{y\}\in\mathsf{Y}$, Eqs. (7.33) and (7.34) give

$$\{y\}^T\{b\} = 0, \tag{7.35}$$

and hence this condition must hold if the system (7.31) has at least one solution. We thus have the following result. *A necessary condition for the existence of at least one solution to the inhomogeneous linear system* $\mathbf{A}\{x\} = \{b\}$ *is that*

$$\{y\}^T\{b\} = 0$$

be true for all $\{y\}$ *that satisfy the homogeneous adjoint equation* $\mathbf{A}^T\{y\} = \{0\}$. It can also be shown that this condition is sufficient.

Problems

7.1. Prove that the following sets of vectors $\mathbf{u}_i$ are linearly dependent and determine [to within a constant factor] *all* sets of coefficients c_i such that $\Sigma c_i\mathbf{u}_i = \mathbf{0}$ where $\Sigma c_i^2 \neq 0$:

$$\text{(a)} \begin{Bmatrix}6\\-2\\-4\end{Bmatrix}, \begin{Bmatrix}-3\\1\\2\end{Bmatrix}, \begin{Bmatrix}24\\-7\\-14\end{Bmatrix}; \quad \text{(b)} \begin{Bmatrix}5\\15\\10\end{Bmatrix}, \begin{Bmatrix}6\\18\\12\end{Bmatrix};$$

$$\text{(c)} \begin{Bmatrix}8\\-1\\4\end{Bmatrix}, \begin{Bmatrix}-6\\1\\-3\end{Bmatrix}, \begin{Bmatrix}4\\1\\2\end{Bmatrix}; \quad \text{(d)} \begin{Bmatrix}3\\5\\7\end{Bmatrix}, \begin{Bmatrix}2\\0\\4\end{Bmatrix}, \begin{Bmatrix}0\\10\\2\end{Bmatrix};$$

$$\text{(e)} \begin{Bmatrix}7\\0\\3\\2\end{Bmatrix}, \begin{Bmatrix}0\\3\\2\\6\end{Bmatrix}, \begin{Bmatrix}7\\3\\5\\9\end{Bmatrix}, \begin{Bmatrix}7\\-12\\-5\\-23\end{Bmatrix}; \quad \text{(f)} \begin{Bmatrix}1\\2\\3\end{Bmatrix}, \begin{Bmatrix}3\\12\\15\end{Bmatrix}, \begin{Bmatrix}1\\6\\7\end{Bmatrix}.$$

7.2. Prove that the following sets of vectors span the same vector space:

$$\text{(a)} \begin{Bmatrix}1\\2\end{Bmatrix}, \begin{Bmatrix}-3\\4\end{Bmatrix}; \quad \begin{Bmatrix}11\\-8\end{Bmatrix}, \begin{Bmatrix}-21\\8\end{Bmatrix};$$

$$\text{(b)} \begin{Bmatrix}1\\2\\-3\end{Bmatrix}, \begin{Bmatrix}-3\\-8\\12\end{Bmatrix}, \begin{Bmatrix}2\\6\\-12\end{Bmatrix}; \quad \begin{Bmatrix}0\\0\\-3\end{Bmatrix}, \begin{Bmatrix}0\\2\\-6\end{Bmatrix}, \begin{Bmatrix}1\\0\\3\end{Bmatrix};$$

$$\text{(c)} \begin{Bmatrix}1\\3\\2\end{Bmatrix}, \begin{Bmatrix}2\\1\\4\end{Bmatrix}, \begin{Bmatrix}3\\-1\\6\end{Bmatrix}; \quad \begin{Bmatrix}0\\5\\0\end{Bmatrix}, \begin{Bmatrix}5\\0\\10\end{Bmatrix};$$

$$\text{(d)} \begin{Bmatrix}2\\-3\\5\end{Bmatrix}, \begin{Bmatrix}5\\0\\2\end{Bmatrix}, \begin{Bmatrix}1\\6\\-9\end{Bmatrix}; \quad \begin{Bmatrix}0\\1\\5\end{Bmatrix}, \begin{Bmatrix}0\\3\\0\end{Bmatrix}, \begin{Bmatrix}1\\13\\7\end{Bmatrix};$$

$$\text{(e)} \begin{Bmatrix}1\\1\\2\end{Bmatrix}, \begin{Bmatrix}3\\-1\\6\end{Bmatrix}, \begin{Bmatrix}5\\-3\\10\end{Bmatrix}; \quad \begin{Bmatrix}2\\3\\4\end{Bmatrix}, \begin{Bmatrix}-1\\1\\-2\end{Bmatrix};$$

$$\text{(f)} \begin{Bmatrix}1\\-2\\3\end{Bmatrix}, \begin{Bmatrix}-3\\1\\-9\end{Bmatrix}, \begin{Bmatrix}2\\1\\6\end{Bmatrix}; \quad \begin{Bmatrix}2\\1\\6\end{Bmatrix}, \begin{Bmatrix}-1\\2\\-3\end{Bmatrix}, \begin{Bmatrix}1\\1\\3\end{Bmatrix}.$$

7.3. Determine whether the following sets of vectors form a minimal spanning set for V_3:

$$\text{(a)}\ \left\{\begin{matrix}1\\2\\3\end{matrix}\right\},\left\{\begin{matrix}3\\4\\5\end{matrix}\right\},\left\{\begin{matrix}1\\4\\7\end{matrix}\right\};\quad \text{(b)}\ \left\{\begin{matrix}3\\2\\1\end{matrix}\right\},\left\{\begin{matrix}2\\3\\4\end{matrix}\right\},\left\{\begin{matrix}7\\3\\1\end{matrix}\right\};$$

$$\text{(c)}\ \left\{\begin{matrix}1\\3\\2\end{matrix}\right\},\left\{\begin{matrix}0\\5\\2\end{matrix}\right\},\left\{\begin{matrix}3\\4\\5\end{matrix}\right\};\quad \text{(d)}\ \left\{\begin{matrix}-1\\2\\-4\end{matrix}\right\},\left\{\begin{matrix}7\\6\\13\end{matrix}\right\},\left\{\begin{matrix}3\\14\\-3\end{matrix}\right\};$$

$$\text{(e)}\ \left\{\begin{matrix}-1\\2\\0\end{matrix}\right\},\left\{\begin{matrix}6\\5\\7\end{matrix}\right\},\left\{\begin{matrix}15\\4\\14\end{matrix}\right\};\quad \text{(f)}\ \left\{\begin{matrix}2\\0\\3\end{matrix}\right\},\left\{\begin{matrix}9\\12\\15\end{matrix}\right\},\left\{\begin{matrix}7\\5\\11\end{matrix}\right\}.$$

7.4. Determine α so that the vectors

$$\text{(a)}\ \left\{\begin{matrix}-1\\\alpha^2-4\alpha+12\\\alpha+12\end{matrix}\right\},\quad \text{(b)}\ \left\{\begin{matrix}-1\\\alpha+2\\-2\\\alpha^2+\alpha+1\end{matrix}\right\},\quad \text{(c)}\ \left\{\begin{matrix}1\\\alpha^2+3\\3\alpha+6\end{matrix}\right\},$$

belong, respectively, to the vector space spanned by

$$\text{(a)}\ \left\{\begin{matrix}1\\3\\2\end{matrix}\right\},\left\{\begin{matrix}-1\\2\\4\end{matrix}\right\};\quad \text{(b)}\ \left\{\begin{matrix}1\\0\\2\\4\end{matrix}\right\},\left\{\begin{matrix}3\\1\\1\\2\end{matrix}\right\},\left\{\begin{matrix}5\\1\\5\\3\end{matrix}\right\};\quad \text{(c)}\ \left\{\begin{matrix}2\\11\\3\end{matrix}\right\},\left\{\begin{matrix}1\\5\\2\end{matrix}\right\}.$$

7.5. Use the row echelon algorithm to obtain $\mathbf{A}_R$ and give the corresponding elementary matrix ($\mathbf{E}_{\text{I}}$, $\mathbf{E}_{\text{II}}$, or $\mathbf{E}_{\text{III}}$) for each step of the algorithm when $\mathbf{A}$ is

$$\text{(a)}\begin{pmatrix}0&0&2\\0&2&0\\0&1&0\end{pmatrix},\quad \text{(b)}\begin{pmatrix}1&2&0&4\\2&3&2&10\\1&3&-2&2\\0&1&-2&-2\end{pmatrix},$$

$$\text{(c)}\begin{pmatrix}3&0&6\\1&2&0\\0&0&1\end{pmatrix},\quad \text{(d)}\begin{pmatrix}0&3&0\\1&0&1\\2&6&0\end{pmatrix},$$

$$\text{(e)}\begin{pmatrix}1&2&4\\0&3&9\\2&5&8\end{pmatrix},\quad \text{(f)}\begin{pmatrix}0&3&6\\2&4&8\\3&6&10\end{pmatrix}.$$

In each case determine $\mathbf{S}_A$ by calculating the corresponding ordered product of elementary matrices.

7.6. By row reducing the appropriate augmented matrix calculate $\mathbf{S}_A$ when $\mathbf{A}$ is

$$\text{(a)}\begin{pmatrix}2&3\\4&5\end{pmatrix};\quad \text{(b)}\begin{pmatrix}1&2\\3&5\\4&7\end{pmatrix};\quad \text{(c)}\begin{pmatrix}1&-1&0\\0&2&4\\6&12&4\end{pmatrix};$$

$$\text{(d)}\begin{pmatrix}1&2&3\\2&3&4\\2&4&6\end{pmatrix};\quad \text{(e)}\begin{pmatrix}3&0&5\\9&4&8\\6&0&10\end{pmatrix};\quad \text{(f)}\begin{pmatrix}1&2&5\\2&5&11\\3&7&16\end{pmatrix}.$$

$S_A A = A_R$

Row reduce $[A/E]$ — final result — obtain $[A_R / S_A]$

7.7. Determine whether the following systems are consistent and, if so, give the general solution:

(a) $6x_1 + 3x_2 = 12$, $4x_1 + 2x_2 = 9$ (b) $8x_1 + 12x_2 = 16$, $6x_1 + 9x_2 = 13$

(c) $x_1 + x_2 + x_3 + 9x_4 = 8$, $x_2 + 2x_3 + 8x_4 = 7$, $-3x_1 + x_3 - 7x_4 = 9$ (d) $x_1 + 2x_2 = 1$, $2x_1 + 5x_2 = 2$, $3x_1 + 6x_2 = 3$

(e) $x_1 + 2x_2 + 3x_3 = 4$, $x_2 + 2x_3 = 3$, $3x_1 + 5x_2 + 7x_3 = 15$ (f) $2x_1 + 3x_2 = 8$, $3x_1 + 7x_2 = 17$, $7x_1 + 13x_2 = 33$

When the system is not consistent solve the corresponding homogeneous system and give a basis for its solution space and a basis for the row space of the matrix **A**.

7.8. By row reducing the appropriate augmented matrix find the general solution of the system $\mathbf{A}\{x\} = \{b\}$ where **A** and $\{b\}$ are given, respectively, by

(a) $\begin{pmatrix} 2 & -1 \\ 4 & 2 \end{pmatrix}, \begin{pmatrix} 1 \\ 2 \end{pmatrix}$; (b) $\begin{pmatrix} 6 & -2 \\ 3 & -1 \end{pmatrix}, \begin{pmatrix} 4 \\ 2 \end{pmatrix}$;

(c) $\begin{pmatrix} 1 & 2 & 3 \\ 0 & 4 & 2 \\ 5 & 0 & 1 \end{pmatrix}, \begin{pmatrix} 0 \\ 2 \\ 3 \end{pmatrix}$; (d) $\begin{pmatrix} 0 & 1 & 2 \\ 2 & 3 & 0 \\ -8 & -9 & 6 \end{pmatrix}, \begin{pmatrix} 4 \\ 2 \\ 4 \end{pmatrix}$;

(e) $\begin{pmatrix} 2 & 5 & 7 \\ 6 & 13 & 12 \\ 2 & 3 & -2 \\ -6 & -11 & -3 \end{pmatrix}, \begin{pmatrix} 1 \\ 2 \\ 0 \\ -1 \end{pmatrix}$; (f) $\begin{pmatrix} 1 & 2 & 3 & 4 \\ 3 & 2 & 4 & 1 \\ 1 & -2 & -2 & -7 \\ 8 & 4 & 9 & -1 \end{pmatrix}, \begin{pmatrix} 1 \\ 2 \\ 0 \\ 5 \end{pmatrix}$.

In each case state whether the solution is unique. If the solution is not unique give a particular solution of the inhomogeneous system, the general solution of the corresponding homogeneous system $\mathbf{A}\{x\} = \{0\}$, a basis for the solution space of $\mathbf{A}\{x\} = \{0\}$ and a basis for the row space of the matrix **A**.

7.9. Prove the relation (7.7).

7.10. Show that $\text{rank}([\mathbf{A}|\mathbf{B}]) \geq \text{rank}(\mathbf{A})$.

7.11. Show that $\dim(\mathsf{V}_n) = n$ and that any set of n linearly independent vectors of order n is a basis for V_n.

7.12. If for the vector space S of order n we have $\dim(\mathsf{S}) = n$ then S is the total vector space V_n.

7.13. Let S be a vector space with $\dim(\mathsf{S}) = d$. If S_1 is a subspace of S with $\dim(\mathsf{S}_1) = d_1$ then show that $d_1 \leq d$. If $d_1 = d$ then show that $\mathsf{S} = \mathsf{S}_1$.

7.14. Let $\mathbf{u}_1, \ldots, \mathbf{u}_p$ be p linearly independent elements of a subspace S. Show that the set $\mathbf{u}_1, \ldots, \mathbf{u}_p$ is part of a basis of S.

7.15. Show that if the nonzero vectors $\mathbf{u}_1, \ldots, \mathbf{u}_n$ of order n are mutually orthogonal they form a basis of V_n.

7.16. If $\mathbf{x}_1, \ldots, \mathbf{x}_n$ is an orthonormal basis of V_n, then show that for any $\mathbf{x} \in V_n$,

$$(\mathbf{x} \circ \mathbf{x}_1)^2 + \ldots + (\mathbf{x} \circ \mathbf{x}_n)^2 = ||\mathbf{x}||^2.$$

Give a geometrical interpretation of this equality for $n = 3$.

7.17. Prove that $\mathbf{u}$ belongs to the subspace spanned by $\mathbf{w}_1, \ldots, \mathbf{w}_p$ if and only if

$$\text{rank}\begin{Bmatrix} \{w_1\}^T \\ \cdot \\ \cdot \\ \cdot \\ \{w_p\}^T \\ \{u\}^T \end{Bmatrix} = \text{rank}\begin{Bmatrix} \{w_1\}^T \\ \cdot \\ \cdot \\ \cdot \\ \{w_p\}^T \end{Bmatrix}.$$

7.18. Prove that $\mathbf{u}$ belongs to the subspace spanned by $\mathbf{w}_1, \ldots, \mathbf{w}_p$ if and only if the solutions of the system

$$\mathbf{w}_1 \circ \mathbf{x} = 0, \ldots, \mathbf{w}_p \circ \mathbf{x} = 0$$

satisfy

$$\mathbf{u} \circ \mathbf{x} = 0.$$

7.19. Show that $\mathbf{A}\{x\} = \{0\}$ and $\mathbf{B}\{x\} = \{0\}$ are equivalent systems if and only if the row spaces of $\mathbf{A}$ and $\mathbf{B}$ are identical. [Use problem (7.10).]

7.20. Let $\mathbf{A} \in M_{p,n}$ and $\mathbf{B} \in M_{p,n}$. Prove that $\mathbf{A}\{x\} = \{0\}$ and $\mathbf{B}\{x\} = \{0\}$ are equivalent systems if and only if $\mathbf{B}$ can be obtained from $\mathbf{A}$ by a finite number of row operations.

7.21. Let $\mathbf{B}\{x\} = \{0\}$ and $\mathbf{C}\{x\} = \{0\}$ be two equivalent systems where $\mathbf{B}$ and $\mathbf{C}$ have the row echelon form. Prove that the corresponding nonzero rows of $\mathbf{B}$ and $\mathbf{C}$ are identical.

7.22. Prove that the system $\mathbf{A}\{x\} = \{b\}$ is always consistent if the number of equations is equal to or less than the number of unknowns AND the rank of $\mathbf{A}$ is equal to the number of equations.

7.23. Prove that the solutions of $\mathbf{A}\{x\} = \{b\}$ form a subspace if and only if the system is homogeneous.

7.24. Prove that the transpose of an elementary row operation matrix is an elementary matrix. Also prove that if $\mathbf{A} \in M_{n,n}$ is any elementary row operation matrix

$$\text{rank}(\mathbf{A}) = \text{rank}(\mathbf{A}^T) = n.$$

7.25. If $\mathbf{B}$ is an elementary row operation matrix the product $\mathbf{B}_{m,m} \cdot \mathbf{A}_{m,n}$ corresponds to a row operation on $\mathbf{A}$. Give a similar interpretation of the product $\mathbf{A}_{m,n} \cdot \mathbf{B}_{n,n}$ and prove that

$$\text{rank}(\mathbf{B}_{m,m} \cdot \mathbf{A}_{m,n}) = \text{rank}(\mathbf{A}_{m,n} \cdot \mathbf{B}_{n,n}) = \text{rank}(\mathbf{A}_{m,n}).$$

7.26. If $\mathbf{A}_R$ is the row reduced form of a matrix $\mathbf{A}$ then

$$\text{rank}(\mathbf{A}_R) = \text{rank}[(\mathbf{A}_R)^T].$$

7.27. Use problems (7.25) and (7.26) to prove that

$$\text{rank}(\mathbf{A}) = \text{rank}(\mathbf{A}^T).$$

7.28. We define the **column space** of **A** as the space spanned by the columns of **A**. Prove that the column and row spaces of **A** have the same dimension.

7.29. Let $\mathbf{A} \in \mathsf{M}_{p,n}$. Show that if the dimension of the solution space of $\mathbf{A}\{x\} = \{0\}$ is $n - r$ then the dimension of the solution space of $\mathbf{A}^T\{y\} = \{0\}$ is $p - r$. Deduce that if **A** is a square matrix, the solution spaces of $\mathbf{A}\{x\} = \{0\}$ and $\mathbf{A}^T\{x\} = \{0\}$ have the same dimensions.

7.30. Express $\mathbf{E}_{\text{I}}(r, s)$ as a product of elementary row operation matrices of the type $\mathbf{E}_{\text{II}}(r; a)$ and $\mathbf{E}_{\text{III}}(r, s; a)$.

7.31. Show that a subspace of V_3 represents in E_3 one of the following sets of points; (1) the origin, (2) points on a line through the origin, (3) points on a plane through the origin, and (4) all points in E_3.

7.32. Let $\mathbf{A} = (a_{ij}) \in \mathsf{M}_{3,3}$. Show that the three planes in E_3 represented by $\{a_i\}^T\{x\} = b_i$, $i = 1, 2, 3$,

(i) have one and only one common point if and only if rank $(\mathbf{A}) = 3$,

(ii) pass through the same straight line (but they don't coincide) if and only if $\text{rank}(\mathbf{A}) = \text{rank}([\mathbf{A}|\{b\}]) = 2$,

(iii) coincide if and only if $\text{rank}(\mathbf{A}) = \text{rank}([\mathbf{A}|\{b\}]) = 1$,

(iv) are parallel to the same line (but not to each other) and have no common point if and only if $2 = \text{rank}(\mathbf{A}) \neq \text{rank}([\mathbf{A}|\{b\}])$,

(v) are parallel but have no common point if and only if $1 = \text{rank}(\mathbf{A}) \neq \text{rank}([\mathbf{A}|\{b\}])$.

LECTURE 8.

Matrix Equations

Study of $\mathbf{AB}=\mathbf{E}$ • Conditions for the existence of $\mathbf{B}$ • Conditions for uniqueness of $\mathbf{B}$ • Singular and nonsingular matrices • The inverse of a square matrix • Properties of the inverse • Inverses of elementary row operation matrices • Inverse of a matrix in terms of its row reducing matrix • Representation of a matrix in terms of its row reduced matrix and the row reducing matrix • Calculation of the inverse by row reduction • Problems

If $\mathbf{A}$ belongs to $\mathsf{M}_{n,p}$ and $\mathbf{B}$ belongs to $\mathsf{M}_{p,n}$, we know that we can form the product $\mathbf{AB}$ and that this product will belong to $\mathsf{M}_{n,n}$. There are many problems in which it is particularly important to know when we can find a matrix $\mathbf{B}$, for given $\mathbf{A}$, so that

$$\mathbf{AB}=\mathbf{E}, \tag{8.1}$$

where $\mathbf{E}$ is the identity matrix of $\mathsf{M}_{n,n}$. This problem can be solved by using the results that we have already established concerning linear inhomogeneous equations $\mathbf{A}\{x\}=\{b\}$.

Since the matrix $\mathbf{B}$ that occurs in Eq. (8.1) is a p-by-n matrix, if it can be found, we know that we can write $\mathbf{B}$ in the form

$$\mathbf{B}=[\{b\}_1, \{b\}_2, \ldots, \{b\}_n], \quad \{b\}_k=\begin{Bmatrix} b_{1k} \\ b_{2k} \\ \cdot \\ \cdot \\ \cdot \\ b_{pk} \end{Bmatrix}, \tag{8.2}$$

where each $\{b\}_k$ belongs to $\mathsf{M}_{p,1}$. Similarly, we can write

$$\mathbf{E}=[\{e\}_1, \{e\}_2, \ldots, \{e\}_n], \quad \{e\}_k \in \mathsf{M}_{n,1}, \tag{8.3}$$

where the column matrices $\{e\}_k$ are obtained from the vectors $\mathbf{e}_k$ that were introduced in lecture 2 [i.e., $\{e\}_k$ has all entries equal to zero but the kth, which is equal to unity]. We can thus write Eq. (8.1) in the equivalent form

$$\mathbf{A}[\{b\}_1, \ldots, \{b\}_n]=[\{e\}_1, \ldots, \{e\}_n].$$

From this, we see that the matrix equation (8.1) is equivalent to a system of n matrix equations

$$\mathbf{A}\{b\}_k=\{e\}_k, \quad k=1, \ldots, n. \tag{8.4}$$

The results established in lecture 7 state that the system (8.4) is a *consistent* system if and only if we have

$$\begin{aligned}\text{rank}(\mathbf{A}) &= \text{rank}([\mathbf{A}|\{e\}_1])\\ \text{rank}(\mathbf{A}) &= \text{rank}([\mathbf{A}|\{e\}_2])\\ &\vdots\\ \text{rank}(\mathbf{A}) &= \text{rank}([\mathbf{A}|\{e\}_n]).\end{aligned}$$

This system of conditions is easily seen to be equivalent to the single condition

$$\text{rank}(\mathbf{A})=\text{rank}([\mathbf{A}|\mathbf{E}]). \tag{8.5}$$

Since $\mathbf{A}$ belongs to $\mathsf{M}_{n,p}$ we know that

$$\text{rank}(\mathbf{A})\leq\min(n, p), \tag{8.6}$$

while

$$\text{rank}(\mathbf{E})=n, \tag{8.7}$$

since $\mathbf{E}$ is the identity matrix of $\mathsf{M}_{n,n}$. We also have

$$\text{rank}([\mathbf{A}|\mathbf{E}])=n, \tag{8.8}$$

the proof of which is left as an exercise. When we combine Eqs. (8.5) and (8.8) we obtain the requirement

$$\text{rank}(\mathbf{A})=n. \tag{8.9}$$

From this result and (8.6) we derive the further requirement

$$p\geq n. \tag{8.10}$$

We have thus established the following result. If $\mathbf{A}$ belongs to $\mathsf{M}_{n,p}$ *there exists a* **generalized right inverse matrix B** *belonging to* $\mathsf{M}_{p,n}$ *such that*

$$\mathbf{AB}=\mathbf{E},$$

if and only if

$$\text{rank}(\mathbf{A})=n \quad \textit{and} \quad p\geq n.$$

We now wish to establish under what conditions is the matrix $\mathbf{B}$ unique. Suppose that we can find two matrices $\mathbf{B}$ and $\mathbf{C}$ such that

$$\mathbf{AB}=\mathbf{E}, \qquad \mathbf{AC}=\mathbf{E}. \tag{8.11}$$

If we subtract the second equation from the first, we then have

$$\mathbf{A}(\mathbf{B}-\mathbf{C})=\mathbf{0}. \tag{8.12}$$

Since we must have rank$(\mathbf{A})=n$ in order that there exist matrices **B** and **C** that satisfy Eqs. (8.11), and since the equation (8.12) is equivalent to a homogeneous system of equations in the same way that Eq. (8.1) is equivalent to the vector system of equations (8.4), Eq. (8.12) will have only the trivial solution if and only if rank$(\mathbf{A})=n$ and $\mathbf{A}\in\mathsf{M}_{n,n}$. If this is the case, then Eq. (8.12) gives us the fact that $\mathbf{B}-\mathbf{C}=\mathbf{0}$, and hence $\mathbf{B}=\mathbf{C}$; that is, **B** is unique. We thus can collect all of the results together in the following statement.

If $\mathbf{A}\in\mathsf{M}_{n,p}$, *there exists a matrix* $\mathbf{B}\in\mathsf{M}_{p,n}$ *such that*

$$\mathbf{AB}=\mathbf{E}$$

if and only if

$$\text{rank}(\mathbf{A})=n,\ \ p\geq n.$$

Further, the matrix **B** *is unique if and only if* **A** *belongs to* $\mathsf{M}_{n,n}$ [i.e., $p=n$], *in which case* **B** *also belongs to* $\mathsf{M}_{n,n}$.

A matrix **A** that belongs to $\mathsf{M}_{n,n}$ and has rank$(\mathbf{A})=n$ is referred to as a **nonsingular** matrix. $\mathbf{A}\in\mathsf{M}_{n,n}$ is said to be **singular** if rank$(\mathbf{A})<n$. From the above theorem it is easily seen that *if* $\mathbf{A}\in\mathsf{M}_{n,n}$ *then* $\mathbf{AB}=\mathbf{E}$ *has a solution* **B** *if and only if* **A** *is nonsingular, in which case the solution* **B** *is unique*. This **unique** matrix **B** is customarily denoted by $\mathbf{A}^{-1}$, the **inverse** of **A**, and we write

$$\mathbf{A}\,\mathbf{A}^{-1}=\mathbf{E}. \tag{8.13}$$

Further, if **A** is nonsingular, then the row echelon form of **A** is **E**, that is $\mathbf{A}_R=\mathbf{E}$. We thus have the matrix $\mathbf{S}_A$ such that

$$\mathbf{S}_A\mathbf{A}=\mathbf{A}_R=\mathbf{E}. \tag{8.14}$$

Now, multiplying Eq. (8.14) on the right by $\mathbf{A}^{-1}$, we have

$$(\mathbf{S}_A\mathbf{A})\mathbf{A}^{-1}=\mathbf{E}\mathbf{A}^{-1}=\mathbf{A}^{-1}. \tag{8.15}$$

However, by Eq. (8.13),

$$(\mathbf{S}_A\mathbf{A})\mathbf{A}^{-1}=\mathbf{S}_A(\mathbf{A}\mathbf{A}^{-1})=\mathbf{S}_A\mathbf{E}=\mathbf{S}_A, \tag{8.16}$$

and hence, on combining Eqs. (8.15) and (8.16), we obtain

$$\mathbf{S}_A=\mathbf{A}^{-1}. \tag{8.17}$$

Since the inverse of a nonsingular matrix **A** is *unique,* it also follows that any matrix $\mathbf{S}\in\mathsf{S}$ such that

$$\mathbf{SA}=\mathbf{A}_R=\mathbf{E}$$

is the inverse of **A** and we have

$$\mathbf{S}=\mathbf{S}_A=\mathbf{A}^{-1}.$$

If we put Eq. (8.17) back into Eq. (8.14) we have

$$\mathbf{A}^{-1}\mathbf{A}=\mathbf{E}. \tag{8.18}$$

If $\mathbf{A}$ and $\mathbf{B}$ belong to $\mathsf{M}_{n,n}$ and both are nonsingular, their product $\mathbf{AB}$ belongs to $\mathsf{M}_{n,n}$. Since we have $\mathbf{AA}^{-1}=\mathbf{E}$, $\mathbf{BB}^{-1}=\mathbf{E}$, we then have $\mathbf{ABB}^{-1}=\mathbf{AE}=\mathbf{A}$. From this we obtain that

$$\mathbf{ABB}^{-1}\mathbf{A}^{-1}=\mathbf{AA}^{-1}=\mathbf{E};$$

that is, *if* $\mathbf{A}$ *and* $\mathbf{B}$ *are nonsingular elements of* $\mathsf{M}_{n,n}$ *then* $\mathbf{AB}$ *is nonsingular and*

$$(\mathbf{AB})^{-1}=\mathbf{B}^{-1}\mathbf{A}^{-1}. \tag{8.19}$$

If we apply this result to the product $\mathbf{AA}^{-1}$, we have

$$(\mathbf{AA}^{-1})^{-1}=(\mathbf{A}^{-1})^{-1}\mathbf{A}^{-1}=\mathbf{E}^{-1}=\mathbf{E},$$

and we thus have

$$(\mathbf{A}^{-1})^{-1}=\mathbf{A}. \tag{8.20}$$

If we apply this result to Eq. (8.17), we obtain

$$\mathbf{S}_A{}^{-1}=(\mathbf{A}^{-1})^{-1}=\mathbf{A}. \tag{8.21}$$

It is easily seen that *the inverses of the three classes of matrices that generate the elementary row operations are, themselves, elementary row operation matrices* and they can be obtained by inspection.

(1) If we interchange the ith and jth columns and then interchange them again, we obtain the original matrix; that is $\mathbf{E}_{\mathrm{I}}{}^{-1}=\mathbf{E}_{\mathrm{I}}$: $\mathbf{E}=\mathbf{E}_{\mathrm{I}}(r, s)\times\mathbf{E}_{\mathrm{I}}(r, s)$, that is $\mathbf{E}_{\mathrm{I}}{}^{-1}(r, s)=\mathbf{E}_{\mathrm{I}}(r, s)$.

(2) If we multiply the ith row by a and then multiply the ith row by $1/a$, the matrix is unchanged under the combination of these two operations: $\mathbf{E}=\mathbf{E}_{\mathrm{II}}\left(r; \dfrac{1}{a}\right)\mathbf{E}_{\mathrm{II}}(r; a) \;\Rightarrow\; \mathbf{E}_{\mathrm{II}}{}^{-1}(r; a)=\mathbf{E}_{\mathrm{II}}\left(r; \dfrac{1}{a}\right)$.

(3) If we replace the ith row by itself plus b times the jth row, and then replace the ith row by itself plus $(-b)$ times the jth row, the matrix is unchanged under the combination of these two operations: $\mathbf{E}=\mathbf{E}_{\mathrm{III}}(i, j; b)\mathbf{E}_{\mathrm{III}}(i, j; -b) \;\Rightarrow\; \mathbf{E}_{\mathrm{III}}{}^{-1}(i, j; b)=\mathbf{E}_{\mathrm{III}}(i, j; -b)$.

When $\mathbf{A}$ is nonsingular, the relation (8.21) establishes the fact that $\mathbf{A}=\mathbf{S}_A{}^{-1}$. On the other hand, the row-echelon algorithm gives us a specific procedure for computing elementary row-operation matrices whose ordered product is $\mathbf{S}_A$. We have also seen that the inverse of elementary row-operation matrices are again elementary row-operation matrices, and hence $\mathbf{S}_A{}^{-1}$ is also a product of elementary row-operation matrices. The formula $\mathbf{A}=\mathbf{S}_A{}^{-1}$ thus gives the following result: *each nonsingular matrix* $\mathbf{A}$ *is equal to a product* $\mathbf{S}_A{}^{-1}$ *of elementary row-operation matrices. Furthermore, the product* $\mathbf{S}_A$ *of elementary row-operation matrices is* **unique** [*since* $\mathbf{A}^{-1}=\mathbf{S}_A$ *and* $\mathbf{A}^{-1}$ *is unique*] *even though there is a lack of uniqueness in the choices of the elementary row-operation matrices that comprise* $\mathbf{S}_A$. For instance, if we change the sequence of steps in the row-echelon algorithm, then we will obtain a different set of elementary row-operation matrices whose ordered product again gives the matrix $\mathbf{S}_A$ that row reduces $\mathbf{A}$.

We have shown that any matrix $\mathbf{S}$ that is comprised of a finite product of elementary row-operation matrices is nonsingular. This fact can be used to obtain a representation for any matrix whether it is singular or not. We know that there exists a matrix $\mathbf{S} \in \mathsf{S}$ such that

$$\mathbf{SA}=\mathbf{A}_R. \tag{8.22}$$

multiplication on the left by $\mathbf{S}^{-1}$ thus gives us

$$\mathbf{A}=\mathbf{S}^{-1}\mathbf{A}_R: \tag{8.23}$$

each matrix $\mathbf{A}$ *is equal to a product of elementary row-operation matrices multiplied by the row reduced form of the matrix* $\mathbf{A}$. If $\mathbf{A} \in \mathsf{M}_{n,n}$ and $\mathbf{A}$ is nonsingular, then $\mathbf{A}_R=\mathbf{E}$, $\mathbf{S}=\mathbf{S}_A$ and we recover Eq. (8.21) from Eq. (8.23).

We now come down to the question of how to compute the inverse of a nonsingular matrix. We know that if $\mathbf{A}$ is nonsingular, then the row operation matrix $\mathbf{S}_A$ that reduces $\mathbf{A}$ to row echelon form is the matrix $\mathbf{A}^{-1}$; that is, if

$$\mathbf{S}_A\mathbf{A}=\mathbf{A}_R=\mathbf{E}, \text{ then } \mathbf{S}_A=\mathbf{A}^{-1}.$$

Thus, in order to compute the inverse of a given matrix $\mathbf{A} \in \mathsf{M}_{n,n}$, we have to check that $\operatorname{rank}(\mathbf{A})=n$ and then compute $\mathbf{S}_A$. We have already found an efficient algorithm for computing $\mathbf{S}_A$ in the last lecture. This algorithm is given by

$$\mathbf{S}_A[\mathbf{A}|\mathbf{E}]=[\mathbf{A}_R|\mathbf{S}_A], \tag{8.24}$$

which says that if we row reduce $[\mathbf{A}|\mathbf{E}]$ and "stop" when we have row reduced $\mathbf{A}$, we obtain $[\mathbf{A}_R|\mathbf{S}_A]$. We also have to check that $\operatorname{rank}(\mathbf{A})=n$, for if $\operatorname{rank}(\mathbf{A})\neq n$ then $\mathbf{A}^{-1}$ does not exist. Since $\mathbf{A} \in \mathsf{M}_{n,n}$ $\operatorname{rank}(\mathbf{A})=n$ if and only if $\mathbf{S}_A\mathbf{A}=\mathbf{A}_R=\mathbf{E}$. When this is substituted into Eq. (8.24), we have

$$\mathbf{S}_A[\mathbf{A}|\mathbf{E}]=[\mathbf{E}|\mathbf{S}_A]. \tag{8.25}$$

This gives us the following algorithm for calculating $\mathbf{A}^{-1}$: *If the row reduction of* $[\mathbf{A}|\mathbf{E}]$ *is* $[\mathbf{E}|\mathbf{S}_A]$, *then* $\mathbf{A}^{-1}$ *exists and is given by* $\mathbf{A}^{-1}=\mathbf{S}_A$.

An immediate formal use of the inverse of a matrix is provided by the problem

$$\mathbf{A}\{x\}=\{b\}$$

where $\mathbf{A} \in \mathsf{M}_{n,n}$, $\{x\}$ and $\{b\}$ belong to $\mathsf{M}_{n,1}$. If $\text{rank}(\mathbf{A}) = n$, then $\mathbf{A}^{-1}$ exists. Multiplying the above matrix equation on the left by $\mathbf{A}^{-1}$ gives

$$\mathbf{A}^{-1}\mathbf{A}\{x\} = \mathbf{A}^{-1}\{b\},$$

and hence we have

$$\{x\} = \mathbf{A}^{-1}\{b\}.$$

This is the unique solution of $\mathbf{A}\{x\} = \{b\}$ since $\text{rank}(\mathbf{A}) = n = \text{rank}(\mathbf{A}|\{b\})$.

EXAMPLE 1

$$\mathbf{A} = \begin{pmatrix} 1 & 3 & 6 \\ 0 & 2 & 4 \\ 2 & 1 & 2 \end{pmatrix}; \quad [\mathbf{A}|\mathbf{E}] = \left(\begin{array}{ccc|ccc} 1 & 3 & 6 & 1 & 0 & 0 \\ 0 & 2 & 4 & 0 & 1 & 0 \\ 2 & 1 & 2 & 0 & 0 & 1 \end{array}\right)$$

$$\Omega \left(\begin{array}{ccc|ccc} 1 & 3 & 6 & 1 & 0 & 0 \\ 0 & 2 & 4 & 0 & 1 & 0 \\ 0 & -5 & -10 & -2 & 0 & 1 \end{array}\right)$$

$$\Omega \left(\begin{array}{ccc|ccc} 1 & 3 & 6 & 1 & 0 & 0 \\ 0 & 1 & 2 & 0 & \frac{1}{2} & 0 \\ 0 & -5 & -10 & -2 & 0 & 1 \end{array}\right)$$

$$\Omega \left(\begin{array}{ccc|ccc} 1 & 3 & 6 & 1 & 0 & 0 \\ 0 & 1 & 2 & 0 & \frac{1}{2} & 0 \\ 0 & 0 & 0 & -2 & \frac{5}{2} & 1 \end{array}\right)$$

$$\Omega \left(\begin{array}{ccc|ccc} 1 & 0 & 0 & 1 & -\frac{3}{2} & 0 \\ 0 & 1 & 2 & 0 & \frac{1}{2} & 0 \\ 0 & 0 & 0 & -2 & \frac{5}{2} & 1 \end{array}\right)$$

$$= [\mathbf{A}_R|\mathbf{S}_A];$$

since $\mathbf{A}_R \neq \mathbf{E}$, $\mathbf{A}^{-1}$ does not exist; however, we have

$$\mathbf{S}_A = \begin{pmatrix} 1 & -\frac{3}{2} & 0 \\ 0 & \frac{1}{2} & 0 \\ -2 & \frac{5}{2} & 1 \end{pmatrix},$$

and this $\mathbf{S}_A$ has the property that

$$\mathbf{S}_A\mathbf{A}=\mathbf{A}_R=\begin{pmatrix}1 & 0 & 0\\ 0 & 1 & 2\\ 0 & 0 & 0\end{pmatrix};$$

further, $\operatorname{rank}(\mathbf{S}_A)=3$,

$$[\mathbf{S}_A|\mathbf{E}]=\left(\begin{array}{ccc|ccc}1 & -\frac{3}{2} & 0 & 1 & 0 & 0\\ 0 & \frac{1}{2} & 0 & 0 & 1 & 0\\ -2 & \frac{5}{2} & 1 & 0 & 0 & 1\end{array}\right)$$

$$\Omega\left(\begin{array}{ccc|ccc}1 & 0 & 0 & 1 & 3 & 0\\ 0 & 1 & 0 & 0 & 2 & 0\\ 0 & 0 & 1 & 2 & 1 & 1\end{array}\right)$$

$$=[\mathbf{E}|\mathbf{S}_A^{-1}],$$

so that

$$\mathbf{S}_A^{-1}=\begin{pmatrix}1 & 3 & 0\\ 0 & 2 & 0\\ 2 & 1 & 1\end{pmatrix}$$

and we have the representation of $\mathbf{A}$ given by

$$\mathbf{A}=\mathbf{S}_A^{-1}\mathbf{A}_R=\begin{pmatrix}1 & 3 & 0\\ 0 & 2 & 0\\ 2 & 1 & 1\end{pmatrix}\begin{pmatrix}1 & 0 & 0\\ 0 & 1 & 2\\ 0 & 0 & 0\end{pmatrix}=\begin{pmatrix}1 & 3 & 6\\ 0 & 2 & 4\\ 2 & 1 & 2\end{pmatrix}.$$

EXAMPLE 2

$$\mathbf{A}=\begin{pmatrix}2 & 3\\ 3 & 6\end{pmatrix};$$

$$[\mathbf{A}|\mathbf{E}]=\left(\begin{array}{cc|cc}2 & 3 & 1 & 0\\ 3 & 6 & 0 & 1\end{array}\right)\Omega\left(\begin{array}{cc|cc}1 & \frac{3}{2} & \frac{1}{2} & 0\\ 3 & 6 & 0 & 1\end{array}\right)$$

$$\Omega\left(\begin{array}{cc|cc}1 & \frac{3}{2} & \frac{1}{2} & 0\\ 0 & \frac{3}{2} & -\frac{3}{2} & 1\end{array}\right)\Omega\left(\begin{array}{cc|cc}1 & \frac{3}{2} & \frac{1}{2} & 0\\ 0 & 1 & -1 & \frac{3}{2}\end{array}\right)$$

$$\Omega\left(\begin{array}{cc|cc} 1 & 0 & 2 & -1 \\ 0 & 1 & -1 & \frac{2}{3} \end{array}\right)=[\mathbf{E}|\mathbf{S}_A],$$

$$\mathbf{S}_A=\mathbf{A}^{-1}=\begin{pmatrix} 2 & -1 \\ -1 & \frac{2}{3} \end{pmatrix}$$

since

$$\mathbf{S}_A\mathbf{A}=\mathbf{A}_R=\mathbf{E}.$$

EXAMPLE 3

$$\mathbf{A}=\begin{pmatrix} 0 & 0 & 1 & 1 \\ 0 & 0 & 1 & -1 \\ 1 & -1 & 0 & 0 \\ 1 & 1 & 0 & 0 \end{pmatrix}.$$

In this example, we will first interchange rows of $[\mathbf{A}|\mathbf{E}]$ and then proceed with the row echelon reduction. This saves a number of steps in the reduction process!

$$[\mathbf{A}|\mathbf{E}]=\left(\begin{array}{cccc|cccc} 0 & 0 & 1 & 1 & 1 & 0 & 0 & 0 \\ 0 & 0 & 1 & -1 & 0 & 1 & 0 & 0 \\ 1 & -1 & 0 & 0 & 0 & 0 & 1 & 0 \\ 1 & 1 & 0 & 0 & 0 & 0 & 0 & 1 \end{array}\right)$$

$$\Omega\left(\begin{array}{cccc|cccc} 1 & -1 & 0 & 0 & 0 & 0 & 1 & 0 \\ 1 & 1 & 0 & 0 & 0 & 0 & 0 & 1 \\ 0 & 0 & 1 & 1 & 1 & 0 & 0 & 0 \\ 0 & 0 & 1 & -1 & 0 & 1 & 0 & 0 \end{array}\right)$$

$$\Omega\left(\begin{array}{cccc|cccc} 1 & -1 & 0 & 0 & 0 & 0 & 1 & 0 \\ 0 & 2 & 0 & 0 & 0 & 0 & -1 & 1 \\ 0 & 0 & 1 & 1 & 1 & 0 & 0 & 0 \\ 0 & 0 & 0 & -2 & -1 & 1 & 0 & 0 \end{array}\right)$$

$$\Omega\left(\begin{array}{cccc|cccc} 1 & 0 & 0 & 0 & 0 & 0 & \frac{1}{2} & \frac{1}{2} \\ 0 & 1 & 0 & 0 & 0 & 0 & -\frac{1}{2} & \frac{1}{2} \\ 0 & 0 & 1 & 0 & \frac{1}{2} & \frac{1}{2} & 0 & 0 \\ 0 & 0 & 0 & 1 & \frac{1}{2} & -\frac{1}{2} & 0 & 0 \end{array}\right)$$

$$=[\mathbf{E}|\mathbf{S}],$$

$$S = A^{-1} = \begin{pmatrix} 0 & 0 & \frac{1}{2} & \frac{1}{2} \\ 0 & 0 & -\frac{1}{2} & \frac{1}{2} \\ \frac{1}{2} & \frac{1}{2} & 0 & 0 \\ \frac{1}{2} & -\frac{1}{2} & 0 & 0 \end{pmatrix}.$$

See problem 8.7 for a justification.

Problems

8.1. For the following values of the matrix **A** obtain all matrices **B** such that **AB** = **E**:

$$\text{(a)} \begin{pmatrix} 1 & 2 & 0 \\ 2 & 3 & 1 \end{pmatrix}; \quad \text{(b)} \begin{pmatrix} 1 & 2 \\ 2 & 3 \end{pmatrix}; \quad \text{(c)} \begin{pmatrix} 2 & 3 & 0 \\ 4 & 6 & 0 \end{pmatrix};$$

$$\text{(d)} \begin{pmatrix} 1 & 2 \\ 3 & 4 \\ 5 & 6 \end{pmatrix}; \quad \text{(e)} \begin{pmatrix} 2 & 3 & 4 \\ 4 & 7 & 6 \end{pmatrix}; \quad \text{(f)} \begin{pmatrix} 1 & 3 \\ 2 & 6 \end{pmatrix};$$

$$\text{(g)} \begin{pmatrix} 3 & 6 \\ 1 & 2 \\ 4 & 5 \end{pmatrix}; \quad \text{(h)} \begin{pmatrix} 1 & 0 & 2 \\ 0 & 1 & 3 \\ 2 & 3 & 5 \end{pmatrix}; \quad \text{(i)} \begin{pmatrix} 1 & 2 & 3 & 4 \\ 2 & 5 & 6 & 8 \\ 3 & 6 & 10 & 12 \end{pmatrix}.$$

State when the matrix **B** is unique.

8.2. Obtain all matrices **B** such that **BA** = **E** when **A** is given as in problem 8.1. State when the matrix **B** is unique.

8.3. Represent the matrix **A** in the form $\mathbf{A} = \mathbf{S}^{-1}\mathbf{A}_R$ and write $\mathbf{S}^{-1}$ as a product of elementary row operation matrices when **A** is given by problem 8.1. State when the matrix $\mathbf{S}^{-1}$ is unique.

8.4. By row reducing the appropriate augmented matrix compute $\mathbf{A}^{-1}$ when **A** is given by

$$\text{(a)} \begin{pmatrix} 1 & 3 \\ 4 & 5 \end{pmatrix}; \quad \text{(b)} \begin{pmatrix} 2 & 4 \\ 3 & 7 \end{pmatrix}; \quad \text{(c)} \begin{pmatrix} 1 & 2 \\ 3 & 5 \end{pmatrix};$$

$$\text{(d)} \begin{pmatrix} 1 & 2 & 3 \\ 2 & 3 & 4 \\ 0 & 1 & 3 \end{pmatrix}; \quad \text{(e)} \begin{pmatrix} 2 & 4 & 8 \\ 3 & 7 & 12 \\ 1 & 3 & 5 \end{pmatrix}; \quad \text{(f)} \begin{pmatrix} 1 & 3 & 12 \\ 0 & 4 & 8 \\ 2 & 6 & 13 \end{pmatrix}.$$

8.5. Solve the system $\mathbf{A}\{x\} = \{b\}$ by calculating $\mathbf{A}^{-1}$ and using the formula $\{x\} = \mathbf{A}^{-1}\{b\}$ when $\mathbf{A}$ and $\{b\}$ are given respectively by

$$\text{(a) } \begin{pmatrix} 3 & 9 \\ 2 & 5 \end{pmatrix}, \begin{Bmatrix} 1 \\ 2 \end{Bmatrix}; \quad \text{(b) } \begin{pmatrix} 1 & 0 \\ 2 & -3 \end{pmatrix}, \begin{Bmatrix} 2 \\ 3 \end{Bmatrix}; \quad \text{(c) } \begin{pmatrix} 0 & 4 \\ 5 & -10 \end{pmatrix}, \begin{Bmatrix} 1 \\ 5 \end{Bmatrix};$$

$$\text{(d) } \begin{pmatrix} 1 & 2 & 3 \\ 2 & 3 & 4 \\ 3 & 5 & 8 \end{pmatrix}, \begin{Bmatrix} 1 \\ 3 \\ 2 \end{Bmatrix}; \quad \text{(e) } \begin{pmatrix} 0 & 1 & 2 \\ 3 & 0 & 4 \\ 0 & 0 & 5 \end{pmatrix}, \begin{Bmatrix} -3 \\ 2 \\ 1 \end{Bmatrix}; \quad \text{(f) } \begin{pmatrix} 1 & 2 & 0 \\ 0 & 2 & 4 \\ 1 & 0 & 3 \end{pmatrix}, \begin{Bmatrix} 5 \\ -3 \\ 2 \end{Bmatrix}.$$

8.6. Prove Eq. (8.8).

8.7. If $[\mathbf{A}|\mathbf{E}]$ is row reduced to $[\mathbf{E}|\mathbf{S}]$ by elementary row operations, which do not necessarily follow the order of the row echelon algorithm, then $\mathbf{A}^{-1}$ exists and is given by $\mathbf{A}^{-1} = \mathbf{S}$.

8.8. Prove that

$$\text{rank}([\mathbf{A}|\mathbf{B}]) \geq \max(\text{rank}(\mathbf{A}), \text{rank}(\mathbf{B})).$$

8.9. Let $\mathbf{F} = [\mathbf{A}|\mathbf{B}]$.

(a) Show, by way of example, that if $\text{rank}([\mathbf{A}|\mathbf{B}]) = r$ and $\text{rank}([\mathbf{A}|\mathbf{C}]) = r$, the relation $\text{rank}([\mathbf{F}|\mathbf{C}]) = r$ need NOT be true.

(b) Prove that if $\text{rank}([\mathbf{A}|\mathbf{B}]) = \text{rank}([\mathbf{A}|\mathbf{C}]) = \text{rank}(\mathbf{A})$, then $\text{rank}([\mathbf{F}|\mathbf{C}]) = \text{rank}(\mathbf{A})$. Generalize this result.

8.10. Prove that rank $([\mathbf{A}|\mathbf{B}]) = \text{rank}([\mathbf{B}|\mathbf{A}])$. [Use problem 7.27.]

8.11. Let $\mathbf{A} \in \mathsf{M}_{n,p}$ and $\text{rank}(\mathbf{A}) = n$. Prove that

$$\text{rank}([\mathbf{A}|\mathbf{B}]) = n.$$

8.12. Let $\mathbf{A} \in \mathsf{M}_{n,p}$. Prove that there exists a matrix $\mathbf{B} \in \mathsf{M}_{p,n}$ such that $\mathbf{BA} = \mathbf{E}$ if and only if

$$\text{rank}(\mathbf{A}) = p, \qquad n \geq p.$$

Moreover, the matrix $\mathbf{B}$ is unique if and only if

$$\text{rank}(\mathbf{A}) = p, \qquad n = p$$

in which case $\mathbf{B} \in \mathsf{M}_{p,p}$.

8.13. Let $\mathbf{A} \in \mathsf{M}_{n,q}$, $\mathbf{B} \in \mathsf{M}_{n,p}$ where $\mathbf{B} = [\{b\}_1, \ldots, \{b\}_p]$. Show that

$$\text{rank}(\mathbf{A}) = \text{rank}([\mathbf{A}|\mathbf{B}])$$

if and only if

$$\text{rank}(\mathbf{A}) = \text{rank}([\mathbf{A}|\{b\}_1]) = \ldots = \text{rank}([\mathbf{A}|\{b\}_p]).$$

8.14. Show, by way of example, that from the relations $\mathbf{AX} = \mathbf{AY}$, $\mathbf{A} \neq \mathbf{0}$, it does not necessarily follow that $\mathbf{X} = \mathbf{Y}$. Similarly, show that the relations $\mathbf{XA} = \mathbf{YA}$, $\mathbf{A} \neq \mathbf{0}$, do not necessarily imply $\mathbf{X} = \mathbf{Y}$.

8.15. If $\mathbf{A}$ is a nonsingular matrix, show that $\mathbf{X} = \mathbf{Y}$ follows from either of the relations $\mathbf{AX} = \mathbf{AY}$ or $\mathbf{XA} = \mathbf{YA}$.

8.16. If $\mathbf{A}$ is a square matrix and $\mathbf{AB} = \mathbf{E}$ or $\mathbf{BA} = \mathbf{E}$ then $\mathbf{A}$ is nonsingular and $\mathbf{B} = \mathbf{A}^{-1}$.

8.17. If $\mathbf{A}$ is a nonsingular matrix, show that $(\mathbf{A}^T)^{-1} = (\mathbf{A}^{-1})^T$.

8.18. If the n-by-n matrices $\mathbf{A}_1, \ldots, \mathbf{A}_p$ are nonsingular, show that $(\mathbf{A}_1 \cdots \mathbf{A}_p)^{-1} = \mathbf{A}_p^{-1} \cdots \mathbf{A}_1^{-1}$.

8.19. Prove that if the product of a finite number of n-by-n matrices is a singular matrix at least one of the factors is a singular matrix.

8.20. Let the matrix $\mathbf{S}$ be defined by $\mathbf{SA} = \mathbf{A}_R$. Give an example to show that the factorization of $\mathbf{S}$ into elementary row operation matrices is not unique.

8.21. Show that every square matrix can be represented as a product of triangular matrices. [Use $\mathbf{A} = \mathbf{S}_A^{-1}\mathbf{A}_R$ and problem 7.30.]

8.22. Show that if $\mathbf{A}$ is a nonsingular matrix which commutes with $\mathbf{B}$, then $\mathbf{B}$ commutes with $\mathbf{A}^{-1}$.

8.23. If m is a positive integer and $\mathbf{A}$ a nonsingular matrix, we define

$$\mathbf{A}^{-m} = (\mathbf{A}^{-1})^m.$$

Show that if m, n are (positive or negative) integers and $\mathbf{A}$ a nonsingular matrix, then

$$\mathbf{A}^r\mathbf{A}^s = \mathbf{A}^{r+s}, \qquad (\mathbf{A}^r)^s = \mathbf{A}^{rs}.$$

8.24. Let $\mathbf{A}$ and $\mathbf{B}$ be nonsingular commuting matrices and m, n two (not necessarily positive) integers. Show that $\mathbf{A}^m$ and $\mathbf{B}^n$ commute.

8.25. Let $\mathbf{AB} = \mathbf{C}$ where $\mathbf{A}$, $\mathbf{B}$ are square matrices, and $\mathbf{C}$ is a nonzero scalar matrix. Show that the matrices $\mathbf{A}$ and $\mathbf{B}$ commute.

8.26. If $\mathbf{A}$ and $\mathbf{B}$ are two diagonal matrices, the diagonal elements of which are the same (but not necessarily in the same order), show that there exists a nonsingular symmetric matrix $\mathbf{H}$ such that

$$\mathbf{A} = \mathbf{H}\,\mathbf{B}\,\mathbf{H}.$$

[See problem 7.25.]

8.27. Let $f(x)$, $g(x)$ be two polynomials and $\mathbf{A}$ a square matrix such that the matrix $g(\mathbf{A})$ is nonsingular. Show that

$$\{g(\mathbf{A})\}^{-1}f(\mathbf{A}) = f(\mathbf{A})\{g(\mathbf{A})\}^{-1}.$$

Either side of this equation is defined as the **ratio of the two matrices** $f(\mathbf{A})$ and $g(\mathbf{A})$ and it is denoted by

$$\frac{f(\mathbf{A})}{g(\mathbf{A})}.$$

[See problem 4.26, and use the equality $f(\mathbf{A})g(\mathbf{A}) = g(\mathbf{A})f(\mathbf{A})$.]

8.28. Let $f(x)$, $g(x)$, $h(x)$, $k(x)$ be four polynomials and $\mathbf{A}$ a square matrix such that $g(\mathbf{A})$ *and* $k(\mathbf{A})$ are nonsingular. Show that

$$\frac{f(\mathbf{A})}{g(\mathbf{A})} = \frac{h(\mathbf{A})}{k(\mathbf{A})} \quad \text{if} \quad \frac{f(x)}{g(x)} = \frac{h(x)}{k(x)}.$$

8.29. Show that any identity between rational functions of a variable x remains valid if x is replaced by a square matrix $\mathbf{A}$ provided that all the matrix functions involved are defined.

LECTURE 9.

Elementary Properties of Matrices

Symmetric and skew-symmetric matrices • Representation of a matrix in terms of its symmetric and skew-symmetric parts • The trace of a matrix • Properties of the trace • Representation of a matrix as the sum of a scalar matrix, a trace free symmetric matrix and a skew-symmetric matrix • Positive definite matrices • Representation of positive definite matrices • Substitutions $\{y\} = \mathbf{A}\{x\}$ that preserve norms • Differentials of $\{x\}^T\mathbf{B}\{x\}$ • Orthogonal matrices • Properties of orthogonal matrices • Quadratic forms • Extremals of quadratic forms • Problems

There are several elementary properties of square matrices which occur so often in applications that we would be remiss if we neglected them.

All of the matrices that are designated by bold capital Latin letters in this lecture are square n-by-n matrices.

A matrix $\mathbf{A}$ is said to be **symmetric** if and only if

$$\mathbf{A}^T = \mathbf{A}. \tag{9.1}$$

A matrix $\mathbf{A}$ is said to be **skewsymmetric** or **antisymmetric** if and only if

$$\mathbf{A}^T = -\mathbf{A}. \tag{9.2}$$

If we define the matrix $\mathbf{U}$ by the relation

$$\mathbf{U} = \frac{1}{2}(\mathbf{A} + \mathbf{A}^T), \tag{9.3}$$

then $\mathbf{U}$ is a symmetric matrix. The matrix $\mathbf{U}$ given by Eq. (9.3) is called the **symmetric part** of the matrix $\mathbf{A}$. Similarly, if we define the matrix $\mathbf{V}$ by the relation

$$\mathbf{V} = \frac{1}{2}(\mathbf{A} - \mathbf{A}^T), \tag{9.4}$$

then $\mathbf{V}$ is a skewsymmetric matrix. The matrix $\mathbf{V}$ given by Eq. (9.4) is called the **skewsymmetric part** of the matrix $\mathbf{A}$. If we combine Eqs. (9.3) and (9.4), we obtain

$$\mathbf{A} = \mathbf{U} + \mathbf{V}, \quad \mathbf{U} = \frac{1}{2}(\mathbf{A} + \mathbf{A}^T), \quad \mathbf{V} = \frac{1}{2}(\mathbf{A} - \mathbf{A}^T). \tag{9.5}$$

We have thus established that *any n-by-n matrix can be represented as a sum of a symmetric matrix and a skewsymmetric matrix.* In fact, this representation is *unique,* as we shall now show. Suppose that we had another such representation, say

$$\mathbf{A}=\mathbf{U}_1+\mathbf{V}_1, \quad \mathbf{U}_1{}^T=\mathbf{U}_1, \quad \mathbf{V}_1{}^T=-\mathbf{V}_1. \tag{9.6}$$

Then, subtracting Eq. (9.6) from Eq. (9.5) gives us

$$\mathbf{0}=(\mathbf{U}-\mathbf{U}_1)+(\mathbf{V}-\mathbf{V}_1). \tag{9.7}$$

However, $\mathbf{0}^T=\mathbf{0}$, and hence Eq. (9.7) gives

$$\mathbf{0}=\mathbf{0}^T=(\mathbf{U}-\mathbf{U}_1)^T+(\mathbf{V}-\mathbf{V}_1)^T=(\mathbf{U}-\mathbf{U}_1)-(\mathbf{V}-\mathbf{V}_1), \tag{9.8}$$

where the last equality is obtained by noting that $\mathbf{U}$, $\mathbf{U}_1$ are symmetric while $\mathbf{V}$, $\mathbf{V}_1$ are skewsymmetric. Adding Eq. (9.8) and Eq. (9.7) gives us $2(\mathbf{U}-\mathbf{U}_1)=\mathbf{0}$, that is, $\mathbf{U}=\mathbf{U}_1$. When we put this back into Eq. (9.7) we then obtain $(\mathbf{V}-\mathbf{V}_1)=\mathbf{0}$, so that $\mathbf{U}=\mathbf{U}_1$, $\mathbf{V}=\mathbf{V}_1$, and the uniqueness is established.

There is another important operation that can be applied to square matrices. The **trace** of an n-by-n matrix $\mathbf{A}$, written $\mathrm{tr}(\mathbf{A})$, is defined by

$$\begin{aligned}\mathrm{tr}(\mathbf{A}) &= (\text{sum of the entries of the matrix } \mathbf{A} \\ &\qquad \text{that sit on the principle diagonal of } \mathbf{A}) \\ &= \sum_{i=1}^{n} a_{ii}.\end{aligned} \tag{9.9}$$

The trace of a matrix is thus a number and the operation tr has the following properties:

$$\mathrm{tr}(\mathbf{A}+\mathbf{B})=\mathrm{tr}(\mathbf{A})+\mathrm{tr}(\mathbf{B}), \tag{9.10}$$

$$\mathrm{tr}(c\mathbf{A})=c\,\mathrm{tr}(\mathbf{A}), \tag{9.11}$$

$$\mathrm{tr}(\mathbf{A}^T)=\mathrm{tr}(\mathbf{A}), \tag{9.12}$$

$$\mathrm{tr}(\mathbf{AB})=\mathrm{tr}(\mathbf{BA}), \quad \mathrm{tr}(\mathbf{ABC})=\mathrm{tr}(\mathbf{BCA})=\mathrm{tr}(\mathbf{CAB}). \tag{9.13}$$

A matrix $\mathbf{A}$ is said to be **trace free** if and only if

$$\mathrm{tr}(\mathbf{A})=0. \tag{9.14}$$

If $\mathbf{E}$ is the n-by-n identity matrix, we have

$$\mathrm{tr}(\mathbf{E})=n. \tag{9.15}$$

We can use this observation to write

$$\mathbf{A}=\frac{1}{n}\mathrm{tr}(\mathbf{A})\mathbf{E}+(\mathbf{A}-\frac{1}{n}\mathrm{tr}(\mathbf{A})\mathbf{E}). \tag{9.16}$$

Now, by Eqs. (9.10), (9.11), and (9.15), we have

$$\mathrm{tr}(\mathbf{A}-\frac{1}{n}\mathrm{tr}(\mathbf{A})\mathbf{E})=\mathrm{tr}(\mathbf{A})-\frac{1}{n}\mathrm{tr}(\mathbf{A})\ \mathrm{tr}(\mathbf{E})=\mathrm{tr}(\mathbf{A})-\mathrm{tr}(\mathbf{A})=0,$$

and hence Eq. (9.16) states that *any n-by-n matrix* **A** *can be represented as the sum of a scalar matrix* $\frac{1}{n}\,\mathrm{tr}(\mathbf{A})\mathbf{E}$ *and a trace free matrix* $\mathbf{A}-\frac{1}{n}\,\mathrm{tr}(\mathbf{A})\mathbf{E}$. We leave the proof that this representation is *unique* to the student as an exercise. We can now combine Eqs. (9.5) and (9.16) so as to obtain the following *unique representation of an n-by-n matrix:*

$$\mathbf{A}=\frac{1}{n}\mathrm{tr}(\mathbf{A})\mathbf{E}+\mathbf{U}+\mathbf{V},$$

$$\mathrm{tr}(\mathbf{U})=\mathrm{tr}(\mathbf{V})=0,\quad \mathbf{U}^T=\mathbf{U},\quad \mathbf{V}^T=-\mathbf{V}. \tag{9.17}$$

The matrices **U** and **V** are given by

$$\mathbf{U}=\frac{1}{2}(\mathbf{A}+\mathbf{A}^T)-\frac{1}{n}\,\mathrm{tr}(\mathbf{A})\mathbf{E},\quad \mathbf{V}=\frac{1}{2}(\mathbf{A}-\mathbf{A}^T). \tag{9.18}$$

Incidently, we have used the fact that

$$\mathbf{B}^T=-\mathbf{B}\ \text{ implies }\ \mathrm{tr}(\mathbf{B})=0, \tag{9.19}$$

which follows directly from Eqs. (9.11) and (9.12).

A *symmetric* matrix **A** is said to be **positive definite** if and only if

$$\{x\}^T\,\mathbf{A}\{x\}>0, \tag{9.20}$$

holds for all $\{x\}\in \mathsf{M}_{n,1}$ such that $\{x\}\neq\{0\}$. If $\mathrm{rank}(\mathbf{A})<n$, then $\mathbf{A}\{x\}=\{0\}$ has at least a one-dimensional subspace of solutions. In this event, there is certainly an element $\{x_0\}$ of $\mathsf{M}_{n,1}$ such that $\{x_0\}\neq\{0\}$ and $\mathbf{A}\{x_0\}=\{0\}$. With this $\{x_0\}$, we then have $\{x_0\}^T\,\mathbf{A}\{x_0\}=\{x_0\}^T\,\{0\}=0$, and hence such a matrix **A** can not be positive definite. Thus, we have the following result: *if a matrix* $\mathbf{A}\in\mathsf{M}_{n,n}$ *is positive definite, then* $\mathrm{rank}(\mathbf{A})=n$ (i.e., **A** is nonsingular). On the other hand, a symmetric *n*-by-*n* matrix of rank *n* need not be positive definite; for example, $n=2$,

$$\mathbf{B}=\begin{pmatrix}0 & -2\\ -2 & 0\end{pmatrix},\quad [1,1]\,\mathbf{B}\begin{Bmatrix}1\\1\end{Bmatrix}=-4\not>0.$$

We thus need to obtain conditions that will allow us to construct positive definite matrices.

Let $\mathbf{B}\in\mathsf{M}_{n,n}$, $\mathrm{rank}(\mathbf{B})=n$, and set

$$\mathbf{A}=\mathbf{B}^T\mathbf{B}. \tag{9.21}$$

We then have

$$\{x\}^T\mathbf{A}\{x\}=\{x\}^T\mathbf{B}^T\mathbf{B}\{x\}=(\mathbf{B}\{x\})^T(\mathbf{B}\{x\})=\|\mathbf{B}\{x\}\|^2\geq 0,$$

for all $\{x\}\in\mathsf{M}_{n,1}$. Now, $\|\mathbf{B}\{x\}\|=0$ if and only if $\mathbf{B}\{x\}=\{0\}$. But

$\mathbf{B}\{x\}=\{0\}$ holds only when $\{x\}=\{0\}$ since $\text{rank}(\mathbf{B})=n$. We thus have $\{x\}^T\mathbf{B}^T\mathbf{B}\{x\}>0$ for all $\{x\}\in \mathsf{M}_{n,1}$ such that $\{x\}\neq\{0\}$; that is, *if* $\mathbf{B}$ *is any n-by-n matrix with* $\text{rank}(\mathbf{B})=n$, *then the matrix* $\mathbf{A}=\mathbf{B}^T\mathbf{B}$ *is positive definite.* In fact, it can be shown that *any positive definite n-by-n matrix can be written in the form* $\mathbf{B}^T\mathbf{B}$ *for some n-by-n matrix* $\mathbf{B}$ *such that* $\text{rank}(\mathbf{B})=n$. This result is important in many applications, for quantities such as $\{x\}^T\mathbf{A}\{x\}$ occur very often in physical problems where it is essential that we have $\{x\}^T\mathbf{A}\{x\}>0$ whenever $\{x\}\neq\{0\}$.

If $\mathbf{A}\in \mathsf{M}_{n,n}$, then for each $\{x\}\in \mathsf{M}_{n,1}$ we obtain a new element of $\mathsf{M}_{n,1}$ by the prescription

$$\{y\}=\mathbf{A}\{x\}. \tag{9.22}$$

We now enquire into what conditions must be placed on the matrix $\mathbf{A}$ so that the length of $\{y\}$ will be the same as the length of $\{x\}$ no matter what $\{x\}\in \mathsf{M}_{n,1}$ we start with. From the definition of the length of a vector, we have

$$||\{y\}||^2=\{y\}^T\{y\}=(\mathbf{A}\{x\})^T(\mathbf{A}\{x\})=\{x\}^T\mathbf{A}^T\mathbf{A}\{x\},$$

and

$$||\{x\}||^2=\{x\}^T\{x\}\equiv\{x\}^T\mathbf{E}\{x\}.$$

The matrix $\mathbf{A}$ will thus have the desired property, namely, $||\{x\}||^2=||\{y\}||^2$, if and only if

$$\{x\}^T\mathbf{E}\{x\}=\{x\}^T\mathbf{A}^T\mathbf{A}\{x\},$$

or

$$\{x\}^T(\mathbf{E}-\mathbf{A}^T\mathbf{A})\{x\}=0, \tag{9.23}$$

holds for every $\{x\}\in \mathsf{M}_{n,1}$. It is clear from Eq. (9.23) that the condition

$$\mathbf{A}^T\mathbf{A}=\mathbf{E} \tag{9.24}$$

implies that the lengths of $\{x\}$ and $\{y\}$ are the same for each $\{x\}$ and $\{y\}=\mathbf{A}\{x\}$ belonging to $\mathsf{M}_{n,1}$. We want to show that Eq. (9.24) is also a necessary condition. Although this can be shown by strictly algebraic means, we shall use the methods of the differential calculus in order to establish this result. In the course of doing this, we shall establish a result which will be needed later in this lecture.

Let $\mathbf{B}$ be a given element of $\mathsf{M}_{n,n}$ and define the function $Q(x_1, x_2, \ldots, x_n)$ of n variables by the relation

$$Q(\{x\})=\{x\}^T\mathbf{B}\{x\},\quad \{x\}^T=[x_1, x_2, \ldots, x_n]. \tag{9.25}$$

The differential of $Q(\{x\})$, as a function of n variables, is then given by

$$dQ=\{dx\}^T\mathbf{B}\{x\}+\{x\}^T\mathbf{B}\{dx\},\quad \{dx\}^T=[dx_1, \ldots, dx_n].$$

However, $\{dx\}^T\mathbf{B}\{x\}$ is a scalar so that

$$\{dx\}^T\mathbf{B}\{x\}=(\{dx\}^T\mathbf{B}\{x\})^T=\{x\}^T\mathbf{B}^T\{dx\},$$

and hence we have

$$dQ=\{x\}^T(\mathbf{B}^T+\mathbf{B})\{dx\}=\{dx\}^T(\mathbf{B}^T+\mathbf{B})\{x\}. \tag{9.26}$$

We also know that

$$dQ=\sum_{i=1}^{n}\frac{\partial Q}{\partial x_i}dx_i,$$

which can be written in the equivalent form

$$dQ=\left\{\frac{\partial Q}{\partial x}\right\}^T\{dx\}=\{dx\}^T\left\{\frac{\partial Q}{\partial x}\right\},\quad \left\{\frac{\partial Q}{\partial x}\right\}^T=\left[\frac{\partial Q}{\partial x_1},\ \ldots,\frac{\partial Q}{\partial x_n}\right].$$

A comparison of this result with Eq. (9.26) then gives us

$$\left\{\frac{\partial Q}{\partial x}\right\}=(\mathbf{B}^T+\mathbf{B})\{x\},\ Q=\{x\}^T\mathbf{B}\{x\}. \tag{9.27}$$

Thus, Eqs. (9.26) and (9.27) give a quick and convenient manner of computing differentials and partial derivatives of quantities such as $Q(\{x\})$. We shall return to these formulae later in this lecture. For the time being, we shall use it to show that Eq. (9.24) is a necessary condition in order that Eq. (9.23) shall hold for all $\{x\}\in \mathsf{M}_{n,1}$.

If we set $\mathbf{B}=\mathbf{E}-\mathbf{A}^T\mathbf{A}$, then Eq. (9.23) becomes

$$\{x\}^T\mathbf{B}\{x\}=0, \tag{9.28}$$

and this result must hold for all $\{x\}\in \mathsf{M}_{n,1}$. The requirement that Eq. (9.28) hold for all $\{x\}\in \mathsf{M}_{n,1}$ says that the left-hand side of Eq. (9.28), namely $Q(\{x\})=\{x\}^T\mathbf{B}\{x\}$ has the constant value zero for all $\{x\}\in \mathsf{M}_{n,1}$. Accordingly, we must have $dQ(\{x\})=0$ for all $\{x\}\in \mathsf{M}_{n,1}$ and all $\{dx\}\in \mathsf{M}_{n,1}$ since the differential of a constant valued function is zero for every choice of $\{dx\}$. When Eq. (9.26) is used, we then have the requirement that

$$dQ(x)=\{x\}^T(\mathbf{B}+\mathbf{B}^T)\{dx\}=0 \tag{9.29}$$

must hold for all $\{x\}\in \mathsf{M}_{n,1}$ and all $\{dx\}\in \mathsf{M}_{n,1}$. The vector $(\mathbf{B}+\mathbf{B}^T)\{dx\}$ must thus be orthogonal to every vector $\{x\}\in \mathsf{M}_{n,1}$. This can be the case only if the vector $(\mathbf{B}+\mathbf{B}^T)$ $\{dx\}$ is the zero vector:

$$(\mathbf{B}+\mathbf{B}^T)\{dx\}=\{0\}. \tag{9.30}$$

Now, Eq. (9.30) must also hold for all $\{dx\}\in \mathsf{M}_{n,1}$ and hence the rank of the coefficient matrix $(\mathbf{B}+\mathbf{B}^T)$ must be zero [i.e., the dimensions of the space of solutions of Eq. (9.30) must be n]. We thus conclude that

$\mathbf{B}+\mathbf{B}^T=\mathbf{0}$. However, since $\mathbf{B}=\mathbf{E}-\mathbf{A}^T\mathbf{A}=\mathbf{B}^T$, we have $(\mathbf{B}+\mathbf{B}^T)=2(\mathbf{E}-\mathbf{A}^T\mathbf{A})=\mathbf{0}$ and the desired result has been established.

Any square matrix that satisfies Eq. (9.24), namely

$$\mathbf{A}^T\mathbf{A}=\mathbf{E}, \quad \mathbf{A}\in\mathsf{M}_{n,n}, \tag{9.31}$$

is referred to as an **orthogonal** matrix, and we have established that *the substitution* $\{y\}=\mathbf{A}\{x\}$ *preserves the lengths of all elements of* $\mathsf{M}_{n,1}$ *if and only if* $\mathbf{A}$ *is an orthogonal matrix.* The definition of an orthogonal matrix given by Eq. (9.31) may also be read to say that $\mathbf{A}^T$ is the inverse of $\mathbf{A}$. We thus have that $\mathbf{A}$ *is an orthogonal matrix if and only if*

$$\mathbf{A}^{-1}=\mathbf{A}^T. \tag{9.32}$$

An orthogonal matrix thus has an inverse which is simplicity itself to compute. In addition, the existence of the inverse of an orthogonal matrix, as stated by Eqs. (9.31) or (9.32) implies that *the rank of an orthogonal n-by-n matrix is always equal to n.* Further, we can use Eq. (9.32) to write the condition that a matrix $\mathbf{A}$ be orthogonal in the equivalent form

$$\mathbf{A}\mathbf{A}^T=\mathbf{E}. \tag{9.33}$$

Obviously, if you have to test whether a given matrix is orthogonal or not, you will use either Eq. (9.31) or Eq. (9.33), since use of Eq. (9.32) would require the computation of the inverse of the matrix $\mathbf{A}$ which is a lot more work than just checking the matrix product $\mathbf{A}^T\mathbf{A}$ or $\mathbf{A}\mathbf{A}^T$ to see whether or not it is equal to the identity matrix.

The norm $||\{x\}||^2=\{x\}^T\{x\}$ we have used for elements of $\mathsf{M}_{n,1}$ is exactly that which one obtains from the norm for elements of V_n under the identification $\{x\}\equiv\mathbf{x}$. We may also carry over the definition of the angle between two nonzero elements of V_n to $\mathsf{M}_{n,1}$ by

$$\cos\,\theta=\frac{\{x\}^T\{y\}}{||\{x\}||\ ||\{y\}||}$$

since $\{x\}^T\{y\}=\mathbf{x}\circ\mathbf{y}$. It is then easily shown that *the substitutions*

$$\{x\}=\mathbf{A}\{u\}, \quad \{y\}=\mathbf{A}\{v\}, \tag{9.34}$$

preserve angles if $\mathbf{A}$ *is orthogonal. The implication does not go the other way,* for if we take $\mathbf{A}=\lambda\mathbf{B}$, $\mathbf{B}^T\mathbf{B}=\mathbf{E}$ and $\lambda\neq(0 \text{ or } 1)$, then the substitutions (9.34) still preserve angles but $\mathbf{A}^T\mathbf{A}=\lambda^2\mathbf{B}^T\mathbf{B}=\lambda^2\mathbf{E}$; that is, $\mathbf{A}$ is not orthogonal. It is true, however, that $\{x\}^T\{y\}=\{u\}^T\{v\}$ for all $\{u\}$ and $\{v\}$ belonging to $\mathsf{M}_{n,1}$ if and only if $\mathbf{A}^T\mathbf{A}=\mathbf{E}$.

If $\mathbf{A}$ and $\mathbf{B}$ are orthogonal matrices, then

$$(\mathbf{AB})^T(\mathbf{AB})=\mathbf{B}^T\mathbf{A}^T\mathbf{A}\mathbf{B}=\mathbf{B}^T\mathbf{B}=\mathbf{E},$$

and hence *the product of any two n-by-n orthogonal matrices is an orthogonal matrix. If we set* $\mathbf{B}=\mathbf{A}^{-1}$, then $\mathbf{B}^T\mathbf{B}=(\mathbf{A}^{-1})^T\mathbf{A}^{-1}$. Thus, if $\mathbf{A}$ is orthogonal, then $\mathbf{A}^{-1}=\mathbf{A}^T$, in which case we have $\mathbf{B}^T\mathbf{B}=(\mathbf{A}^T)^T\mathbf{A}^T=\mathbf{A}\mathbf{A}^T=\mathbf{E}$. Thus, *the inverse of an orthogonal matrix is an orthogonal matrix.* Since the identity matrix is an orthogonal matrix [i.e., $\mathbf{E}^T\mathbf{E}=\mathbf{E}$], those of you who are familiar with the notion of a group will realize that *the set of all orthogonal n-by-n matrices forms a group under the operation of matrix multiplication.* [This simply says that products of orthogonal matrices are orthogonal, inverses of orthogonal matrices are orthogonal and the identity under multiplication is an orthogonal matrix.] We note that

$$\begin{pmatrix} \cos\theta & -\sin\theta \\ \sin\theta & \cos\theta \end{pmatrix}, \quad \begin{pmatrix} \cos\theta & \sin\theta \\ \sin\theta & -\cos\theta \end{pmatrix}$$

are orthogonal matrices for all values of θ. Further,

$$\mathbf{0}_{1,\psi}=\begin{pmatrix} 1 & 0 & 0 \\ 0 & \cos\psi & -\sin\psi \\ 0 & \sin\psi & \cos\psi \end{pmatrix}, \quad \mathbf{0}_{2,\phi}=\begin{pmatrix} \cos\phi & 0 & -\sin\phi \\ 0 & 1 & 0 \\ \sin\phi & 0 & \cos\phi \end{pmatrix},$$

and

$$\mathbf{0}_{3,\theta}=\begin{pmatrix} \cos\theta & -\sin\theta & 0 \\ \sin\theta & \cos\theta & 0 \\ 0 & 0 & 1 \end{pmatrix}$$

are orthogonal matrices for every value of the arguments θ, ϕ, ψ. A full characterization of orthogonal matrices must wait until you study group theory. We simply note here that every 3-by-3 orthogonal matrix can be represented as a product of $\mathbf{0}_1$, $\mathbf{0}_2$, $\mathbf{0}_3$ and

$$\begin{pmatrix} -1 & 0 & 0 \\ 0 & 1 & 0 \\ 0 & 0 & 1 \end{pmatrix}$$

if the arguments θ, ϕ, and ψ are chosen properly. The student will find that the matrices $\mathbf{0}_1$, $\mathbf{0}_2$, and $\mathbf{0}_3$ are very convenient when it comes to solving problems.

Before leaving orthogonal matrices for the present, we establish one more very important property of these matrices. If $\mathbf{B}$ is an n-by-n matrix, then we can write $\mathbf{B}$ in the form

$$\mathbf{B}=[\{b\}_1, \{b\}_2, \ldots, \{b\}_n], \tag{9.35}$$

where $\{b\}_i$ is the ith column of $\mathbf{B}$. We then have

$$\mathbf{B}^T\mathbf{B}=\mathbf{C}, \text{ where } c_{ij}=\{b\}_i^T\{b\}_j. \tag{9.36}$$

Thus, since $\mathbf{B}$ is an orthogonal matrix if and only if we have $\mathbf{B}^T\mathbf{B}=\mathbf{E}$, Eq. (9.36) gives

$$\{b\}_i^T \{b\}_j = \begin{cases} 1 & \text{if } i=j \\ 0 & \text{if } i \neq j; \end{cases} \tag{9.37}$$

each column of an orthogonal matrix is a unit vector and each column of an orthogonal matrix is orthogonal to every other column, and conversely.

The above results can be used to examine a class of problems that arises time and again in the physical sciences. Suppose that we are given a symmetric n-by-n matrix $\mathbf{A}$, so that

$$\mathbf{A}^T = \mathbf{A}. \tag{9.38}$$

With this matrix as an ingredient, we construct the **quadratic form**

$$Q(\{x\}) = \{x\}^T \mathbf{A} \{x\}. \tag{9.39}$$

We can then define a set Q of vectors $\{x\}$ by the requirement that Q is the set of all vectors which satisfy the equation

$$Q(\{x\}) = \{x\}^T \mathbf{A} \{x\} = k, \tag{9.40}$$

where k is a given real number. For example, if $A = \begin{pmatrix} 1 & -3 \\ -3 & 4 \end{pmatrix}$, $k=5$, then Q would consist of all elements of $\mathsf{M}_{2,1}$ that satisfy

$$Q(\{x\}) = (x_1)^2 - 6x_1x_2 + 4(x_2)^2 = 5.$$

What is required is to find those $\{x\}$ belonging to Q which have the largest or smallest lengths. Since the square of the length of a vector $\{x\}$ is given by $\{x\}^T\{x\}$, what we have to do is to find those elements of $\mathsf{M}_{n,1}$ which belong to Q and which are such that the quadratic form $\{x\}^T\{x\} = \{x\}^T\mathbf{E}\{x\}$ has extremal values. If $\{x\}$ were not required to belong to Q then the maximum value of $\{x\}^T\mathbf{E}\{x\}$ is infinity and the minimum value is zero. Since the $\{x\}$'s are required to belong to Q, we can not consider all $\{x\}$, but rather only those that satisfy this constraint. We thus have an extremal problem with a constraint and hence we use a *Lagrange multiplier* in order to account for the constraint. We denote this Lagrange multiplier by h. We thus have to determine the extremal values of the function

$$\begin{aligned} \Gamma(\{x\}) &= \{x\}^T\mathbf{E}\{x\} + h(\{x\}^T\mathbf{A}\{x\} - k) \\ &= \{x\}^T(\mathbf{E} + h\,\mathbf{A})\{x\} - hk \end{aligned} \tag{9.41}$$

with respect to the n variables $x_1, x_2, \ldots, x_n$. We know from calculus that $\Gamma(\{\bar{x}\})$ is extremal only if each of the first partial derivatives of $\Gamma(\{\bar{x}\})$ is equal to zero. Since $\mathbf{E}$ and $\mathbf{A}$ are symmetric matrices, we can use Eq. (9.27) to compute the partial derivatives, and hence we obtain the necessary conditions

$$\left\{\frac{\partial \Gamma}{\partial x}\right\} = 2(\mathbf{E} + h\,\mathbf{A})\{\bar{x}\} = \{0\}. \tag{9.42}$$

Since Eq. (9.42) is a linear homogeneous system, it will have a nontrivial solution $\{\bar{x}\}$ only if the coefficient matrix $\mathbf{E}+h\mathbf{A}$ has rank less than n. It thus turns out that we can find a solution of Eq. (9.42) only if the Lagrange multiplier h is chosen such that

$$\text{rank}(\mathbf{E}+h\,\mathbf{A})<n. \tag{9.43}$$

The next two lectures will be devoted to finding a means of guaranteeing that the rank of a square n-by-n matrix is less than n. Even though we do not have this information now, and hence we do not know how to choose h, we can still make some headway. We simply assume that h has been chosen so that Eq. (9.43) is satisfied, in which case there will exist nontrivial solutions to Eq. (9.42). If $\{\bar{x}\}$ is such a solution of Eq. (9.42), then Eq. (9.41) gives

$$\Gamma(\{\bar{x}\})=-hk. \tag{9.44}$$

On the other hand, if $\{\bar{x}\}$ belongs to Q then Eq. (9.41) gives

$$\Gamma(\{\bar{x}\})=\{\bar{x}\}^T\{\bar{x}\}=||\{\bar{x}\}||^2,$$

from which we conclude that the critical values of $||\{\bar{x}\}||^2$ that belong to Q are given by $-hk$.

Since we do not know a direct method of choosing h so that the condition $\text{rank}(\mathbf{E}+h\,\mathbf{A})<n$ is satisfied, let us see if we can't come at the problem another way. Suppose that we can find an orthogonal matrix $\mathbf{B}$ (i.e., $\mathbf{B}^T=\mathbf{B}^{-1}$) such that

$$\mathbf{B}^{-1}\mathbf{A}\,\mathbf{B}=\mathbf{D}(\lambda_1, \lambda_2, \ldots, \lambda_n). \tag{9.45}$$

Since the matrix $\mathbf{B}$ is assumed to be orthogonal, we know that if we set

$$\{x\}=\mathbf{B}\{y\}, \tag{9.46}$$

then

$$||\{x\}||=||\{y\}||. \tag{9.47}$$

On the other hand, Eqs. (9.31) and (9.46) give

$$\Gamma(\{x\})=\Gamma(\mathbf{B}\{y\})=\bar{\Gamma}(\{y\})=\{y\}^T\mathbf{B}^T(\mathbf{E}+h\,\mathbf{A})\mathbf{B}\{y\}-hk.$$

Thus, when we use Eq. (9.45) and $\mathbf{B}^{-1}=\mathbf{B}^T$, we have

$$\Gamma(\{x\})=\{y\}^T(\mathbf{E}+h\,\mathbf{D}(\lambda_1, \ldots, \lambda_n))\{y\}-hk. \tag{9.48}$$

Proceeding in exactly the same fashion as we did above (i.e., differentiating with respect to the y's and setting the derivatives equal to zero), we obtain the conditions

$$\begin{aligned}\left\{\frac{\partial\bar{\Gamma}}{\partial y}\right\}&=(\mathbf{E}+h\,\mathbf{D}(\lambda_1, \ldots, \lambda_n))\{\bar{y}\}=0,\\ \{\bar{x}\}&=\mathbf{B}\{\bar{y}\}.\end{aligned} \tag{9.49}$$

The reason for all of this is that the requirement

$$\operatorname{rank}(\mathbf{E}+h\,\mathbf{D}(\lambda_1, \ldots, \lambda_n))<n \tag{9.50}$$

is now seen to be satisfied only if we choose

$$h=\frac{-1}{\lambda_i}, \tag{9.51}$$

for some value of i between 1 and n. In fact, Eq. (9.51) gives a value for h which will satisfy the condition (9.50) for each value of i. From this and Eq. (9.48) we conclude that

$$||\{\bar{x}\}||^2=||\{\bar{y}\}||^2=-h\,k=k/\lambda_i \tag{9.52}$$

gives a stationary value for each choice of i.

This problem illustrates one of an important class of problems in which it is useful to be able to find a matrix **B**, for given **A**, such that

$$\mathbf{B}^T=\mathbf{B}^{-1},\ \ \mathbf{B}^{-1}\mathbf{A}\,\mathbf{B}=\mathbf{D}(\lambda_1, \ldots, \lambda_n).$$

If there is one equation that can be said to be the most popular equation in the physical sciences, it is, without doubt,

$$\mathbf{B}^{-1}\mathbf{A}\,\mathbf{B}=\mathbf{D}(\lambda_1, \ldots, \lambda_n). \tag{9.53}$$

The rest of the lectures in this book are, in fact, devoted to the theory and applications of finding a matrix **B** and the numbers $\lambda_1, \ldots, \lambda_n$ that satisfy Eq. (9.53). This theory, like the above problem, requires conditions which guarantee that an n-by-n matrix has rank less than n when the matrix contains one or more unknowns, such as the matrix $(\mathbf{E}+h\,\mathbf{A})$ where h was the unknown. We shall thus spend the next two lectures on the study of determinants, which provide the required conditions, and then head full bent into the study of Eq. (9.53).

Problems

9.1. Obtain the symmetric and skewsymmetric part, as well as the trace, of the following matrices:

$$\text{(a)}\begin{pmatrix}1&2&3\\3&4&5\\0&0&2\end{pmatrix};\quad \text{(b)}\begin{pmatrix}2&0&1\\0&3&2\\2&0&4\end{pmatrix};\quad \text{(c)}\begin{pmatrix}3&4&0\\7&2&0\\0&3&4\end{pmatrix};$$

$$\text{(d)}\begin{pmatrix}0&1&2\\3&0&0\\0&5&7\end{pmatrix};\quad \text{(e)}\begin{pmatrix}1&0&3\\0&2&0\\4&0&3\end{pmatrix};\quad \text{(f)}\begin{pmatrix}1&2&3\\2&3&4\\5&0&3\end{pmatrix}.$$

9.2. Represent the matrices in problem 9.1 as the sum of a scalar matrix and a trace free matrix.

9.3. Represent the matrices in problem 9.1 as the sum of a scalar matrix, a trace free symmetric matrix and a skewsymmetric matrix.

9.4. Write the following quadratic forms in the form $\{x\}^T\mathbf{A}\{x\}$ where $\mathbf{A} = \mathbf{A}^T$:

(a) $x_1^2 + x_2^2 + x_3^2$, (b) $2x_1^2 + 3x_1x_2 + 5x_2^2$, (c) $3x_1^2 + 6x_1x_2 + 2x_2^2$,
(d) $x_1^2 + x_2^2 + x_3^2 + 4x_1x_2 + 6x_1x_3 + 8x_2x_3$, (e) $3x_1^2 + 6x_1x_4 + 4x_2x_3$.

9.5. Which of the following matrices are orthogonal?

(a) $\begin{pmatrix} \frac{\sqrt{3}}{2} & -\frac{1}{2} \\ \frac{1}{2} & \frac{\sqrt{3}}{2} \end{pmatrix}$; (b) $\begin{pmatrix} \frac{\sqrt{5}}{9} & \frac{2}{9} \\ \frac{1}{9} & \frac{\sqrt{8}}{9} \end{pmatrix}$; (c) $\begin{pmatrix} \frac{\sqrt{5}}{9} & \frac{2}{9} \\ \frac{-2}{9} & \frac{\sqrt{5}}{9} \end{pmatrix}$;

(d) $\begin{pmatrix} \frac{3}{7} & \frac{6}{7} & \frac{2}{7} \\ \frac{6}{7} & \frac{-2}{7} & \frac{-3}{7} \\ \frac{2}{7} & \frac{-3}{7} & \frac{6}{7} \end{pmatrix}$; (e) $\begin{pmatrix} \frac{\sqrt{2}}{5} & \frac{1}{\sqrt{5}} \\ \frac{-1}{\sqrt{5}} & \frac{2}{\sqrt{5}} \end{pmatrix}$; (f) $\begin{pmatrix} \frac{3}{10} & \frac{1}{10} \\ \frac{2}{10} & \frac{\sqrt{6}}{10} \end{pmatrix}$.

9.6. Prove that the symmetric part of a skewsymmetric matrix is zero. Also prove that the skewsymmetric part of a symmetric matrix is zero.

9.7. Let $\mathbf{A}^T = -\mathbf{A}$. Prove that the diagonal elements of $\mathbf{A}$ are zero.

9.8. Prove the formulae (9.10) through (9.13) and generalize Eq. (9.13).

9.9. Prove that the representation of a square matrix as the sum of a scalar matrix and a trace free matrix is unique.

9.10. Prove that the representation of a square matrix as the sum of a scalar matrix, a trace free symmetric matrix and a skewsymmetric matrix is unique.

9.11. Prove algebraically that:

(a) $\{x\}^T\mathbf{A}\{x\} = 0$ for all $\{x\}$ if and only if $\mathbf{A}$ is a skewsymmetric matrix.
(b) If $\{x\}^T\mathbf{A}\{x\} = 0$ for all $\{x\}$, where $\mathbf{A}$ is symmetric, then $\mathbf{A} = \mathbf{0}$.

9.12. Prove that $\{x\}^T\mathbf{A}\{x\} = \{x\}^T\mathbf{B}\{x\}$, $\mathbf{B}^T = \mathbf{B}$, is valid for all $\{x\}$ if and only if $\mathbf{B}$ is the symmetric part of $\mathbf{A}$.

9.13. Prove algebraically that if $||\mathbf{A}\{x\}|| = ||\{x\}||$ for all $\{x\} \in \mathsf{V}_n$ then $\mathbf{A}$ is an orthogonal matrix.

9.14. Let $\{x\} = \mathbf{A}\{u\}$, $\{y\} = \mathbf{A}\{v\}$. Prove that $\{x\}^T\{y\} = \{u\}^T\{v\}$ for all $\{u\}$ and $\{v\}$ if and only if $\mathbf{A}$ is an orthogonal matrix.

9.15. A set of vectors $\mathbf{a}_1, \ldots, \mathbf{a}_m$ is **orthonormal** if $\mathbf{a}_i \cdot \mathbf{a}_j = 0$ and $||\mathbf{a}_i|| = 1$ for $i \neq j$, $i, j = 1, \ldots, m$. Prove that the rows of an orthogonal matrix are orthonormal vectors.

9.16. Show that $\text{rank}(\mathbf{E} + h\mathbf{D}(\lambda_1, \ldots, \lambda_n)) < n$ if and only if $1 + h\lambda_i = 0$ for at least one value of i between 1 and n.

9.17. Let $\{p\}_i = [p_{1i}, p_{2i}, p_{3i}]^T$, $i = 1, 2, 3$, be three orthonormal vectors. Show that

(i) $\{p\}_i$ form an orthonormal basis of V_3

(ii) if $\{x\} = \sum_j y_j \{p\}_j$, then

$$\{x\} = \mathbf{P}\{y\}, \quad \{y\} = \mathbf{P}^T\{x\},$$

where $\mathbf{P}$ is the orthogonal matrix $[\{p\}_1, \{p\}_2, \{p\}_3]$.

9.18. Let OX_i and OY_i, $i = 1, 2, 3$, be two systems of orthogonal cartesian axes in E_3. If P_i is a point on OY_i such that the distance OP is equal to one and the positive direction of OY_i is from O towards P_i, then P_i is called the **unit point** of OY_i. Moreover, the coordinates p_{1i}, p_{2i}, p_{3i} of P_i with respect to the axes OX_i are called **direction cosines** of OY_i and the matrix $\mathbf{P} = [\{p\}_1, \{p\}_2, \{p\}_3]$ **matrix of direction cosines** of the axes OY_i with respect to the axes OX_i. Finally, $\{p\}_i$ is the **unit vector** of OY_i. Show that

(i) $\mathbf{P}$ is an orthogonal matrix;

(ii) if x_1, x_2, x_3 and y_1, y_2, y_3 are the coordinates of the same point referred to the axes OX_i and OY_i, then

$$\{x\} = \mathbf{P}\{y\}, \qquad \{y\} = \mathbf{P}^T\{x\};$$

(iii) $\mathbf{P}^T$ is the matrix of the direction cosines of the axes OX_i with respect to the axes OY_i.

9.19. Show that the matrices given on page 110 are orthogonal.

9.20. Two half-lines OP_1, OP_2, which do not coincide, separate the plane OP_1P_2 in two parts. Either one is called the (**elementary**) **angle** OP_1P_2. We extend the definition to include the case in which OP_1, OP_2 coincide: In this particular case we say that the one of the angles is zero and the other includes the whole plane (i.e. is equal to 2π). Let OX, OY be a system of axes in a plane where OX is considered the first axis. The direction in which the first positive half-axis should turn in order to coincide with the second while sweeping the smallest of the two angles of the positive half-axes is called the **positive direction of rotation** in the plane. Note that *the order (orientation) of the axes in a plane determines the positive direction of rotation in that plane.* We say that **the ray** OP **is rotated about** O **through the (signed) angle** θ when OP is rotated about O in the positive or negative direction if $\theta > O$ or $\theta < O$ respectively and sweeps an (elementary) angle equal to $|\theta|$. Show that if the point $\mathbf{x}$ is rotated about the origin through an angle θ, its new coordinates y_1, y_2 are given by $\{y\} = \mathbf{A}\{x\}$ where $\mathbf{A}$ is the orthogonal matrix

$$\mathbf{A} = \begin{pmatrix} \cos\theta & -\sin\theta \\ \sin\theta & \cos\theta \end{pmatrix}.$$

9.21. Show that

$$(\mathbf{E} - \mathbf{O}_{1,\psi})(\mathbf{E} + \mathbf{O}_{1,\psi})^{-1} = \tan\frac{\psi}{2}\begin{pmatrix} 0 & 0 & 0 \\ 0 & 0 & 1 \\ 0 & -1 & 0 \end{pmatrix}.$$

LECTURE 10

Determinants

Notation for determinants • The minor matrix of an element of a given matrix • Definition of the determinant • The two basic properties of determinants • Row expansion • Column expansion • Determinants of the elementary row operation matrices • Properties of determinants • Relations between rank($\mathbf{A}$) and det($\mathbf{A}$) • Problems

If $\mathbf{A}$ is a given square n-by-n matrix of known numbers, we can row reduce $\mathbf{A}$ by the row echelon algorithm and thereby determine the rank of $\mathbf{A}$. If $\mathbf{A}$ is not a given matrix, such as $\mathbf{B}-\lambda\mathbf{E}$ where λ is unknown, then we can not row reduce such a matrix since the row echelon algorithm demands that we find nonzero entries and we don't know which of the entries are nonzero if λ is not given to us. However, one of the essential ingredients in solving problems is to know when an arbitrary n-by-n matrix $\mathbf{A}$ has $\text{rank}(\mathbf{A})=n$ or $\text{rank}(\mathbf{A})<n$. This information is supplied in a concise fashion by the study of what are known as determinants. In particular, determinants allow us to find values of λ such that $\text{rank}(\mathbf{B}-\lambda\mathbf{E})=n$ and values of λ for which $\text{rank}(\mathbf{B}-\lambda\mathbf{E})<n$.

We assume throughout this lecture that all matrices that are denoted by capital letters are square n-by-n matrices. Associated with each such square matrix $\mathbf{A}$ is a number called the **determinant** of $\mathbf{A}$ and denoted by $\det(\mathbf{A})$. If the matrix $\mathbf{A}$ is written as

$$\mathbf{A}=\begin{pmatrix} a_{11} & a_{12} & \cdots & a_{1n} \\ a_{21} & a_{22} & \cdots & a_{2n} \\ \vdots & \vdots & & \vdots \\ a_{n1} & a_{n2} & \cdots & a_{nn} \end{pmatrix},$$

then the customary notation for the determinant is

$$\det(\mathbf{A})=\begin{vmatrix} a_{11} & a_{12} & \cdots & a_{1n} \\ a_{21} & a_{22} & \cdots & a_{2n} \\ \vdots & \vdots & & \vdots \\ a_{n1} & a_{n2} & \cdots & a_{nn} \end{vmatrix}.$$

$\det(\mathbf{A})$ is said to be an nth **order** determinant when $\mathbf{A}\in \mathsf{M}_{n,n}$. If $\mathbf{A}$ is a 1-by-1 matrix, $\mathbf{A}=(a_{11})$, we define $\det(\mathbf{A})=a_{11}$. If $\mathbf{A}$ is a 2-by-2 matrix

$$\mathbf{A}=\begin{pmatrix} a_{11} & a_{12} \\ a_{21} & a_{22} \end{pmatrix},$$

we define

$$\det(\mathbf{A})=\begin{vmatrix} a_{11} & a_{12} \\ a_{21} & a_{22} \end{vmatrix}=a_{11}a_{22}-a_{21}a_{12}. \tag{10.1}$$

For instance

$$\begin{vmatrix} 6 & 4 \\ -5 & 3 \end{vmatrix}=(6)(3)-(-5)(4)=38.$$

The definition of the determinant of an n-by-n matrix (a determinant of nth order) requires some additional notation, which we now introduce. Let $\mathbf{A}$ be an n-by-n matrix. We can form an $(n-1)$-by-$(n-1)$ matrix $\mathbf{A}_{ij}$ from the matrix $\mathbf{A}$ by deleting the ith row and the jth column from the matrix $\mathbf{A}$. The $(n-1)$-by-$(n-1)$ matrix $\mathbf{A}_{ij}$ is referred to as the **minor matrix of the entry** a_{ij} of the original matrix $\mathbf{A}$. Thus, since $\mathbf{A}$ has n^2 entries, there are n^2 minor matrices of the entries of $\mathbf{A}$. For example, if

$$\mathbf{A}=\begin{pmatrix} 1 & 2 & 3 & 4 \\ 5 & 6 & 7 & 8 \\ -1 & -2 & -3 & -4 \\ -5 & -6 & -7 & -8 \end{pmatrix},$$

then

$$\mathbf{A}_{11}=\begin{pmatrix} 6 & 7 & 8 \\ -2 & -3 & -4 \\ -6 & -7 & -8 \end{pmatrix};$$

$$\mathbf{A}_{23}=\begin{pmatrix} 1 & 2 & 4 \\ -1 & -2 & -4 \\ -5 & -6 & -8 \end{pmatrix},$$

$$\mathbf{A}_{34}=\begin{pmatrix} 1 & 2 & 3 \\ 5 & 6 & 7 \\ -5 & -6 & -7 \end{pmatrix}.$$

Since the minor of any entry of a square matrix is again a square matrix, this suggests a recursive method of defining the determinant since we know how to compute determinants of 1-by-1 and 2-by-2 matrices. Indeed, this is the case, for the determinant of an n-by-n matrix $\mathbf{A}$ is defined by

$$\det(\mathbf{A})=\sum_{j=1}^{n} a_{1j}(-1)^{1+j}\det(\mathbf{A}_{1j}). \tag{10.2}$$

The definition (10.2) simply says that we take the entries of the first row of $\mathbf{A}$ (that is a_{1j}) multiply each by the determinant of its minor matrix and then add them up with appropriate factors of $+1$ and -1 as given by Eq. (10.2). For $n=2$, Eq. (10.2) gives us

$$\det(\mathbf{A}) = a_{11}(-1)^{1+1}\det(a_{22}) + a_{12}(-1)^{1+2}\det(a_{21})$$
$$= a_{11}a_{22} - a_{21}a_{21},$$

which agrees with the definition of determinants of 2-by-2 matrices that we have already given. For a 3-by-3 matrix, Eq. (10.2) gives

$$\det(\mathbf{A}) = a_{11}(-1)^{1+1}\det(\mathbf{A}_{11}) + a_{12}(-1)^{1+2}\det(\mathbf{A}_{12}) + a_{13}(-1)^{1+3}\det(\mathbf{A}_{13})$$
$$= a_{11}\det(\mathbf{A}_{11}) - a_{12}\det(\mathbf{A}_{12}) + a_{13}\det(\mathbf{A}_{13}).$$

Since $\mathbf{A}_{11}$, $\mathbf{A}_{12}$, and $\mathbf{A}_{13}$ are 2-by-2 matrices, Eq. (10.1) can be used to evaluate $\det(\mathbf{A}_{11})$, $\det(\mathbf{A}_{12})$ and $\det(\mathbf{A}_{13})$:

$$\det(\mathbf{A}) = a_{11}\begin{vmatrix} a_{22} & a_{23} \\ a_{32} & a_{33} \end{vmatrix} - a_{12}\begin{vmatrix} a_{21} & a_{23} \\ a_{31} & a_{33} \end{vmatrix} + a_{13}\begin{vmatrix} a_{21} & a_{22} \\ a_{31} & a_{32} \end{vmatrix}.$$

Further, Eq. (10.2) can be used to reduce determinants of 4-by-4 matrices to sums of determinants of 3-by-3 matrices with appropriate factors, and each of these determinants of 3-by-3 matrices can be reduced to sums of determinants of 2-by-2 matrices with appropriate factors. The formula (10.2) is thus indeed recursive since it reduces the calculation of a determinant of nth order to sums that involve calculations of determinants of $(n-1)$th order.

For example, if $\mathbf{E}$ denotes the n-by-n identity matrix, then Eq. (10.2) gives

$$\det(\mathbf{E}) = 1(-1)^{1+1}\det(\mathbf{E}_{11}) = \det(\mathbf{E}_{11}), \qquad (10.3)$$

since $e_{11}=1$ and $e_{12}=e_{13}= \ldots =e_{1n}=0$. Now, $\mathbf{E}_{11}$ is the $(n-1)$-by-$(n-1)$ identity matrix since it is the minor matrix of the entry e_{11} of the n-by-n identity matrix. Equation (10.3) thus says that the determinant of the identity matrix has the same value of all $n=1, 2, \ldots$, and in particular, $\det(\mathbf{E}) = \det((1)) = 1$ since (1) is the 1-by-1 identity matrix. We thus have

$$\det(\mathbf{E}) = 1. \qquad (10.4)$$

The recursive property of the definition (10.2) can be used to establish the following two basic results:

$$\det(\mathbf{A}^T) = \det(\mathbf{A}), \qquad (10.5)$$

$$\det(\mathbf{AB}) = \det(\mathbf{A})\det(\mathbf{B}), \qquad (10.6)$$

when both $\mathbf{A}$ and $\mathbf{B}$ belong to $\mathsf{M}_{n,n}$. We shall simply ask the reader to accept the validity of these results since the actual calculations for their proofs by induction takes a number of pages (see problems).

As a first use of Eq. (10.5), we derive another formula for $\det(\mathbf{A})$. Let $\mathbf{B}=\mathbf{A}^T$, so that $b_{ij}=a_{ji}$ and $\mathbf{B}_{ij}=(\mathbf{A}_{ji})^T$. We then have

$$\det(\mathbf{A}^T)=\det(\mathbf{B})=\sum_{j=1}^{n} b_{1j}(-1)^{1+j}\det(\mathbf{B}_{1j})$$

$$=\sum_{j=1}^{n} a_{j1}(-1)^{1+j}\det((\mathbf{A}_{j1})^T)\,. \qquad (10.7)$$

However, Eq. (10.5) tells us that $\det((\mathbf{A}_{j1})^T)=\det(\mathbf{A}_{j1})$ and $\det(\mathbf{A}^T)=\det(\mathbf{A})$. When these results are substituted into Eq. (10.7) we obtain the formula

$$\det(\mathbf{A})=\sum_{j=1}^{n} a_{j1}(-1)^{1+j}\det(\mathbf{A}_{j1}). \qquad (10.8)$$

The formula (10.2) tells us how to evaluate $\det(\mathbf{A})$ in terms of the entries of the first row of $\mathbf{A}$ and the determinants of the minor matrices of the entries of the first row of $\mathbf{A}$. It is thus customary to refer to Eq. (10.2) as the expansion of the determinant by the first row, or **row expansion** for short. The formula (10.8) evaluates the determinant of $\mathbf{A}$ by expansion by the first column, or first **column expansion** for short. It thus follows that $\det(\mathbf{A})=\det(\mathbf{A}^T)$ *allows us to translate all information concerning row expansion properties of a determinant into corresponding column expansion properties of a determinant.*

There are several properties of $\det(\mathbf{A})$ that can be derived from the basic formula $\det(\mathbf{AB})=\det(\mathbf{A})\det(\mathbf{B})$. The easiest way to proceed in this is first to establish the following results for the elementary row operation matrices, which we leave to the student as exercises:

$$\det(\mathbf{E}_{\mathrm{I}}(i,j))=-1, \qquad (10.9)$$

$$\det(\mathbf{E}_{\mathrm{II}}(i;b))=b, \qquad (10.10)$$

$$\det(\mathbf{E}_{\mathrm{III}}(i,j;b))=1. \qquad (10.11)$$

Thus, Eq. (10.6) gives $\det(\mathbf{S})\neq 0$ for any $\mathbf{S}\in\mathrm{S}$. The first property we establish is the following: *if two rows (columns) of* $\mathbf{A}$ *are interchanged, then the determinant of the resulting matrix is equal to* $-\det(\mathbf{A})$. Suppose that we interchange the ith and jth rows of $\mathbf{A}$ and denote the resulting matrix by $\mathbf{B}$, that is

$$\mathbf{B}=\mathbf{E}_{\mathrm{I}}(i,j)\mathbf{A}. \qquad (10.12)$$

When we take the determinant of both sides of Eq. (10.12) and use Eqs. (10.6) and (10.9), we have

$$\det(\mathbf{B})=\det(\mathbf{E}_{\mathrm{I}}(i,j)\mathbf{A})=\det(\mathbf{E}_{\mathrm{I}}(i,j))\det(\mathbf{A})=-\det(\mathbf{A}),$$

and hence the result is established for interchanging rows of $\mathbf{A}$. However,

Eq. (10.5) states that any result that holds for rows of **A** also holds for columns of **A**, so that the result also holds for interchanging columns of **A**. In the succeeding proofs, we will only obtain the results for rows since they will then hold for columns by Eq. (10.5).

The result we have just established allows us to derive new formulae for det(**A**). Let **B** be obtained from **A** by interchanging the first and the ith rows of **A**, that is,

$$\mathbf{B}=\mathbf{E}_{\mathrm{I}}(1, i)\mathbf{A}. \tag{10.13}$$

We then have

$$b_{1j}=a_{ij}, \quad b_{ij}=a_{1j}. \tag{10.14}$$

We know, however, that

$$-\det(\mathbf{A})=\det(\mathbf{B})=\sum_{j=1}^{n} b_{1j}(-1)^{1+j}\det(\mathbf{B}_{1j}). \tag{10.15}$$

Now, Eq. (10.13) gives us

$$\det(\mathbf{B}_{1j})=\begin{vmatrix} a_{2\,1} & \cdots & a_{2\,j-1} & a_{2\,j+1} & \cdots & a_{2n} \\ \vdots & & \vdots & \vdots & & \vdots \\ a_{i-1\,1} & \cdots & a_{i-1\,j-1} & a_{i-1\,j+1} & \cdots & a_{i-1n} \\ a_{1\,1} & \cdots & a_{1\,j-1} & a_{1\,j+1} & \cdots & a_{1n} \\ a_{i+1\,1} & \cdots & a_{i+1\,j-1} & a_{i+1\,j+1} & \cdots & a_{i+1n} \\ \vdots & & \vdots & \vdots & & \vdots \\ a_{n\,1} & \cdots & a_{n\,j-1} & a_{n\,j+1} & \cdots & a_{nn} \end{vmatrix}$$

If we successively interchange the rows $i-2$ times and use the result we established concerning interchange of rows, we have

$$\det(\mathbf{B}_{1j})=(-1)^{i-2}\begin{vmatrix} a_{1\,1} & \cdots & a_{1\,j-1} & a_{1\,j+1} & \cdots & a_{1n} \\ a_{2\,1} & \cdots & a_{2\,j-1} & a_{2\,j+1} & \cdots & a_{2n} \\ \vdots & & \vdots & \vdots & & \vdots \\ a_{i-1\,1} & \cdots & a_{i-1\,j-1} & a_{i-1\,j+1} & \cdots & a_{i-1n} \\ a_{i+1\,1} & \cdots & a_{i+1\,j-1} & a_{i+1\,j+1} & \cdots & a_{i+1n} \\ \vdots & & \vdots & \vdots & & \vdots \\ a_{n\,1} & \cdots & a_{n\,j-1} & a_{n\,j+1} & \cdots & a_{nn} \end{vmatrix} \tag{10.16}$$

$$=(-1)^{i-2}\det(\mathbf{A}_{ij}).$$

When Eqs. (10.14) and (10.16) are substituted into Eq. (10.15), the result is

$$-\det(\mathbf{A}) = \sum_{j=1}^{n} a_{ij}(-1)^{1+j}(-1)^{i-2}\det(\mathbf{A}_{ij}),$$

that is

$$\det(\mathbf{A}) = \sum_{j=1}^{n} a_{ij}(-1)^{i+j}\det(\mathbf{A}_{ij}), \tag{10.17}$$

for any value of i from 1 through n. The formula (10.17) gives the ith **row expansion** of $\det(\mathbf{A})$. The corresponding ith **column expansion**

$$\det(\mathbf{A}) = \sum_{j=1}^{n} a_{ji}(-1)^{j+i}\det(\mathbf{A}_{ji}) \tag{10.18}$$

follows from Eq. (10.17) and $\det(\mathbf{A}) = \det(\mathbf{A}^T)$.

If every element in a row (column) of $\mathbf{A}$ *is zero, then* $\det(\mathbf{A}) = 0$. This result follows directly from Eqs. (10.17) and (10.18) since we need only expand by the zero row or column in order to establish the result. An expansion of $\det(\mathbf{A})$ by the appropriate row or column also establishes the following result. *If the ith row of* $\mathbf{A}$ *is of the form*

$$\{a_i\}^T = \{b_i\}^T + \{c_i\}^T,$$

then

$$\det(\mathbf{A}) = \det\begin{pmatrix} \{a_1\}^T \\ \cdot \\ \cdot \\ \cdot \\ \{a_{i-1}\}^T \\ \{a_i\}^T \\ \{a_{i+1}\}^T \\ \cdot \\ \cdot \\ \cdot \\ \{a_n\}^T \end{pmatrix} = \det\begin{pmatrix} \{a_1\}^T \\ \cdot \\ \cdot \\ \cdot \\ \{a_{i-1}\}^T \\ \{b_i\}^T + \{c_i\}^T \\ \{a_{i+1}\}^T \\ \cdot \\ \cdot \\ \cdot \\ \{a_n\}^T \end{pmatrix}$$

$$= \det\begin{pmatrix} \{a_1\}^T \\ \cdot \\ \cdot \\ \cdot \\ \{a_{i-1}\}^T \\ \{b_i\}^T \\ \{a_{i+1}\}^T \\ \cdot \\ \cdot \\ \cdot \\ \{a_n\}^T \end{pmatrix} + \det\begin{pmatrix} \{a_1\}^T \\ \cdot \\ \cdot \\ \cdot \\ \{a_{i-1}\}^T \\ \{c_i\}^T \\ \{a_{i+1}\}^T \\ \cdot \\ \cdot \\ \cdot \\ \{a_n\}^T \end{pmatrix}.$$

If every element in a row (column) of **A** *is multiplied by a number b, then the determinant of the resulting matrix is equal to b* det(**A**). Suppose that the ith row of **A** is multiplied by b and the resulting matrix is denoted by **B**, then

$$\mathbf{B}=\mathbf{E}_{\mathrm{II}}(i;b)\mathbf{A}. \tag{10.19}$$

Taking the determinant of both sides of Eq. (10.19) and using Eqs. (10.6) and (10.10), we have

$$\det(\mathbf{B})=\det(\mathbf{E}_{\mathrm{II}}(i;b)\mathbf{A})=\det(\mathbf{E}_{\mathrm{II}}(i;b))\det(\mathbf{A})=b\det(\mathbf{A}).$$

If every element in a row of **A** *is multiplied by a number b and then added to another row of* **A**, *the determinant of the new matrix is equal to* det(**A**). Since $\mathbf{E}_{\mathrm{III}}(i,j;b)$ accomplishes this operation, we have $\mathbf{B}=\mathbf{E}_{\mathrm{III}}(i,j;b)\mathbf{A}$. Taking determinants of both sides and using Eqs. (10.6) and (10.11), we have

$$\det(\mathbf{B})=\det(\mathbf{E}_{\mathrm{III}}(i,j;b))\det(\mathbf{A})=\det(\mathbf{A}).$$

Suppose that two rows of **A** are identical. We can then replace one of these identical rows of **A** by itself minus the other identical row without changing the value of det(**A**). We will then have a row of the new matrix that is comprised only of zeros, and the determinant of this new matrix is thus equal to zero. Thus, *if two rows (columns) of* **A** *are identical, then* det(**A**) = 0. Further, if any row of **A** is a linear combination of the other rows of **A**, then we can arrive at a matrix with a zero row by application of the elementary row operations. This simply says that there is a matrix $\mathbf{S}\in\mathsf{S}$ such that

$$\mathbf{SA}=\mathbf{B},\quad \det(\mathbf{S})\neq 0,$$

and that **B** has a row of zeros whenever a row of **A** is a linear combination of other rows of **A**. Taking determinants of both sides of $\mathbf{SA}=\mathbf{B}$, we have $\det(\mathbf{S})\det(\mathbf{A})=\det(\mathbf{B})=0$ since **B** has a row of zeros. Thus, since $\det(\mathbf{S})\neq 0$, we have established the following result: *if a row (column) of* **A** *is a linear combination of the other rows (columns) of* **A**, *then* det(**A**) = 0.

For the purpose of this course, the basic reason for studying determinants is the following result: *An n-by-n matrix* **A** *has* $\mathrm{rank}(\mathbf{A})=n$ *if and only if* $\det(\mathbf{A})\neq 0$, *and* $\mathrm{rank}(\mathbf{A})<n$ *if and only if* $\det(\mathbf{A})=0$. We know that there exists a matrix $\mathbf{S}_A\in\mathsf{S}$, such that

$$\mathbf{S}_A\mathbf{A}=\mathbf{A}_R,\quad \det(\mathbf{S}_A)\neq 0. \tag{10.20}$$

Taking determinants of both sides of Eq. (10.20) and using Eq. (10.6), we have $\det(\mathbf{S}_A)\det(\mathbf{A})=\det(\mathbf{A}_R)$, that is

$$\det(\mathbf{A})=\det(\mathbf{A}_R)/\det(\mathbf{S}_A). \tag{10.21}$$

Since $\mathbf{A} \in \mathsf{M}_{n,n}$, $\text{rank}(\mathbf{A}) = n$ if and only if $\mathbf{A}_R = \mathbf{E}$, in which case Eq. (10.21) gives $\det(\mathbf{A}) = 1/\det(\mathbf{S}_A) \neq 0$. On the other hand, $\text{rank}(\mathbf{A}) < n$ if and only if at least the last row of $\mathbf{A}_R$ is a zero row. In this case, $\det(\mathbf{A}_R) = 0$, and Eq. (10.21) gives $\det(\mathbf{A}) = 0$.

The last property we state follows directly by column expansion:

$$\begin{vmatrix} a_{11} & a_{12} & a_{13} & \cdots & a_{1n} \\ 0 & a_{22} & a_{23} & \cdots & a_{2n} \\ & 0 & a_{33} & \cdots & a_{3n} \\ & & & & \vdots \\ & 0 & & 0 & a_{nn} \end{vmatrix} = a_{11}a_{22} \cdots a_{nn}. \qquad (10.22)$$

Problems

10.1. For the following matrices $\mathbf{B}$ write the minor matrices $\mathbf{B}_{12}$, $\mathbf{B}_{23}$, and $\mathbf{B}_{32}$ and calculate their determinants:

$$\text{(a)} \begin{pmatrix} 1 & 2 & 3 \\ 3 & 4 & 5 \\ 5 & 6 & 7 \end{pmatrix}; \quad \text{(b)} \begin{pmatrix} 0 & 1 & 1 \\ 2 & 5 & 6 \\ 3 & 0 & 8 \end{pmatrix}; \quad \text{(c)} \begin{pmatrix} 1 & 0 & 2 \\ 3 & 4 & 0 \\ 0 & 5 & 6 \end{pmatrix};$$

$$\text{(d)} \begin{pmatrix} 0 & 0 & 1 \\ 3 & 4 & 0 \\ 5 & 6 & 8 \end{pmatrix}; \quad \text{(e)} \begin{pmatrix} 8 & 4 & 0 \\ 0 & 6 & 7 \\ 1 & 3 & 0 \end{pmatrix}; \quad \text{(f)} \begin{pmatrix} 0 & 3 & 4 \\ 5 & 1 & 2 \\ 1 & 0 & 3 \end{pmatrix}.$$

10.2. Calculate the determinants of the following matrices (choose the appropriate row or column expansion to simplify the calculation):

$$\text{(a)} \begin{pmatrix} 1 & 2 & 3 \\ 0 & 1 & -4 \\ 0 & -5 & 6 \end{pmatrix}; \quad \text{(b)} \begin{pmatrix} 3 & 4 & -5 \\ 0 & 1 & 0 \\ 3 & -4 & 5 \end{pmatrix}; \quad \text{(c)} \begin{pmatrix} 3 & -4 & 0 \\ -8 & 1 & -1 \\ 3 & 4 & 1 \end{pmatrix};$$

$$\text{(d)} \begin{pmatrix} 3 & 5 & -7 \\ 1 & 3 & 0 \\ 5 & -8 & 4 \end{pmatrix}; \quad \text{(e)} \begin{pmatrix} 1 & 2 & 5 & 0 \\ 0 & -3 & 1 & 0 \\ 5 & 6 & 7 & -8 \\ 1 & 0 & 0 & 1 \end{pmatrix};$$

$$\text{(f)} \begin{pmatrix} 5 & 6 & -1 & 0 \\ 2 & 5 & -3 & 1 \\ 1 & 0 & 0 & 1 \\ -3 & -1 & 2 & 0 \end{pmatrix}.$$

10.3. Use the properties of determinants to show that

(a) $$\begin{vmatrix} 1 & a & bc \\ 1 & b & ca \\ 1 & c & ab \end{vmatrix} = (b-a)(c-a)(c-b),$$

(b) $$\begin{vmatrix} x & 1 & \cdots & 1 \\ 1 & x & \cdots & 1 \\ \cdot & \cdot & \cdots & \cdot \\ 1 & 1 & \cdots & x \end{vmatrix} = (x+n-1)(x-1)^{n-1},$$

(c) $$\begin{vmatrix} 1 & 1 & 1 & \cdots & 1 \\ 1 & 1+a_2 & 1 & \cdots & 1 \\ 1 & 1 & 1+a_3 & \cdots & 1 \\ \cdot & \cdot & \cdot & \cdots & \cdot \\ 1 & 1 & \cdot & \cdots & 1+a_n \end{vmatrix} = a_2 a_3 \cdots a_n,$$

(d) $$\begin{vmatrix} 1+a_1 & 1 & 1 & \cdots & 1 \\ 1 & 1+a_2 & 1 & \cdots & 1 \\ 1 & 1 & 1+a_3 & \cdots & 1 \\ \cdot & \cdot & \cdot & \cdots & \cdot \\ 1 & 1 & 1 & \cdots & 1+a_n \end{vmatrix}$$
$$= a_1 \cdots a_n\left(1 + \frac{1}{a_1} + \cdots + \frac{1}{a_n}\right),$$

(e) $$\begin{vmatrix} 1+a_1 & a_2 & a_3 & \cdots & a_n \\ a_1 & 1+a_2 & a_3 & \cdots & a_n \\ a_1 & a_2 & 1+a_3 & \cdots & a_n \\ \cdot & \cdot & \cdot & \cdots & \cdot \\ a_1 & a_2 & a_3 & \cdots & 1+a_n \end{vmatrix} = 1 + a_1 + a_2 + \cdots + a_n.$$

10.4. Show that

$$D = \begin{vmatrix} a_1^{n-1} & a_1^{n-2} & \cdots & a_1 & 1 \\ a_2^{n-1} & a_2^{n-2} & \cdots & a_2 & 1 \\ \cdot & \cdot & \cdots & \cdot & \cdot \\ a_n^{n-1} & a_n^{n-2} & \cdots & a_n & 1 \end{vmatrix} = (a_1 - a_2) \cdots (a_1 - a_n)(a_2 - a_3) \cdots \cdots (a_2 - a_n) \cdots \cdots (a_{n-1} - a_n).$$

[If two of the $a_1, \ldots, a_n$ are equal the equality is obvious. If $a_i \neq a_j$ when $i \neq j$, then the first row expansion gives a polynomial of degree $(n-1)$ in a_1 with roots $a_2, \ldots, a_n$. Hence $D = (a_1 - a_2) \ldots (a_1 - a_n) D_1(a_2, a_3, \ldots, a_n)$ where D_1 does not contain a_1. Now prove that $D_1(a_3, a_3, \ldots, a_n) = 0$ etc.] D is referred to as the **Vandermonde** determinant.

10.5. Show that the sum of the products of the elements on the diagonal lines of the table

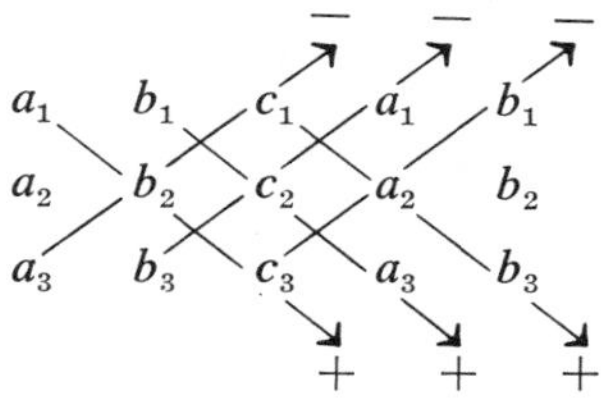

taken with the corresponding signs give the value of the third-order determinant

$$\begin{vmatrix} a_1 & b_1 & c_1 \\ a_2 & b_2 & c_2 \\ a_3 & b_3 & c_3 \end{vmatrix}.$$

This rule applies to third-order determinants *only.*

10.6. Prove the formulae (10.9) through (10.11).

10.7. If **A** is an n-by-n matrix, α a given number and k a positive integer, then show that

$$|\alpha \mathbf{A}| = \alpha^n |\mathbf{A}|, \qquad |\mathbf{A}^k| = |\mathbf{A}|^k.$$

10.8. The function sgn x (read: sign x) is defined as follows:

$$\operatorname{sgn} x = \begin{cases} 1 \text{ if } x > 0 \\ 0 \text{ if } x = 0. \\ -1 \text{ if } x < 0 \end{cases}$$

Show that: $\operatorname{sgn}(x_1 x_2) = (\operatorname{sgn} x_1)(\operatorname{sgn} x_2)$. Use this result to derive:

$$\operatorname{sgn}(x_1 \ . \ . \ . \ x_n) = (\operatorname{sgn} x_1) \ . \ . \ . \ (\operatorname{sgn} x_n).$$

10.9. If $p_1, \ldots, p_n$ are the elements of the set of distinct positive integers $\{k_1, \ldots, k_n\}$ *taken in a specific order*, then $(p_1, \ldots, p_n)$ is a **permutation** of $\{k_1, \ldots, k_n\}$. For example (1, 3, 2) and (2, 1, 3) are two different permutations of 1, 2, 3.

Let $(k_1, k_2, k_3) = (2, 1, 3)$

(i) Write all possible permutations (j_1, j_2, j_3) of 1, 2, 3 and the corresponding permutations $(j_{k_1}, j_{k_2}, j_{k_3})$.

(ii) Write all possible permutations (j_1, j_2, j_3) of 1, 2, 3 and the corresponding permutations (m_1, m_2, m_3) where $(j_{m_1}, j_{m_2}, j_{m_3}) = (k_1, k_2, k_3)$.

(iii) Write all possible permutations (j_1, j_2, j_3) of 1, 2, 3 and the corresponding permutations $(k_{j_1}, k_{j_2}, k_{j_3})$.

[For example, if $(j_1, j_2, j_3) = (2, 3, 1)$, then

(1) $(j_{k_1}, j_{k_2}, j_{k_3}) = (j_2, j_1, j_3) = (3, 2, 1)$

(2) $(k_1, k_2, k_3) = (2, 1, 3) = (j_{m_1}, j_{m_2}, j_{m_3})$ and $(m_1, m_2, m_3) = (1, 3, 2)$

(3) $(k_{j_1}, k_{j_2}, k_{j_3}) = (k_2, k_3, k_1) = (1, 3, 2)$.]

10.10. Let $(k_1, \ldots, k_n)$, $(j_1, \ldots, j_n)$ and $(l_1, \ldots, l_n)$ be three permutations of the integers $1, 2, \ldots, n$. Show that:

(i) as $(j_1, \ldots, j_n)$ varies over all permutations of $1, \ldots, n$ so does $(k_{j_1}, \ldots, k_{j_n})$;

(ii) as $(k_1, \ldots, k_n)$ varies over all permutations of $1, \ldots, n$ so does $(k_{j_1}, \ldots, k_{j_n})$;

(iii) if, for any $(j_1, \ldots, j_n)$ and $(l_1, \ldots, l_n)$, $(k_1, \ldots, k_n)$ is such that $(j_{k_1}, \ldots, j_{k_n}) = (l_1, \ldots, l_n)$ then as $(j_1, \ldots, j_n)$ varies over all permutations of $(1, \ldots, n)$ so does $(k_1, \ldots, k_n)$.

10.11. The **permutation symbol** $e_{j_1 \ldots j_n}$, where $j_1, \ldots, j_n$ are positive integers $\leq n$, not necessarily distinct, is defined by

$$\begin{aligned} e_{j_1 \ldots j_n} &= \operatorname{sgn} \prod_{1 \leq r < s \leq n} (j_s - j_r) \\ &= \operatorname{sgn}\, (j_2 - j_1)(j_3 - j_2)(j_3 - j_1) \ . \ . \ . \ (j_n - j_1). \end{aligned}$$

Show that

(i) If $j_1 < j_2 < \ldots < j_n$ then $e_{j_1 \ldots j_n} = 1$.
(ii) $e_{j_1 \ldots j_n} = 0$ if and only if two of the $j_1, \ldots, j_n$ are equal.
(iii) The interchange of any two successive indices changes the sign of the permutation symbol.
(iv) Use the above result to show that the interchange of any two indices changes the sign of the permutation symbol.

10.12. (i) Write all permutation symbols with two indices and their values.

(ii) Find a method to tabulate systematically all permutation symbols with three indices and give their values. Generalize this result.

10.13. Let J_k be the number of indices which follow j_k and are less than j_k in the permutation symbol $e_{j_1 \ldots j_n}$ with *distinct* indices. Show that $e_{j_1 \ldots j_n} = -1$ if and only if $J_1 + \ldots + J_n$ is odd.

10.14. Let $j_1, \ldots, j_n$ be the n *distinct* indices of $e_{j_1 j_2 \ldots j_n}$ and

$$\begin{aligned} k_p &= j_p && \text{if} \quad j_p < j_1 \\ k_p &= j_p - 1 && \text{if} \quad j_p > j_1 \end{aligned} \qquad \text{where } p = 2, \ldots, n.$$

Show that

(i) The integers $k_2, \ldots, k_n$ are distinct and $\leq n - 1$.
(ii) As the indices $j_2, \ldots, j_n$ vary over all possible permutations of the integers $1, \ldots, j_1 - 1, j_1 + 1, \ldots, n$ the indices $k_2, \ldots, k_n$ vary over all possible permutations of the integers $1, \ldots, n - 1$.
(iii) $e_{j_1 j_2 \ldots j_n} = (-1)^{j_1+1} e_{k_2 \ldots k_n}$.

10.15. Show that

$$e_{k_1 \ldots k_n} e_{j_1 \ldots j_n} = e_{k_{\mu_1} \ldots k_{\mu_n}} e_{j_{\mu_1} \ldots j_{\mu_n}},$$

where $(\mu_1, \ldots, \mu_n)$ is a permutation of $1, \ldots, n$. [Note that $e_{k_{\mu_1} \ldots k_{\mu_n}}$ and $e_{j_{\mu_1} \ldots j_{\mu_n}}$ are obtained from $e_{k_1 \ldots k_n}$ and $e_{j_1 \ldots j_n}$, respectively, by the same interchange of indices.]

10.16. If $(\mu_1, \ldots, \mu_n)$ is a permutation of $1, \ldots, n$, use problem 10.15 to show that

(i) $e_{k_1 \ldots k_n} = e_{k_1 \ldots k_n} e_{12 \ldots n} = e_{k_{\mu_1} \ldots k_{\mu_n}} e_{\mu_1 \ldots \mu_n}$.

Use (i) to derive

(ii) $e_{k_1 \ldots k_n} e_{\mu_1 \ldots \mu_n} = e_{k_{\mu_1} \ldots k_{\mu_n}}$,

where $\mu_1, \ldots, \mu_n$ need not be distinct.

10.17. We define the determinant of the n-by-n matrix $\mathbf{A} = (a_{ij})$ to be the sum

$$\det(\mathbf{A}) = \sum_{j_1, j_2, \ldots, j_n = 1}^{n} e_{j_1 j_2 \ldots j_n} a_{1j_1} a_{2j_2} \ldots a_{nj_n}$$

$$= a_{11} \sum_{j_2, \ldots, j_n = 1}^{n} e_{1 j_2 \ldots j_n} a_{2j_2} \ldots a_{nj_n}$$

$$+ \ldots + a_{1n} \sum_{j_2, \ldots, j_n = 1}^{n} e_{n j_2 \ldots j_n} a_{2j_2} \ldots a_{nj_n}.$$

Show that this definition agrees with the definition given in the text; that is, show that the above definition gives

$$\det(\mathbf{A}) = a_{11}(-1)^{1+1}\det(\mathbf{A}_{11}) + a_{12}(-1)^{2+1}\det(\mathbf{A}_{12})$$
$$+ \ldots + a_{1n}(-1)^{n+1}\det(\mathbf{A}_{1n}).$$

[Use problem 10.14.]

10.18. Show that

$$\det(\mathbf{A}) = \sum_{j=1}^{n} a_{ij}(-1)^{i+j}\det(\mathbf{A}_{ij}).$$

This formula gives the ith row expansion of $\det(\mathbf{A})$. [Follow the steps of problem 10.17 but sum first with respect to j_i instead of j_1.]

10.19. Justify each step in the following proof:

$$\det(\mathbf{A}) e_{k_1 \ldots k_n} = \sum_{j_1, \ldots, j_n = 1}^{n} e_{j_1 \ldots j_n} e_{k_1 \ldots k_n} a_{1j_1} \ldots a_{nj_n}$$

$$= \sum_{j_1, \ldots, j_n = 1}^{n} e_{j_{k_1} \ldots j_{k_n}} a_{1j_1} \ldots a_{nj_n}$$

$$= \sum_{j_1, \ldots, j_n = 1}^{n} e_{j_{k_1} \ldots j_{k_n}} a_{k_1 j_{k_1}} \ldots a_{k_n j_{k_n}}$$

$$= \sum_{p_1, \ldots, p_n = 1}^{n} e_{p_1 \ldots p_n} a_{k_1 p_1} \ldots a_{k_n p_n},$$

from which

$$\det(\mathbf{A}) e_{k_1 \ldots k_n} = \sum_{p_1, \ldots, p_n = 1}^{n} e_{p_1 \ldots p_n} a_{k_1 p_1} \ldots a_{k_n p_n}.$$

[See problems 10.10, 10.14, and 10.16.]

10.20. Show that

$$\det(\mathbf{A}) = \sum_{i=1}^{n} a_{ij}(-1)^{i+j}\det(\mathbf{A}_{ij}).$$

This formula gives the jth column expansion of det(**A**). [See problem 10.18.]

10.21. Justify each step of the following proof:

Let $(j_1, \ldots, j_n)$, $(\mu_1, \ldots, \mu_n)$, and $(l_1, \ldots, l_n)$ be three permutations of the integers $1, \ldots, n$ such that $(j_{\mu_1}, \ldots, j_{\mu_n}) = (l_1, \ldots, l_n)$. Then .

$$\begin{aligned} e_{j_1 \ldots j_n} a_{1j_1} \ldots a_{nj_n} &= e_{j_1 \ldots j_n} e_{\mu_1 \ldots \mu_n} e_{\mu_1 \ldots \mu_n} a_{1j_1} \ldots a_{nj_n} \\ &= e_{j_{\mu_1} \ldots j_{\mu_n}} e_{\mu_1 \ldots \mu_n} a_{1j_1} \ldots a_{nj_n} \\ &= e_{j_{\mu_1} \ldots j_{\mu_n}} e_{\mu_1 \ldots \mu_n} a_{\mu_1 j_{\mu_1}} \ldots a_{\mu_n j_{\mu_n}} \\ &= e_{l_1 \ldots l_n} e_{\mu_1 \ldots \mu_n} a_{\mu_1 l_1} \ldots a_{\mu_n l_n}; \end{aligned}$$

hence

$$\begin{aligned} \det(\mathbf{A}) e_{l_1 \ldots l_n} &= e_{l_1 \ldots l_n} \sum_{j_1, \ldots, j_n = 1}^{n} e_{j_1 \ldots j_n} a_{1j_1} \ldots a_{nj_n} \\ &= \sum_{\mu_1, \ldots, \mu_n = 1}^{n} e_{\mu_1 \ldots \mu_n} a_{\mu_1 l_1} \ldots a_{\mu_n l_n}. \end{aligned}$$

10.22. Show that $\det(\mathbf{A}) = \det(\mathbf{A}^T)$.

10.23. Justify each step in the following proof:

$$\begin{aligned} \det(\mathbf{AB}) = &\sum_{j_1, \ldots, j_n = 1}^{n} e_{j_1 \ldots j_n} \left(\sum_{p_1 = 1}^{n} a_{j_1 p_1} b_{p_1 1} \right) \ldots \left(\sum_{p_n = 1}^{n} a_{j_n p_n} b_{p_n n} \right) \\ &\sum_{p_1, \ldots, p_n = 1}^{n} \left(\sum_{j_1, \ldots, j_n = 1}^{n} e_{j_1 \ldots j_n} a_{j_1 p_1} \ldots a_{j_n p_n} b_{p_1 1} \ldots b_{p_n n} \right) \\ &= \sum_{p_1, \ldots, p_n = 1}^{n} \det(\mathbf{A}) e_{p_1 \ldots p_n} b_{p_1 1} \ldots b_{p_n n} = \det(\mathbf{A})\det(\mathbf{B}) \end{aligned}$$

so that

$$\det(\mathbf{AB}) = \det(\mathbf{A})\det(\mathbf{B}).$$

LECTURE 11

The Calculation of Determinants

The cofactor of an entry of a matrix • The matrix of cofactors • Formulas involving cofactor matrices • Cramer's rule • Calculation of determinants by row reduction methods • Problems

Let **A** be a given *n*-by-*n* matrix. We saw in the last lecture that the determinant of **A** could be evaluated by use of either the row expansion formula

$$\det(\mathbf{A}) = \sum_{j=1}^{n} a_{ij}(-1)^{i+j}\det(\mathbf{A}_{ij}). \tag{11.1}$$

or by the column expansion formula

$$\det(\mathbf{A}) = \sum_{j=1}^{n} a_{ji}(-1)^{j+i}\det(\mathbf{A}_{ji}). \tag{11.2}$$

The $(n-1)$-by-$(n-1)$ matrix $\mathbf{A}_{ij}$ is the minor matrix of a_{ij} and is obtained from **A** by deletion of the *i*th row and the *j*th column. Both of the above formulae involve terms of the form $(-1)^{i+j}\det(\mathbf{A}_{ij})$ or $(-1)^{j+i}\det(\mathbf{A}_{ji})$. It is customary to refer to the number

$$c_{ij}(\mathbf{A}) = (-1)^{i+j}\det(\mathbf{A}_{ij}) \tag{11.3}$$

as the **cofactor** of the element a_{ij} of **A**. Since there are n^2 cofactors of the entries of **A**, the n^2 numbers $c_{ij}(\mathbf{A})$ can be arranged as an *n*-by-*n* matrix

$$\mathbf{C}(\mathbf{A}) = (c_{ij}(\mathbf{A})), \tag{11.4}$$

called the **matrix of cofactors** of **A**. This matrix is a useful tool in certain calculations.

The first thing we do is to rewrite the row and column expansion formulae (11.1) and (11.2) in terms of the entries of the matrix of cofactors:

$$\det(\mathbf{A}) = \sum_{j=1}^{n} a_{ij}\, c_{ij}(\mathbf{A}), \tag{11.5}$$

$$\det(\mathbf{A}) = \sum_{j=1}^{n} a_{ji}\, c_{ji}(\mathbf{A}). \tag{11.6}$$

The next facts we establish are the following:

$$\sum_{j=1}^{n} a_{ij}\, c_{kj}(\mathbf{A}) = \det(\mathbf{A})\, e_{ik}, \tag{11.7}$$

$$\sum_{j=1}^{n} a_{ji}\, c_{jk}(\mathbf{A}) = \det(\mathbf{A})\, e_{ik}, \tag{11.8}$$

where $\mathbf{E}=(e_{ik})$; that is, $e_{ik}=1$ if $i=k$ and $e_{ik}=0$ if $i\neq k$. If $i=k$, then Eq. (11.7) is the same as Eq. (11.5) and Eq. (11.8) is the same as Eq. (11.6). The row expansion formula for $\det(\mathbf{A})$ gives us

$$\sum_{j=1}^{n} a_{ij}\, c_{kj}(\mathbf{A}) = \sum_{j=1}^{n} a_{ij}(-1)^{k+j} \det(\mathbf{A}_{kj})$$

$$= \begin{vmatrix} a_{11} & \cdots & a_{1n} \\ \cdot & & \cdot \\ \cdot & & \cdot \\ \cdot & & \cdot \\ a_{k-1\,1} & \cdots & a_{k-1\,n} \\ a_{i1} & \cdots & a_{in} \\ \cdot & & \cdot \\ \cdot & & \cdot \\ a_{k+1\,1} & \cdots & a_{k+1\,n} \\ \cdot & & \cdot \\ a_{n1} & \cdots & a_{nn} \end{vmatrix}.$$

If $i\neq k$, two of the rows of the determinant are equal and hence the value of the determinant is zero. The formula (11.8) is established in the same way using the same argument for the column expansion.

The summations in the above formula are reminiscent of matrix multiplication, and indeed, Eqs. (11.7) and (11.8) can be formulated in terms of matrix multiplication. With $\mathbf{C}(\mathbf{A})=(c_{ij}(\mathbf{A}))$, we have $\mathbf{C}(\mathbf{A})^T= (c_{ji}(\mathbf{A}))$. Thus, if we set $\mathbf{W}=\mathbf{A}\,\mathbf{C}(\mathbf{A})^T$ and evaluate the matrix product, we have

$$w_{ik} = \sum_{j=1}^{n} a_{ij}\, c_{kj}(\mathbf{A}).$$

The formula (11.7) then gives $w_{ik}=\det(\mathbf{A})e_{ik}$ where $\mathbf{E}=(e_{ik})$, that is,

$$\mathbf{A}\,\mathbf{C}(\mathbf{A})^T = \det(\mathbf{A})\,\mathbf{E}, \tag{11.9}$$

"or $\mathrm{tr}[\mathbf{A}\mathbf{C}(\mathbf{A})^T]=n\,\det(\mathbf{A})$. This can also be written as $\mathbf{A}(\mathbf{C}(\mathbf{A})^T/\det(\mathbf{A})) = \mathbf{E}$ if $\det(\mathbf{A})\neq 0$. Hence we obtain the result

$$\mathbf{A}^{-1} = \mathbf{C}(\mathbf{A})^T/\det(\mathbf{A}), \quad \det(\mathbf{A})\neq 0. \tag{11.10}$$

In most instances, however, it is much quicker to find $\mathbf{A}^{-1}$ by row reducing $[\mathbf{A}|\mathbf{E}]$. Similarly, Eq. (11.8) can be used to establish

$$\mathbf{C}(\mathbf{A})^T\mathbf{A}=\det(\mathbf{A})\ \mathbf{E}. \tag{11.11}$$

Note also that $\mathbf{A}\,\mathbf{C}(\mathbf{A})^T=\mathbf{C}(\mathbf{A})^T\mathbf{A}$.

Let $\mathbf{B}_k$ be the matrix that is obtained from the matrix $\mathbf{A}$ by replacing the kth column of $\mathbf{A}$ by the column matrix $\{b\}$. *Cramer's rule* states that if $\det(\mathbf{A})\neq 0$ then the linear inhomogeneous system $\mathbf{A}\{x\}=\{b\}$ has the unique solution $\{x\}$ given by

$$x_k=\det(\mathbf{B}_k)/\det(\mathbf{A}). \tag{11.12}$$

We first note that $\det(\mathbf{A})\neq 0$ and $\mathbf{A}\in \mathsf{M}_{n,n}$, so that $\operatorname{rank}(\mathbf{A})=n$. Thus, $\mathbf{A}^{-1}$ exists and the system $\mathbf{A}\{x\}=\{b\}$ has the unique solution $\{x\}=\mathbf{A}^{-1}\{b\}$. When Eq. (11.10) is used to evaluate $\mathbf{A}^{-1}$, we thus have

$$\{x\}=\frac{1}{\det(\mathbf{A})}\mathbf{C}(\mathbf{A})^T\{b\},$$

that is,

$$x_i=\sum_{j=1}^{n}\frac{1}{\det(\mathbf{A})}\,c_{ji}(\mathbf{A})b_j=\sum_{j=1}^{n}\frac{1}{\det(\mathbf{A})}\,b_jc_{ji}\ =\frac{1}{\det(\mathbf{A})}\sum_{j=1}^{n}b_j(-1)^{j+i}A_{ji}.$$

However,

$$\sum_{j=1}^{n}b_j(-1)^{j+i}A_{ji}=\det(\mathbf{B}_i),$$

and the result is established. Cramer's rule is often useful in theoretical investigations, but for actual calculations with $n>4$, it is much longer and more inefficient than the method we have already learned for solving inhomogeneous systems, namely row reduction of $[\mathbf{A}|\{b\}]$.

We now come down to the actual details of calculating determinants when the given matrix is a numerical matrix. It should be clear to the student that the properties of determinants established in the previous lecture can be used to simplify the calculations by reducing a large number of the terms involved in the row or column expansion formula to zero. There is, however, a straightforward and systematic method of determinant evaluation that is based directly on the row echelon algorithm. If $\mathbf{S}\in\mathsf{S}$, then $\det(\mathbf{S})\neq 0$. Thus $\mathbf{SA}=\mathbf{B}$ gives

$$\det(\mathbf{A})=\frac{1}{\det(\mathbf{S})}\det(\mathbf{B}). \tag{11.13}$$

Equations (10.9) through (10.11) of the last lecture give the values of the determinants of the three elementary row operation matrices that we use in the row echelon algorithm. Thus, *if we row reduce* **A** *and keep track of the determinants of the row operation matrices that row reduce* **A**, *then* $\det(\mathbf{A})\neq 0$ *if and only if* $\mathbf{A}_R=\mathbf{E}$, *in which case* $\det(\mathbf{A})$ *is equal to the reciprocal of the product of the determinants of the row operation matrices that were used,* that is $\mathbf{S}_A\mathbf{A}=\mathbf{E}$, then $\det(\mathbf{A})=1/\det(\mathbf{S}_A)$.

For example:

$$\begin{pmatrix} 1 & 3 & -2 & 0 \\ 1 & 1 & 0 & -1 \\ 2 & 0 & 2 & 0 \\ 0 & 1 & 1 & 1 \end{pmatrix} \underset{\Omega}{(1)} \begin{pmatrix} 1 & 3 & -2 & 0 \\ 0 & -2 & 2 & -1 \\ 0 & -6 & 6 & 0 \\ 0 & 1 & 1 & 1 \end{pmatrix}$$

$$\underset{\Omega}{(-\tfrac{1}{2})} \begin{pmatrix} 1 & 3 & -2 & 0 \\ 0 & 1 & -1 & \tfrac{1}{2} \\ 0 & -6 & 6 & 0 \\ 0 & 1 & 1 & 1 \end{pmatrix} \underset{\Omega}{(1)} \begin{pmatrix} 1 & 3 & -2 & 0 \\ 0 & 1 & -1 & \tfrac{1}{2} \\ 0 & 0 & 0 & 3 \\ 0 & 0 & 2 & \tfrac{1}{2} \end{pmatrix}$$

$$\underset{\Omega}{(-1)} \begin{pmatrix} 1 & 3 & -2 & 0 \\ 0 & 1 & -1 & \tfrac{1}{2} \\ 0 & 0 & 2 & \tfrac{1}{2} \\ 0 & 0 & 0 & 3 \end{pmatrix},$$

(a)
where Ω denotes that the determinant of the elementary row operation matrix which accomplishes the step is equal to a. In this example, we have

$$\mathbf{SA}=\begin{pmatrix} 1 & 3 & 2 & 0 \\ 0 & 1 & -1 & \tfrac{1}{2} \\ 0 & 0 & 2 & \tfrac{1}{2} \\ 0 & 0 & 0 & 3 \end{pmatrix}, \qquad \det(\mathbf{S})=(1)\left(\frac{-1}{2}\right)(1)(-1)=\frac{1}{2}.$$

Thus, since

$$\begin{vmatrix} 1 & 3 & -2 & 0 \\ 0 & 1 & -1 & \tfrac{1}{2} \\ 0 & 0 & 2 & \tfrac{1}{2} \\ 0 & 0 & 0 & 3 \end{vmatrix} =(1)(1)(2)(3)=6,$$

taking determinants gives

$$\frac{1}{2}\det(\mathbf{A})=6,$$

or

$$\det(\mathbf{A})=12.$$

The full row reduction of **A** does not have to be computed, since we know how to evaluate the determinant when there are only zeros below the principle diagonal as in the above example. [See Eq. (10.22.) There is still further simplification that we should note. *If the row reduction of* $\mathbf{A}$ *leads to a column that does not have a corner element, then* $\det(\mathbf{A})=0$. This follows from the fact that every column of $\mathbf{A}_R$ must have a corner element if $\mathbf{A}_R=\mathbf{E}$ and this is necessary and sufficient for $\text{rank}(\mathbf{A})=n$ when $\mathbf{A}\in\mathbf{M}_{n,n}$. Thus, for example, whenever the row echelon reduction of $\mathbf{A}$ leads to the following form

$$\begin{pmatrix} 0 & X & X & X \\ 0 & 0 & X & X \\ 0 & 0 & 0 & 0 \end{pmatrix},$$

then $\det(\mathbf{A})=0$.

Problems

11.1. By reducing the following matrices to the upper triangular form calculate their determinants:

(a) $\begin{pmatrix} 5 & 3 \\ 10 & -8 \end{pmatrix}$, (b) $\begin{pmatrix} 3 & 14 \\ 9 & 48 \end{pmatrix}$, (c) $\begin{pmatrix} 1 & 3 & 5 \\ 2 & 6 & 14 \\ 4 & 15 & 22 \end{pmatrix}$,

(d) $\begin{pmatrix} 2 & 7 & 13 \\ 8 & 30 & 60 \\ 4 & 15 & 29 \end{pmatrix}$, (e) $\begin{pmatrix} 2 & 0 & 3 & 6 \\ 7 & 1 & 8 & 2 \\ -5 & 1 & 2 & 0 \\ 1 & 0 & 3 & 1 \end{pmatrix}$, (f) $\begin{pmatrix} -3 & 2 & 5 & 1 \\ 5 & -6 & 7 & 0 \\ 2 & 5 & 0 & 0 \\ 1 & 2 & 5 & 1 \end{pmatrix}$.

11.2. Use the Cramer's rule to solve the following systems:

(a) $3x_1 - 2x_2 = 3$, $5x_1 + x_2 = 8$ (b) $x_1 - 3x_2 = 1$, $6x_1 - x_2 = 0$ (c) $3x_1 - x_2 = 0$, $-x_1 + x_3 = 3$

(d) $x_1 - 2x_2 + x_3 = 1$, $x_1 + x_2 = 5$, $6x_1 - x_2 + x_3 = 1$ (e) $x_2 - 2x_3 = 1$, $6x_1 - x_2 - x_3 = 0$, $x_1 - 2x_2 = 1$ (f) $x_1 - 2x_2 + x_3 = 6$, $x_2 - 3x_3 = 7$, $6x_1 + x_3 = 0$

11.3. Show that

$$\begin{vmatrix} a_{11} & a_{12} & \cdots & a_{1n} & p_1 \\ a_{21} & a_{22} & \cdots & a_{2n} & p_2 \\ & & \cdots & \cdot & \\ a_{n1} & a_{12} & \cdots & a_{nn} & p_n \\ q_1 & q_2 & \cdots & q_n & r \end{vmatrix} = r \begin{vmatrix} a_{11} & \cdots & a_{1n} \\ & \cdots & \\ a_{n1} & \cdots & a_{nn} \end{vmatrix} - \sum_{i,j=1}^{n} p_i q_j c_{ij}$$

where c_{ij} are the cofactors of the element a_{ij} of $|a_{ij}|$.

11.4. If $\mathbf{A}$ is a nonsingular matrix and k a (positive or negative) integer, then show that $|\mathbf{A}^k| = |\mathbf{A}|^k$. In particular $|\mathbf{A}^{-1}| = |\mathbf{A}|^{-1}$.

11.5. If $a_{rs}(t)$ are differentiable functions of t and

$$D(t) = \begin{vmatrix} a_{11}(t) & \dots & a_{1n}(t) \\ & \dots & \\ a_{n1}(t) & \dots & a_{nn}(t) \end{vmatrix},$$

show that $D'(t) = D_1(t) + \dots + D_n(t)$ where $D_k(t)$ denotes the determinant obtained from $D(t)$ if we replace the elements of the k column by their derivatives.

11.6. The **principal minor** $M_{i \dots j}$ of a determinant $|\mathbf{A}|$ is the determinant we obtain from $|\mathbf{A}|$ if we keep only the ith, . . . , jth columns and rows of $|\mathbf{A}|$. Show that

$$\begin{aligned} |\mathbf{A} - \lambda\mathbf{E}| &= \begin{vmatrix} a_{11} - \lambda & a_{12} & a_{13} \\ a_{21} & a_{22} - \lambda & a_{23} \\ a_{31} & a_{32} & a_{33} - \lambda \end{vmatrix} \\ &= (-\lambda)^3 + (-\lambda)^2(M_1 + M_2 + M_3) \\ &\quad + (-\lambda)(M_{12} + M_{13} + M_{23}) + |\mathbf{A}|, \end{aligned}$$

where M_i, M_{ij} are principal minors of the determinant $|\mathbf{A}|$.
[Write

$$|\mathbf{A} - \lambda\mathbf{E}| = \begin{vmatrix} a_{11} - \lambda & a_{12} + 0 & a_{13} + 0 \\ a_{12} + 0 & a_{22} - \lambda & a_{23} + 0 \\ a_{13} + 0 & a_{32} + 0 & a_{33} - \lambda \end{vmatrix}$$

and use the theorem on p. 121.

11.7. The matrix $\mathbf{C}(\mathbf{A})^T$, where $\mathbf{C}(\mathbf{A})$ is defined by Eq. (11.4), is called the **adjugate** matrix of $\mathbf{A}$ and it will be denoted by $\mathbf{A}^*$. If $\mathbf{A}$ is an n-by-n matrix, then show that

(i) $\mathbf{A}\mathbf{A}^* = \mathbf{A}^*\mathbf{A} = |\mathbf{A}|\mathbf{E}$,
(ii) $|\mathbf{A}\mathbf{A}^*| = |\mathbf{A}|^n$, $|\mathbf{A}^*| = |\mathbf{A}|^{n-1}$.

11.8. Show that $|\mathbf{A}| = 0$ if and only if a row (or column) of $\mathbf{A}$ is a linear combination of the other rows (or columns) of $\mathbf{A}$. [Use the theorem on p. 122 and the problem 7.19.]

11.9. Let $\mathbf{A}$ be an m-by-n matrix. The matrix formed from $\mathbf{A}$, if we keep only the elements on i rows and j columns, where $i \le m$ and $j \le n$, will be called an i-by-j **submatrix** of $\mathbf{A}$. If $p = \min(m, n)$ and $\operatorname{rank}(\mathbf{A}) = p$, then show that there is at least one p-by-p submatrix $\mathbf{B}$ of $\mathbf{A}$ such that $|\mathbf{B}| \neq 0$. [Use problems 11.8 and 7.19.]

11.10. Let $\mathbf{A}$ be an m-by-n matrix, $m < n$. Show that if the rows of $\mathbf{A}$ are linearly dependent so are the rows of any m-by-m submatrix of $\mathbf{A}$.

11.11. Let $\mathbf{A}$ be an m-by-n matrix and p an integer $< \min(m, n)$. Show that $\operatorname{rank}(\mathbf{A}) = p$ if and only if there is a p-by-p submatrix $\mathbf{B}$ of $\mathbf{A}$ such that $|\mathbf{B}| \neq 0$ *and* if $\mathbf{C}$ is a q-by-q submatrix of $\mathbf{A}$ such that $q > p$ then $|\mathbf{C}| = 0$. [Use problems 11.9 and 11.10.]

11.12. Let **A** be an m-by-n matrix with linearly independent columns and $\mathbf{B} \in M_{n,n}$ a nonsingular matrix. Show that the columns of the matrix **AB** are linearly independent. [Use problems 7.19 and 11.9.]

11.13. Let **A** and **B** be two m-by-n matrices with linearly independent columns. If each of the columns of **B** is a linear combination of the columns of **A**, show that $\mathbf{B} = \mathbf{AC}$ where **C** is a nonsingular n-by-n matrix. [Use problem 11.9.]

11.14. Let $\mathbf{E}(i_1, \ldots, i_n) = [\{e\}_{i_1}, \ldots, \{e\}_{i_n}]$ where $i_1, \ldots, i_n$ is a permutation of the integers $1, 2, \ldots, n$ and $\{e\}_{i_p}$ is the i_p column of the n-by-n identity matrix. Show that

$$|\mathbf{E}(i_1, \ldots, i_n)| = e_{i_1 i_2 \ldots i_n}.$$

11.15. Let **A** and **B** be two m-by-n matrices. Show that each column (row) of **A** is a column (row) of **B** and each column (row) of **B** a column (row) of **A** if and only if $\mathbf{A} = \mathbf{BE}(i_1, \ldots, i_n)$ $[\mathbf{A} = \mathbf{E}(i_1, \ldots, i_m)\mathbf{B}]$.

11.16. Show that

$$n!|\mathbf{A}| = \sum_{i, \ldots, k, r, \ldots, t = 1}^{n} e_{ij \ldots k} e_{rs \ldots t} a_{ir} a_{js} \ldots a_{kt}$$

[Use problem 10.21.]

11.17. If c_{ir} is the cofactor of the element a_{ir} of $|\mathbf{A}| = |a_{ij}|$, then show that

$$(n-1)!\, c_{ir} = \sum_{j, \ldots, k, s, \ldots, t} e_{ij \ldots k} e_{rs \ldots t} a_{js} \ldots a_{kt}$$

[Use problem 10.19 to write

$$|\mathbf{A}| = \sum_{r, s, \ldots, t = 1}^{n} a_{ir}(e_{ij \ldots k} e_{rs \ldots t} a_{js} \ldots a_{kt}) \text{ etc.]}$$

LECTURE 12

Eigenvalues and Eigenvectors

An example from systems of linear first-order differential equations • Similarity of matrices • Diagonalizability and similarity to a diagonal matrix • Conditons for similarity to a diagonal matrix • Eigenvectors and eigenvalues • The characteristic polynomial • Examples • Complex eigenvalues and eigenvectors • Examples • Equality of eigenvalues of similar matrices • Problems

From now on we will deal only with square matrices which will be n-by-n matrices in the general discussion.

Let **A** be a given n-by-n matrix. We saw in lecture 9 that we could find the stationary lengths of vectors that satisfy $\{x\}^T\mathbf{A}\{x\}=k$ if we could find an orthogonal matrix **B** and a diagonal matrix $\mathbf{D}(\lambda_1, \ldots, \lambda_n)$ such that

$$\mathbf{B}^{-1}\mathbf{A}\,\mathbf{B}=\mathbf{D}(\lambda_1, \ldots, \lambda_n).$$

This equation arises time and again in any number of different contexts. Perhaps one of the most important places is in the study of systems of first-order linear differential equations, such as

$$\frac{dx_1(t)}{dt}=3x_1(t)+5x_2(t),$$

$$\frac{dx_2(t)}{dt}=-4x_1(t)+7x_2(t).$$

If we write $\{x(t)\}^T=[x_1(t), x_2(t)]$, and $\frac{d}{dt}\{x(t)\}^T=\left[\frac{dx_1(t)}{dt}, \frac{dx_2(t)}{dt}\right]$, then the above system can be written as

$$\frac{d}{dt}\{x(t)\}=\mathbf{A}\{x(t)\},$$

where

$$\mathbf{A}=\begin{pmatrix} 3 & 5 \\ -4 & 7 \end{pmatrix}.$$

In general, suppose that $\{x(t)\}$ is an n-tuple of functions of the variable t:

$$\{x(t)\}^T = [x_1(t), x_2(t), \ldots, x_n(t)].$$

The derivatives of these functions can then be written as $\frac{d}{dt}\{x(t)\}$, where

$$\frac{d}{dt}\{x(t)\}^T = \left[\frac{dx_1(t)}{dt}, \ldots, \frac{dx_n(t)}{dt}\right].$$

A linear homogeneous system of first-order differential equations with constant coefficients is then given by

$$\frac{d}{dt}\{x(t)\} = \mathbf{A}\{x(t)\}; \tag{12.1}$$

that is,

$$\frac{dx_1}{dt} = a_{11}x_1 + a_{12}x_2 + \ldots + a_{1n}x_n,$$

$$\vdots$$

$$\frac{dx_n}{dt} = a_{n1}x_1 + a_{n2}x_2 + \ldots + a_{nn}x_n,$$

where $a_{11}, \ldots, a_{nn}$ are constants, and $\mathbf{A} = (a_{ij})$. It is an easy matter to show that the single linear homogeneous differential equation

$$\frac{dx}{dt} = \alpha x$$

has the general solution

$$x(t) = c\,e^{\alpha t},$$

where c is an arbitrary constant, and we would like to use this fact to solve the system (12.1). The way we do this is to introduce new dependent variables $\{z(t)\}$ by the substitution

$$\{x(t)\} = \mathbf{B}\{z(t)\}, \tag{12.2}$$

where the entries of the matrix **B** are *constants.* We then have

$$\frac{d}{dt}\{x(t)\} = \frac{d}{dt}(\mathbf{B}\{z(t)\}) = \mathbf{B}\frac{d}{dt}\{z(t)\},$$

and hence the system (12.1) becomes

$$\mathbf{B}\frac{d}{dt}\{z(t)\} = \mathbf{AB}\{z(t)\}. \tag{12.3}$$

Thus, if we require **B** to be nonsingular, then multiplication of Eq. (12.3) by $\mathbf{B}^{-1}$ on the left gives us the system

$$\frac{d}{dt}\{z(t)\}=\mathbf{B}^{-1}\mathbf{A}\,\mathbf{B}\{z(t)\}. \tag{12.4}$$

Now comes the crucial step. Since the matrix **B** is an arbitrary nonsingular matrix, we can choose it in such a fashion as to lead to a simplification of the system (12.4). In particular, suppose that we can choose **B** so as to satisfy

$$\mathbf{B}^{-1}\mathbf{A}\,\mathbf{B}=\mathbf{D}(\lambda_1, \ldots, \lambda_n). \tag{12.5}$$

When Eq. (12.5) is substituted into Eq. (12.4) we have

$$\frac{d}{dt}\{z(t)\}=\mathbf{D}(\lambda_1, \ldots, \lambda_n)\{z(t)\}; \tag{12.6}$$

that is,

$$\frac{d}{dt}z_i(t)=\lambda_i\, z_i(t), \quad i=1, \ldots, n. \tag{12.7}$$

Each of the equations (12.7) can be solved so that we have

$$z_i(t)=c_i\, e^{\lambda_i t}. \tag{12.8}$$

The desired solution of the original system (12.1) is then given by substituting Eq. (12.8) into Eq. (12.2); that is

$$\{x(t)\}=\mathbf{B}\begin{Bmatrix} c_1\, e^{\lambda_1 t} \\ \cdot \\ \cdot \\ \cdot \\ c_n\, e^{\lambda_n t} \end{Bmatrix}.$$

Here again, what did the trick for us was the fact that we supposed the matrix **B** could be chosen so as to satisfy the equation

$$\mathbf{B}^{-1}\mathbf{A}\,\mathbf{B}=\mathbf{D}(\lambda_1, \ldots, \lambda_n).$$

Obviously, we are going to study when we can find such a matrix **B**.

Two n-by-n matrices **A** and **B** are said to be **similar** if and only if there exists a *nonsingular* n-by-n matrix **K** such that

$$\mathbf{K}^{-1}\mathbf{A}\,\mathbf{K}=\mathbf{B}. \tag{12.9}$$

The case we wish to study is that in which **A** *is similar to a diagonal matrix* $\mathbf{D}(\lambda_1, \ldots, \lambda_n)$; that is, there exists a nonsingular matrix **K** such that

$$\mathbf{K}^{-1}\mathbf{A}\,\mathbf{K}=\mathbf{D}(\lambda_1, \ldots, \lambda_n). \tag{12.10}$$

If **A** is similar to a diagonal matrix, we say that **A** is a **diagonalizable** matrix.

If we multiply the defining equation (12.10) on the left by **K**, we have

$$\mathbf{A}\,\mathbf{K}=\mathbf{K}\,\mathbf{D}(\lambda_1, \ldots, \lambda_n). \tag{12.11}$$

If $\{k\}_i$ denotes the ith column of the matrix **K**, then we have

$$\mathbf{K}=[\{k\}_1, \ . \ . \ ., \ \{k\}_n], \tag{12.12}$$

and hence

$$\mathbf{A}\,\mathbf{K}=[\mathbf{A}\{k\}_1, \ . \ . \ ., \ \mathbf{A}\{k\}_n], \tag{12.13}$$

while

$$\mathbf{K}\,\mathbf{D}=[\lambda_1\{k\}_1, \ . \ . \ ., \ \lambda_n\{k\}_n]. \tag{12.14}$$

When Eqs. (12.13) and (12.14) are substituted into Eq. (12.11), we obtain the equivalent system of n vector equations

$$\mathbf{A}\{k\}_i=\lambda_i\{k\}_i, \quad i=1, \ . \ . \ ., \ n. \tag{12.15}$$

Since the matrix **K** is given by Eq. (12.12) and **K** must be nonsingular, each of the vectors $\{k\}_i$ which satisfies Eqs. (12.15) must be a nonzero vector and, in addition, we have to choose the n vectors which satisfy Eq. (12.15) so that they are linearly independent. We can therefore summarize our findings thus far with the following statement.

An n-by-n matrix **A** *is diagonalizable if and only if we can find n numbers* $\lambda_1, \ . \ . \ ., \ \lambda_n$ (which may be complex numbers) *and a collection of n linearly independent vectors* $\{k\}_1, \ . \ . \ ., \ \{k\}_n$ *such that*

$$\mathbf{A}\{k\}_i=\lambda_i\{k\}_i, \quad i=1, \ . \ . \ ., \ n. \tag{12.15}$$

If these conditions are met, then

$$\mathbf{K}=[\{k\}_1, \ . \ . \ ., \ \{k\}_n] \tag{12.16}$$

is such that

$$\mathbf{K}^{-1}\mathbf{A}\,\mathbf{K}=\mathbf{D}(\lambda_1, \ . \ . \ ., \ \lambda_n). \tag{12.17}$$

The reader must make particular note of the fact that λ_1 is associated with $\{k\}_1$, λ_2 is associated with $\{k\}_2$, and so forth, as is shown by Eqs. (12.15). This relation is preserved in writing Eqs. (12.16) and (12.17); that is, if we write Eq. (12.16), then we must use $\mathbf{D}(\lambda_1, \ . \ . \ ., \ \lambda_n)$ in Eq. (12.17) rather than, say, $\mathbf{D}(\lambda_2, \lambda_1, \ . \ . \ ., \ \lambda_n)$. The reader should also note, however, that if we write

$$\mathbf{K}=[\{k\}_2, \{k\}_1, \{k\}_3, \ . \ . \ ., \ \{k\}_n],$$

then we have

$$\mathbf{K}^{-1}\mathbf{A}\,\mathbf{K}=\mathbf{D}(\lambda_2, \lambda_1, \lambda_3, \ . \ . \ ., \ \lambda_n).$$

In other words, it doesn't make any difference what order we use to write **K** in terms of the solutions of Eqs. (12.15) just so we use the same order in writing the diagonal matrix **D** in terms of the λ's.

A *nonzero* vector $\{k\}$ which satisfies

$$\mathbf{A}\{k\} = \lambda\{k\} \tag{12.18}$$

is said to be an **eigenvector** or **characteristic** vector of the matrix $\mathbf{A}$ and the number λ is said to be an **eigenvalue** or **characteristic** value of $\mathbf{A}$. Throughout the remainder of these lectures, we shall use the terms eigenvector and eigenvalue. Thus, *a matrix* $\mathbf{A} \in \mathsf{M}_{n,n}$ *is diagonalizable if and only if* $\mathbf{A}$ *has n linearly independent eigenvectors.* Obviously, if $\{k\}$ is an eigenvector of $\mathbf{A}$ then any nonzero multiple of $\{k\}$ is also an eigenvector of $\mathbf{A}$; that is

$$\mathbf{A}\{k\} = \lambda\{k\}, \text{ then } \mathbf{A}(c\{k\}) = \lambda(c\{k\}), \ c \neq 0.$$

The essential thing concerning diagonalizability of $\mathbf{A}$ is that we must be able to find n linearly independent eigenvectors of $\mathbf{A}$.

An eigenvector of $\mathbf{A}$ has a very important interpretation in terms of substitutions such as $\{y\} = \mathbf{A}\{x\}$. If we ask what vectors are not changed in direction by the substitution $\{y\} = \mathbf{A}\{x\}$, then we require vectors $\{\bar{x}\}$ such that $\{\bar{y}\} = \mathbf{A}\{\bar{x}\} = \lambda\{\bar{x}\}$ for some number λ. Thus, *the vectors that are not changed in direction by the substitution* $\{y\} = \mathbf{A}\{x\}$ *are just the eigenvectors of the matrix* $\mathbf{A}$. We shall have to return to this interpretation of eigenvectors several times in succeeding lectures.

The reasoning of the previous paragraphs has reduced the question of whether a given matrix $\mathbf{A}$ is diagonalizable to the question of whether $\mathbf{A}$ possesses n linearly independent eigenvectors. This is indeed a simplification, for we can first solve the problem of finding eigenvectors of a given matrix $\mathbf{A}$ and then ask whether we can find n linearly independent eigenvectors. By definition a vector $\{k\}$ is an eigenvector of $\mathbf{A}$ if and only if $\{k\}$ is a nonzero vector which satisfies the equation

$$\mathbf{A}\{k\} = \lambda\{k\} \tag{12.19}$$

for some value of λ. Since $\lambda\{k\} \equiv \lambda\, \mathbf{E}\{k\}$, we can write Eq. (12.19) in the equivalent form

$$(\mathbf{A} - \lambda\mathbf{E})\{k\} = \{0\}. \tag{12.20}$$

We are now on familiar ground, for Eq. (12.20) is nothing more than a linear homogeneous system of algebraic equations with $(\mathbf{A} - \lambda\mathbf{E})$ as the coefficient matrix. We know that such a system has a nontrivial solution $\{k\}$ (that is $\{k\} \neq \{0\}$) if and only if $\operatorname{rank}(\mathbf{A} - \lambda\mathbf{E})$, the rank of the coefficient matrix of Eq. (12.20), is less than n. Our study of determinants has shown that a necessary and sufficient condition that an n-by-n matrix have rank less than n is that the determinant of the matrix be equal to zero. Thus, Eq. (12.20) will have a nontrivial solution if and only if

$$\det(\mathbf{A} - \lambda\mathbf{E}) = 0. \tag{12.21}$$

Since $\mathbf{A}$ is a given matrix, the only way that Eq. (12.21) can be satisfied is if we choose λ in such a way that this condition is fulfilled. If λ is so chosen, then Eq. (12.20) will have a nontrivial solution since the dimension of the solution space of Eq. (12.20) will be greater than or equal to one. Thus, a number λ that satisfies (12.21) is an eigenvalue of the matrix **A** and we have established the following result. *If the number λ is chosen so that* $\det(\mathbf{A}-\lambda\mathbf{E})=0$, *then λ is an eigenvalue of* **A** *and there exists a space* $\mathsf{N}(\lambda)\subset\mathsf{M}_{n,1}$ *of vectors* $\{k\}$ *of at least one-dimension whose elements satisfy* $\mathbf{A}\{k\}=\lambda\{k\}$. *Each nonzero vector in* $\mathsf{N}(\lambda)$ *is an eigenvector of* **A** *that is associated with the eigenvalue* λ. The subspace of solutions of $\mathbf{A}\{k\}=\lambda\{k\}$ is of obvious importance, and hence we have introduced the notation $\mathsf{N}(\lambda)$ for this subspace of $\mathsf{M}_{n,1}$. The dimension of this subspace will be of importance to us later when we come to deciding when we can find n linearly independent eigenvectors of a matrix **A**.

We are now at the point in the argument where we can see that everything hinges on finding λ's so that $\det(\mathbf{A}-\lambda\mathbf{E})=0$, for then the calculation of the eigenvectors is a routine problem in linear algebra. Since $\mathbf{A}-\lambda\mathbf{E}$ is an n-by-n matrix, the function

$$p(\lambda)=\det(\mathbf{A}-\lambda\mathbf{E}) \tag{12.22}$$

will be an nth degree polynomial in the variable λ. Thus, *an eigenvalue of a matrix* **A** *is a root of the* **characteristic polynomial** $p(\lambda)=\det(\mathbf{A}-\lambda\mathbf{E})$ *of the matrix* **A**; that is, λ satisfies

$$p(\lambda)=\det(\mathbf{A}-\lambda\mathbf{E})=0. \tag{12.23}$$

At this point, it is worth considering a few examples. Let $n=2$ and let **A** be given by $\begin{pmatrix} 3 & 1 \\ -6 & -4 \end{pmatrix}$. We then have

$$\mathbf{A}-\lambda\mathbf{E}=\begin{pmatrix} 3-\lambda & 1 \\ -6 & -4-\lambda \end{pmatrix},$$

and hence

$$\begin{aligned} p(\lambda)&=\det(\mathbf{A}-\lambda\mathbf{E})=(3-\lambda)(-4-\lambda)+6=\lambda^2+\lambda-6 \\ &=(\lambda-2)(\lambda+3). \end{aligned}$$

Hence, the eigenvalues of **A** are the roots of the equation $(\lambda-2)(\lambda+3)=0$, namely $\lambda_1=2$ and $\lambda_2=-3$. We then have

$$\mathbf{A}-\lambda_1\mathbf{E}=\begin{pmatrix} 1 & 1 \\ -6 & -6 \end{pmatrix}, \qquad \mathbf{A}-\lambda_2\mathbf{E}=\begin{pmatrix} 6 & 1 \\ -6 & -1 \end{pmatrix},$$

so that both of these matrices have rank less than two. In fact, we may as well note it here as later on that *the calculation of eigenvalues is self-checking;* if a number λ_1 has been computed as an eigenvalue of a matrix **A**, then we must have $\operatorname{rank}(\mathbf{A}-\lambda_1\mathbf{E})<n$. This follows directly from the

manner in which we have derived the characteristic polynomial of a matrix, namely, $\det(\mathbf{A}-\lambda\mathbf{E})=0$. Hence, if you do not get the result $\operatorname{rank}(\mathbf{A}-\lambda_1\mathbf{E})<n$, then you have made a mistake in computing the eigenvalue λ_1 of $\mathbf{A}$.

We now have to find the row reduced form of the matrices $(\mathbf{A}-\lambda_1\mathbf{E})$ and $(\mathbf{A}-\lambda_2\mathbf{E})$ since we have to solve the equations

$$(\mathbf{A}-\lambda_1\mathbf{E})\{k\}_1=0, \qquad (\mathbf{A}-\lambda_2\mathbf{E})\{k\}_2=0,$$

in order to determine eigenvectors $\{k\}_1$ and $\{k\}_2$. Thus, in finding the eigenvectors of a matrix after you have found the eigenvalues, you will always have a check on the calculations that gave the eigenvalues, for you must find that the row reduced forms of the coefficient matrices $(\mathbf{A}-\lambda_1\mathbf{E})$ and $(\mathbf{A}-\lambda_2\mathbf{E})$ have at least one zero row so that the rank will be less than n. In this example,

$$(\mathbf{A}-\lambda_1\mathbf{E})_R=\begin{pmatrix}1 & 1\\ 0 & 0\end{pmatrix}, \qquad (\mathbf{A}-\lambda_2\mathbf{E})_R=\begin{pmatrix}1 & 1/6\\ 0 & 0\end{pmatrix},$$

so that

$$\{k\}_1=\alpha\begin{Bmatrix}-1\\ 1\end{Bmatrix}, \qquad \{k\}_2=\beta\begin{Bmatrix}-1/6\\ 1\end{Bmatrix},$$

are eigenvectors of $\mathbf{A}$ corresponding to $\lambda_1=2$, $\lambda_2=-3$ for any nonzero numbers α and β. Thus, the subspace $\mathsf{N}(2)$ is spanned by $\begin{Bmatrix}-1\\ 1\end{Bmatrix}$ and the subspace $\mathsf{N}(-3)$ is spanned by $\begin{Bmatrix}-1/6\\ 1\end{Bmatrix}$. One choice of the numbers α and β is $\alpha=\beta=1$, in which case we have

$$\{k\}_1=\begin{Bmatrix}-1\\ 1\end{Bmatrix}, \qquad \{k\}_2=\begin{Bmatrix}-1/6\\ 1\end{Bmatrix}.$$

Since $\{k\}_1$ and $\{k\}_2$ are linearly independent, we have

$$\mathbf{K}=[\{k\}_1,\ \{k\}_2]=\begin{pmatrix}-1 & -1/6\\ 1 & 1\end{pmatrix}, \qquad \mathbf{D}(\lambda_1,\lambda_2)=\mathbf{D}(2,-3),$$

and we have $\mathbf{K}^{-1}\mathbf{A}\,\mathbf{K}=\mathbf{D}(2,-3)$, as is easily seen by direct calculation. Thus, the matrix $\mathbf{A}$ is diagonalizable. If we make the choice $\alpha=-1$, $\beta=6$, then

$$\{k\}_1=\begin{Bmatrix}1\\ -1\end{Bmatrix}, \qquad \{k\}_2=\begin{Bmatrix}-1\\ 6\end{Bmatrix}, \qquad \mathbf{K}=\begin{pmatrix}1 & -1\\ -1 & 6\end{pmatrix}.$$

Thus, although the eigenvectors have been chosen in a different manner, and hence the matrix $\mathbf{K}$ is different, we still have $\mathbf{K}^{-1}\mathbf{A}\,\mathbf{K}=\mathbf{D}(2,-3)$. We leave it as an exercise to show that $\mathbf{K}^{-1}\mathbf{A}\,\mathbf{K}=\mathbf{D}(2,-3)$ holds for any nonzero choice of the numbers α and β.

For the next example let the matrix **A** be given by

$$\begin{pmatrix} 4 & 1 \\ -1 & 2 \end{pmatrix},$$

so that

$$\mathbf{A}-\lambda\mathbf{E}=\begin{pmatrix} 4-\lambda & 1 \\ -1 & 2-\lambda \end{pmatrix},$$

and hence

$$p(\lambda)=\det(\mathbf{A}-\lambda\mathbf{E})=\lambda^2-6\lambda+9=(\lambda-3)^2.$$

Thus, the roots of the characteristic polynomial are $\lambda_1=3=\lambda_2$. In this case, we have

$$\mathbf{A}-\lambda_1\mathbf{E}=\begin{pmatrix} 1 & 1 \\ -1 & -1 \end{pmatrix}, \qquad \mathbf{A}-\lambda_2\mathbf{E}=\begin{pmatrix} 1 & 1 \\ -1 & -1 \end{pmatrix},$$

and hence the eigenvectors of **A** must satisfy

$$(\mathbf{A}-\lambda_1\mathbf{E})\{k\}_1=\begin{pmatrix} 1 & 1 \\ -1 & -1 \end{pmatrix}\{k\}_1=\{0\}, \qquad \begin{pmatrix} 1 & 1 \\ -1 & -1 \end{pmatrix}\{k\}_2=\{0\}.$$

The solutions of these equations are

$$\{k\}_1=\alpha\begin{Bmatrix} -1 \\ 1 \end{Bmatrix}, \qquad \{k\}_2=\beta\begin{Bmatrix} -1 \\ 1 \end{Bmatrix},$$

so that $\mathsf{N}(\lambda_1)=\mathsf{N}(3)$ and $\mathsf{N}(\lambda_2)=\mathsf{N}(3)$ are both spanned by $\begin{Bmatrix} -1 \\ 1 \end{Bmatrix}$. The totality of eigenvectors of the matrix **A** thus spans only a 1-dimensional subspace of $\mathsf{M}_{2,1}$; we can not find 2 linearly independent eigenvectors and hence **A** is not a diagonalizable matrix. The reader should carefully note that nondiagonalizability of a matrix says only that there are less than n linearly independent eigenvectors of the matrix. This example has a one-dimensional subspace of eigenvectors, so that there is certainly no scarcity of eigenvectors, it is just that there are not two linearly independent eigenvectors of the matrix and this leads to the nondiagonalizability.

Let the matrix **A** be given by

$$\mathbf{A}=\frac{1}{2}\begin{pmatrix} 2 & 0 & 0 \\ 0 & 3 & -1 \\ 0 & -1 & 3 \end{pmatrix},$$

then

$$\mathbf{A}-\lambda\mathbf{E}=\frac{1}{2}\begin{pmatrix} 2-2\lambda & 0 & 0 \\ 0 & 3-2\lambda & -1 \\ 0 & -1 & 3-2\lambda \end{pmatrix}$$

and hence

$$p(\lambda)=\det(\mathbf{A}-\lambda\mathbf{E})=(1-\lambda)(\lambda-1)(\lambda-2).$$

Thus, we have

$$\lambda_1=\lambda_2=1, \quad \lambda_3=2;$$

$$\mathbf{A}-\lambda_1\mathbf{E}=\mathbf{A}-\lambda_2\mathbf{E}=\frac{1}{2}\begin{pmatrix}0 & 0 & 0\\ 0 & 1 & -1\\ 0 & -1 & 1\end{pmatrix},$$

$$\mathbf{A}-\lambda_3\mathbf{E}=\frac{1}{2}\begin{pmatrix}-2 & 0 & 0\\ 0 & -1 & -1\\ 0 & -1 & -1\end{pmatrix},$$

and

$$\operatorname{rank}(\mathbf{A}-\mathbf{E})=1, \qquad \operatorname{rank}(\mathbf{A}-2\mathbf{E})=2.$$

Since $\operatorname{rank}(\mathbf{A}-\mathbf{E})=\operatorname{rank}(\mathbf{A}-\lambda_1\mathbf{E})=1$, we have

$$\dim(\mathsf{N}(\lambda_1))=\dim(\mathsf{N}(1))=2, \ \dim(\mathsf{N}(\lambda_3))=\dim(\mathsf{N}(2))=1.$$

It is a straightforward calculation to show that $\begin{Bmatrix}1\\0\\0\end{Bmatrix}$ and $\begin{Bmatrix}0\\1\\1\end{Bmatrix}$ form a basis for $\mathsf{N}(1)$ and that a basis for $\mathsf{N}(2)$ is $\begin{Bmatrix}0\\1\\-1\end{Bmatrix}$. This tells us that

$$\lambda_1=1, \ \lambda_2=1, \ \lambda_3=2$$

$$\{k\}_1=\begin{Bmatrix}1\\0\\0\end{Bmatrix}, \ \{k\}_2=\begin{Bmatrix}0\\1\\1\end{Bmatrix}, \ \{k\}_3=\begin{Bmatrix}0\\1\\-1\end{Bmatrix}.$$

Since $\{k\}_1$, $\{k\}_2$ and $\{k\}_3$ are linearly independent, $\mathbf{A}$ is diagonalizable and

$$\mathbf{K}=\begin{pmatrix}1 & 0 & 0\\ 0 & 1 & 1\\ 0 & 1 & -1\end{pmatrix}$$

is such that

$$\mathbf{K}^{-1}\mathbf{A}\,\mathbf{K}=\mathbf{D}(1,1,2).$$

Since a real polynomial need not have real roots, we must be prepared to consider instances in which the characteristic polynomial of a matrix $\mathbf{A}$ has complex roots. In other words, an eigenvalue of a matrix can be a complex number. If $\mathbf{A}$ is a real n-by-n matrix, then the characteristic polynomial $p(\lambda)$ of $\mathbf{A}$ will be an nth-order polynomial with real coefficients.

Thus, if $\lambda=\alpha+i\beta$ is a complex root of $p(\lambda)$, then $\bar{\lambda}=\alpha-i\beta$ must also be a complex root of $p(\lambda)$. Hence, *if λ is a complex eigenvalue of* **A** *then its complex conjugate $\bar{\lambda}$ is also an eigenvalue of* **A**. We can actually go further, for suppose that $\{k\}$ is an eigenvector associated with the complex eigenvalue λ. We then have

$$\mathbf{A}\{k\}=\lambda\{k\}. \tag{12.24}$$

Since **A** is real and λ is complex, $\{k\}$ must be complex. If we take the complex conjugate of both sides of Eq. (12.24), we obtain

$$\bar{\mathbf{A}}\{\bar{k}\}=\bar{\lambda}\{\bar{k}\}.$$

But, **A** is a real matrix so that $\mathbf{A}=\bar{\mathbf{A}}$, and we obtain

$$\mathbf{A}\{\bar{k}\}=\bar{\lambda}\{\bar{k}\}. \tag{12.25}$$

If $\{k\}$ is an eigenvector of a real matrix **A** *associated with a complex eigenvalue λ, then $\{\bar{k}\}$ is an eigenvector of* **A** *associated with the eigenvalue $\bar{\lambda}$.* Thus, if we have a complex eigenvalue and an associated eigenvector, then we can obtain another eigenvalue and an associated eigenvector by simply taking complex conjugates. This, in effect cuts the work in half whenever we have complex eigenvalues.

We illustrate these ideas with the following example. Let the matrix **A** be $\begin{pmatrix} 0 & 1 \\ -1 & 0 \end{pmatrix}$, so that the eigenvalues are the roots of

$$p(\lambda)=\begin{vmatrix} -\lambda & 1 \\ -1 & -\lambda \end{vmatrix}=\lambda^2+1,$$

that is $\lambda_1=i$ and $\lambda_2=-i$ where $i=\sqrt{-1}$. Remembering that $i^2=-1$ and that $\frac{1}{i}=\frac{1}{i}\times\frac{i}{i}=\frac{i}{i^2}=-i$, row reduction gives

$$(\mathbf{A}-\lambda_1\mathbf{E})_R=(\mathbf{A}-i\mathbf{E})_R=\begin{pmatrix} 1 & i \\ 0 & 0 \end{pmatrix}, \qquad (\mathbf{A}-\lambda_2\mathbf{E})_R=\begin{pmatrix} 1 & -i \\ 0 & 0 \end{pmatrix},$$

and we have

$$\{k\}_1=\alpha\begin{Bmatrix} -i \\ 1 \end{Bmatrix}, \qquad \{k\}_2=\beta\begin{Bmatrix} i \\ 1 \end{Bmatrix}.$$

For $\alpha=\beta=1$, $\{k\}_1$ and $\{k\}_2$ are linearly independent,

$$\mathbf{K}=\begin{pmatrix} -i & i \\ 1 & 1 \end{pmatrix}, \qquad \mathbf{K}^{-1}=\frac{1}{2}\begin{pmatrix} i & 1 \\ -i & 1 \end{pmatrix}, \text{ and}$$

$$\mathbf{K}^{-1}\mathbf{A}\,\mathbf{K}=\frac{1}{2}\begin{pmatrix} i & 1 \\ -i & 1 \end{pmatrix}\begin{pmatrix} 0 & 1 \\ -1 & 0 \end{pmatrix}\begin{pmatrix} -i & i \\ 1 & 1 \end{pmatrix}=\begin{pmatrix} i & 0 \\ 0 & -i \end{pmatrix}=\mathbf{D}(i,-i)$$

$$=\mathbf{D}(\lambda_1,\lambda_2).$$

Hence, the matrix **A** is diagonalizable but **A** has complex eigenvalues and the matrix **K** has complex numbers as its entries.

For the next example, we take

$$\mathbf{A}=\begin{pmatrix} 1 & 1 & 0 & 0 \\ -1 & 1 & 0 & 0 \\ 0 & 0 & 1 & -1 \\ 0 & 0 & 1 & 1 \end{pmatrix}; \qquad \begin{aligned} p(\lambda) &= \det(\mathbf{A}-\lambda\mathbf{E}) \\ &= (\lambda^2-2\lambda+2)^2 \end{aligned}$$

$$\lambda_1=\lambda_2=1+i, \;\; \lambda_3=\lambda_4=1-i,$$

$$\lambda_1=\lambda_2=\bar{\lambda}_3=\bar{\lambda}_4;$$

$$\mathbf{A}-\lambda_1\mathbf{E}=\begin{pmatrix} -i & 1 & 0 & 0 \\ -1 & -i & 0 & 0 \\ 0 & 0 & -i & -1 \\ 0 & 0 & 1 & -i \end{pmatrix},$$

$$\mathbf{A}-\lambda_3\mathbf{E}=\begin{pmatrix} i & 1 & 0 & 0 \\ -1 & i & 0 & 0 \\ 0 & 0 & i & -1 \\ 0 & 0 & 1 & i \end{pmatrix},$$

so that

$$(\mathbf{A}-\lambda_1\mathbf{E})=(\mathbf{A}-\lambda_2\mathbf{E})=(\overline{\mathbf{A}-\lambda_3\mathbf{E}})=(\overline{\mathbf{A}-\lambda_4\mathbf{E}})=(\mathbf{A}-\bar{\lambda}_3\mathbf{E})=(\mathbf{A}-\bar{\lambda}_4\mathbf{E});$$

$$(\mathbf{A}-\lambda_1\mathbf{E})_R=\begin{pmatrix} 1 & i & 0 & 0 \\ 0 & 0 & 1 & -i \\ 0 & 0 & 0 & 0 \\ 0 & 0 & 0 & 0 \end{pmatrix},$$

$$(\mathbf{A}-\lambda_3\mathbf{E})_R=\begin{pmatrix} 1 & -i & 0 & 0 \\ 0 & 0 & 1 & i \\ 0 & 0 & 0 & 0 \\ 0 & 0 & 0 & 0 \end{pmatrix},$$

$$(\mathbf{A}-\lambda_1\mathbf{E})_R=(\mathbf{A}-\lambda_2\mathbf{E})_R=(\overline{\mathbf{A}-\lambda_3\mathbf{E}})_R=(\overline{\mathbf{A}-\lambda_4\mathbf{E}})_R.$$

For $\lambda_1=\lambda_2=1+i$, $(\mathbf{A}-\lambda_1\mathbf{E})_R\{k\}_1=\{0\}$ implies

$$\{k\}_1=\alpha\begin{Bmatrix} -i \\ 1 \\ 0 \\ 0 \end{Bmatrix}+\beta\begin{Bmatrix} 0 \\ 0 \\ i \\ 1 \end{Bmatrix}$$

and for $\lambda_3=\lambda_4=1-i$, $(\mathbf{A}-\lambda_3\mathbf{E})_R\{k\}_3=\{0\}$ implies

$$\{k\}_3=\gamma\begin{Bmatrix} i \\ 1 \\ 0 \\ 0 \end{Bmatrix}+\delta\begin{Bmatrix} 0 \\ 0 \\ -i \\ 1 \end{Bmatrix}.$$

We can therefore take

$$\lambda_1=\lambda_2=1+i,\ \ \lambda_3=\lambda_4=1-i,$$

$$\{k\}_1=\begin{Bmatrix}-i\\1\\0\\0\end{Bmatrix},\ \ \{k\}_2=\begin{Bmatrix}0\\0\\i\\1\end{Bmatrix},$$

$$\{k\}_3=\begin{Bmatrix}i\\1\\0\\0\end{Bmatrix},\ \ \{k\}_4=\begin{Bmatrix}0\\0\\-i\\1\end{Bmatrix};$$

$$\lambda_1=\bar{\lambda}_3,\ \ \{k\}_1=\{\bar{k}\}_3;\ \ \lambda_2=\bar{\lambda}_4,\ \ \{k\}_2=\{\bar{k}\}_4;$$

$$\mathbf{K}=\begin{pmatrix}-i & 0 & i & 0\\ 1 & 0 & 1 & 0\\ 0 & i & 0 & -i\\ 0 & 1 & 0 & 1\end{pmatrix},$$

$$\mathbf{K}^{-1}=\frac{1}{2}\begin{pmatrix}i & 1 & 0 & 0\\ 0 & 0 & -i & 1\\ -i & 1 & 0 & 0\\ 0 & 0 & i & 1\end{pmatrix}.$$

As a final example, we take

$$\mathbf{A}=\begin{pmatrix}8 & 56 & -8 & -20\\ 0 & -7 & 0 & 5\\ 4 & 25 & -4 & -7\\ 0 & -10 & 0 & 8\end{pmatrix}.$$

We then have

$$p(\lambda)=\det(\mathbf{A}-\lambda\mathbf{E})=(\lambda-4)(\lambda+2)\lambda(\lambda-3),$$

so that

$$\lambda_1=4,\ \ \lambda_2=-2,\ \ \lambda_3=0,\ \ \lambda_4=3,$$

$$\{k\}_1=\begin{Bmatrix}2\\0\\1\\0\end{Bmatrix},\ \ \{k\}_2=\begin{Bmatrix}-6\\1\\-3\\1\end{Bmatrix};$$

$$\{k\}_3=\begin{Bmatrix}1\\0\\1\\0\end{Bmatrix},\ \ \{k\}_4=\begin{Bmatrix}-8\\1\\-3\\2\end{Bmatrix}.$$

Thus

$$\mathbf{K}=\begin{pmatrix} 2 & -6 & 1 & -8 \\ 0 & 1 & 0 & 1 \\ 1 & -3 & 1 & -3 \\ 0 & 1 & 0 & 2 \end{pmatrix}, \quad \mathbf{K}^{-1}=\begin{pmatrix} 1 & 1 & -1 & 2 \\ 0 & 2 & 0 & -1 \\ -1 & 2 & 2 & -2 \\ 0 & -1 & 0 & 1 \end{pmatrix},$$

and $\mathbf{K}^{-1}\mathbf{AK}=\mathbf{D}(4, -2, 0, 3)$.

We conclude this lecture with the demonstration of the following important fact. *If* $\mathbf{A}$ *and* $\mathbf{B}$ *are similar matrices* (that is, $\mathbf{K}^{-1}\mathbf{AK}=\mathbf{B}$) then $\mathbf{A}$ *and* $\mathbf{B}$ *have the same characteristic polynomial and the same eigenvalues.* We first recall that $\det(\mathbf{K}^{-1}\mathbf{WK})=\det(\mathbf{K}^{-1})\det(\mathbf{W})\det(\mathbf{K})=\det(\mathbf{W})$. We thus have $\det(\mathbf{A}-\lambda\mathbf{E})=\det(\mathbf{K}^{-1}(\mathbf{A}-\lambda\mathbf{E})\mathbf{K})=\det(\mathbf{K}^{-1}\mathbf{AK}-\lambda\mathbf{E})=\det(\mathbf{B}-\lambda\mathbf{E})$, and hence the characteristic polynomial of $\mathbf{A}$ is the same as the characteristic polynomial of $\mathbf{B}$ whenever $\mathbf{A}$ and $\mathbf{B}$ are similar.

Problems

12.1. For each of the matrices $\mathbf{A}$ given below,

(i) Find the characteristic polynomial and calculate all distinct eigenvalues $\lambda_1, \ldots, \lambda_p$;

(ii) Obtain the dimension of the solution space $N(\lambda_i)$ of the system $(\mathbf{A}-\lambda_i\mathbf{E})\{k\}=0$, $i=1, \ldots, p$;

(iii) Give a basis for $N(\lambda_i)$, $i=1, \ldots, p$;

(iv) Is $\mathbf{A}$ diagonalizable? If it is, write a matrix of eigenvectors $\mathbf{K}$ and a diagonal matrix $\mathbf{D}(\lambda_1, \ldots, \lambda_p)$ so that $\mathbf{K}^{-1}\mathbf{AK}=\mathbf{D}(\lambda_1, \ldots, \lambda_p)$:

(a) $\begin{pmatrix} 8 & -3 \\ 8 & -2 \end{pmatrix}$, (b) $\begin{pmatrix} 1 & 4 \\ 2 & -1 \end{pmatrix}$, (c) $\begin{pmatrix} 4 & 2 \\ -2 & 8 \end{pmatrix}$,

(d) $\begin{pmatrix} 2 & -5 \\ 4 & -2 \end{pmatrix}$, (e) $\begin{pmatrix} 3 & \frac{1}{2} & -1 \\ -12 & -4 & 6 \\ -4 & -2 & 3 \end{pmatrix}$, (f) $\begin{pmatrix} 5 & -6 & -14 \\ 3 & -6 & -21 \\ -1 & 3 & 10 \end{pmatrix}$,

(g) $\begin{pmatrix} 1 & 0 & 0 \\ -\frac{1}{2} & 0 & 1 \\ -1 & -2 & 3 \end{pmatrix}$, (h) $\begin{pmatrix} 0 & 1 & \frac{1}{2} \\ 0 & 1 & 0 \\ 2 & -2 & 0 \end{pmatrix}$.

12.2. Write fully the systems of ordinary differential equations $d\{x(t)\}/dt = \mathbf{A}\{x(t)\}$ when the matrix $\mathbf{A}$ is as in 12.1.

12.3. If α is a given number, find the maximum number of linearly independent eigenvectors of the following matrices and state whether they are diagonalizable:

(a) $\begin{pmatrix} \alpha & 1 \\ 0 & \alpha \end{pmatrix}$, (b) $\begin{pmatrix} \alpha & 1 & 0 \\ 0 & \alpha & 0 \\ 0 & 0 & \alpha \end{pmatrix}$, (c) $\begin{pmatrix} \alpha & 1 & 0 \\ 0 & \alpha & 1 \\ 0 & 0 & \alpha \end{pmatrix}$,

(d) $\begin{pmatrix} \alpha & 0 & 0 \\ 0 & \alpha & 0 \\ 0 & 0 & \alpha \end{pmatrix}$, (e) $\begin{pmatrix} \alpha & 0 & 1 \\ 0 & \alpha & 0 \\ 0 & 0 & \alpha \end{pmatrix}$, (f) $\begin{pmatrix} \alpha & 1 & 0 & 0 \\ 0 & \alpha & 0 & 0 \\ 0 & 0 & \alpha & 1 \\ 0 & 0 & 0 & \alpha \end{pmatrix}$.

12.4. Show that if a nondiagonal matrix has only one distinct eigenvalue, the matrix is not diagonalizable.

12.5. Show that the characteristic polynomial $p(\lambda) = |\mathbf{A} - \lambda\mathbf{E}|$ of the n-by-n matrix $\mathbf{A}$ is of the nth degree.

12.6. Show that $\mathbf{A}$ and $\mathbf{A}^T$ have the same characteristic polynomial and hence the same characteristic roots.

12.7. Show that if λ is a characteristic root of the nonsingular matrix $\mathbf{A}$, then λ^{-1} is a characteristic root of $\mathbf{A}^{-1}$.

12.8. If $p(\lambda)$ is the characteristic polynomial of the n-by-n matrix $\mathbf{A}$, show that

$$|\mathbf{A} - \lambda\mathbf{E}| = p(\lambda) = (-\lambda)^n + (-\lambda)^{n-1}\mathrm{tr}\mathbf{A} + (-\lambda)^{n-2}\Sigma M_{ij} + (-\lambda)^{n-3}\Sigma M_{ijk} + \cdots + |\mathbf{A}|$$

where $\Sigma M_{i_1 \ldots i_k}$ is the sum of all the principal minors of $|\mathbf{A}|$ of order k. [See problem 11.6.]

12.9. Show that

(i) A matrix is singular if and only if one of its characteristic roots is zero.
(ii) The trace of a matrix is equal to the sum of its characteristic roots.
(iii) The sum of the characteristic roots of a skew-symmetric matrix is zero.

[Use the previous problem and the relations between the roots and the coefficients of a polynomial.]

12.10. If $\mathbf{A}$ and $\mathbf{B}$ are similar n-by-n matrices, show that the sum of all the principal minors of $|\mathbf{A}|$ of order k, $1 \leq k \leq n$, equals the sum of all principal minors of $|\mathbf{B}|$ of the same order.

12.11. Show that if $\mathbf{A}$ is an orthogonal matrix then $|\mathbf{A}| = \pm 1$. [Use (9.31).] The orthogonal matrix $\mathbf{A}$ is called **proper** or **improper** if $|\mathbf{A}| = 1$ or $|\mathbf{A}| = -1$, respectively.

12.12. Let c_{ij} denote the cofactor of the element a_{ij} of $|\mathbf{A}|$. If $\mathbf{A}$ is a proper (improper) orthogonal matrix, show that $a_{ij} = c_{ij}$ $(a_{ij} = -c_{ij})$. [Use (9.32) and (11.10).]

12.13. Show that if λ is a characteristic root of the orthogonal matrix $\mathbf{A}$, then λ^{-1} is also a characteristic root. [See problems 12.6 and 12.7.]

12.14. Show that every characteristic root of an orthogonal matrix has unit modulus. [Multiply (12.24) with the transpose of (12.25).]

12.15. If **A** is an improper orthogonal matrix, show that -1 is a characteristic root of **A**. [Consider the determinants of $\mathbf{A}^T(\mathbf{A}+\mathbf{E}) = (\mathbf{A}+\mathbf{E})^T$.]

12.16. Let **A** be a n-by-n orthogonal matrix. Show that if **A** is proper and n odd or if **A** is improper and n is even, then 1 is a characteristic root of **A**. [Consider the determinants of $\mathbf{A}^T(\mathbf{A}-\mathbf{E}) = -(\mathbf{A}-\mathbf{E})^T$.]

12.17. If **A** is a proper two-by-two orthogonal matrix, show that there exists a unique angle θ, $0 \leq \theta \leq 2\pi$ such that

$$\mathbf{A} = \begin{pmatrix} \cos\theta & -\sin\theta \\ \sin\theta & \cos\theta \end{pmatrix}.$$

12.18. Show that the only two-by-two proper orthogonal matrices with real characteristic roots are

$$\begin{pmatrix} 1 & 0 \\ 0 & 1 \end{pmatrix}, \begin{pmatrix} -1 & 0 \\ 0 & -1 \end{pmatrix}.$$

12.19. Show that any rotation in the plane can be represented by a proper two-by-two orthogonal matrix, i.e. if the point **x** is rotated about the origin to the new position **y** then $\{y\} = \mathbf{A}\{x\}$ where **A** is a proper orthogonal matrix. [See problem 9.20.]

12.20. Show that every proper two-by-two orthogonal matrix **A** represents a rotation in the plane, i.e. if $\{y\} = \mathbf{A}\{x\}$, then we obtain the point **y** if we rotate the point **x** about the origin through an angle θ, $0 \leq \theta \leq 2\pi$, uniquely determined by **A**.

12.21. If **A** is an improper two-by-two orthogonal matrix, show that there exists a unique angle ϕ, $0 \leq \phi \leq \pi$, such that

$$\mathbf{A} = \begin{pmatrix} \cos 2\phi & \sin 2\phi \\ \sin 2\phi & -\cos 2\phi \end{pmatrix}.$$

Use this result to conclude that **A** represents a reflexion on that line through the origin which forms an angle ϕ with the positive axis OX_1.

12.22. Show that the characteristic roots of an improper two-by-two orthogonal matrix are ± 1.

12.23. Show that if **A** is an improper orthogonal matrix, then ϕ, **B**, **C** can be determined so that

$$\mathbf{A} = \begin{pmatrix} \cos 2\phi & \sin 2\phi \\ \sin 2\phi & -\cos 2\phi \end{pmatrix}\mathbf{B} = \mathbf{C}\begin{pmatrix} \cos 2\phi & \sin 2\phi \\ \sin 2\phi & -\cos 2\phi \end{pmatrix},$$

where $0 \leq \phi \leq \pi$ and **B**, **C** are proper orthogonal matrices. Use this result to conclude that a rotation followed by a reflexion on a line through the origin, or a reflexion followed by a rotation, are represented by an improper orthogonal matrix. In either case, if the matrix is given, *either* the line of reflexion *or* the angle of rotation can be specified.

12.24. Let OX_i, OY_i be two cartesian systems of axes in E_3 and **P** the matrix of cosines of the second system with respect to the first. If **P** is a proper orthogonal matrix, we say that **the two systems have the same orientation**. Show that if two systems have the same orientation they can be moved, remaining orthogonal, so as to coincide with each other.

12.25. Let OX_i and OZ_i be two orthogonal cartesian systems, not necessarily distinct, with the same orientation. If P is a point and Q its projecton on Z_2OZ_3, we say that P is **rotated about OZ_1 through an angle** θ if the distance OP remains constant and Q is rotated about O through the angle θ. Show that if the point $\mathbf{x}$ of E_3 is rotated through the angle θ about the OX_i-axis, its new coordinates y_1, y_2, y_3 are given respectively by

$$\{y\} = \mathbf{O}_{i,\theta}\{x\},$$

where the orthogonal matrix $\mathbf{O}_{i,\theta}$ is given on page 110.

LECTURE 13

Diagonalization of Matrices

Multiplicity of roots of the characteristic polynomial • Dimension of the subspace spanned by the eigenvectors associated with an eigenvalue • Necessary and sufficient conditions for the diagonalizability of a matrix • Matrices of eigenvectors • Problems

We now turn to the question of deciding when a given matrix is diagonalizable; that is, *when does* $\mathbf{A} \in \mathsf{M}_{n,n}$ *have* n *linearly independent eigenvectors?* If $\mathbf{A}$ is an n-by-n matrix, then $p(\lambda)$, the characteristic polynomial of $\mathbf{A}$, is an nth-order polynomial of λ and it will have n roots by the fundamental theorem of algebra (that is, there will be n numbers, the eigenvalues of $\mathbf{A}$, that satisfy $p(\lambda)=0$. There is nothing, however, that says that all of the roots of the characteristic polynomial have to be different numbers, for example $p(\lambda)=(\lambda-1)^2(\lambda-2)(\lambda+3)^3$ has the roots $\lambda_1=\lambda_2=1$, $\lambda_3=2$, and $\lambda_4=\lambda_5=\lambda_6=-3$. If we have r roots of the characteristic polynomial equal to the same number α, then the number α is said to be a root, or eigenvalue, of **multiplicity** r. Thus, in the above example, one is a root of multiplicity two, -3 is a root of multiplicity three, and 2 is a root of multiplicity one. A root of multiplicity one is referred to as a **simple** root. We thus have to face the fact that there will be fewer than n distinct numbers which are roots of the characteristic polynomial of $\mathbf{A} \in \mathsf{M}_{n,n}$ whenever there are roots of multiplicity greater than one. If all of the roots of $p(\lambda)$ are simple, however, then there are n distinct numbers that are the roots of the characteristic polynomial of $\mathbf{A} \in \mathsf{M}_{n,n}$ and hence the eigenvalues of $\mathbf{A}$ will be n distinct numbers.

The reason why we have to consider whether or not the characteristic polynomial has simple roots or not is that this information tells us a great deal about whether a matrix is diagonalizable or not. To see why this is the case, we first establish the following result.

If $\lambda_1, \ldots, \lambda_r$, $1 \le r \le n$, *are the distinct eigenvalues of the matrix* $\mathbf{A} \in \mathsf{M}_{n,n}$, d_i, $1 \le i \le r$, *is the dimension of the solution space* $\mathsf{N}(\lambda_i)$ *of* $(\mathbf{A}-\lambda_i\mathbf{E})\{x\}=0$ *and* $\{k\}_{p,1}, \ldots, \{k\}_{p,d_p}$ *are linearly independent eigenvectors associated with the eigenvalue* λ_p, $1 \le p \le r$, *then the* $d_1 + \ldots + d_r$

eigenvectors

$$\{k\}_{1,1}, \ldots, \{k\}_{1,d_1}, \ldots, \{k\}_{r,1}, \ldots, \{k\}_{r,d_r} \qquad (13.1)$$

are linearly independent.

We first note that because d_i is the dimension of the solution space of $(\mathbf{A}-\lambda_i\mathbf{E})\{x\}=0$ we can indeed find d_i linearly independent eigenvectors associated with the eigenvalue λ_i. Suppose now that the italicized statement was not true and let $\{k\}_{p,q+1}$ be the first eigenvector of the set (13.1) that can be expressed linearly in terms of the eigenvectors preceding it. (A similar proof applies if we happen to have $q=0$.) We would then have

$$\begin{aligned}\{k\}_{p,q+1}=c_{1,1}\{k\}_{1,1}+ \ldots +c_{1,d_1}\{k\}_{1,d_1}+ \ldots +\\ c_{p-1,1}\{k\}_{p-1,1}+ \ldots +c_{p-1,d_{p-1}}\{k\}_{p-1,d_{p-1}}\\ +c_{p,1}\{k\}_{p,1}+ \ldots +c_{p,q}\{k\}_{p,q}.\end{aligned} \qquad (13.2)$$

If we multiply both sides of Eq. (13.2) by $(\mathbf{A}-\lambda_p\mathbf{E})$, we obtain

$$\begin{aligned}\mathbf{0}=(\mathbf{A}-\lambda_p\mathbf{E})\{k\}_{p,q+1}=c_{1,1}(\mathbf{A}-\lambda_p\mathbf{E})\{k\}_{1,1}\\ + \ldots +c_{1,d_1}(\mathbf{A}-\lambda_p\mathbf{E})\{k\}_{1,d_1}+ \ldots +c_{p-1,1}(\mathbf{A}-\lambda_p\mathbf{E})\{k\}_{p-1,1}\\ + \ldots +c_{p-1,d_{p-1}}(\mathbf{A}-\lambda_p\mathbf{E})\{k\}_{p-1,d_{p-1}}+c_{p,1}(\mathbf{A}-\lambda_p\mathbf{E})\{k\}_{p,1}\\ + \ldots +c_{p,q}(\mathbf{A}-\lambda_p\mathbf{E})\{k\}_{p,q}=c_{1,1}(\lambda_1-\lambda_p)\{k\}_{1,1}\\ + \ldots +c_{1,d_1}(\lambda_1-\lambda_p)\{k\}_{1,d_1}+ \ldots +c_{p-1,1}(\lambda_{p-1}-\lambda_p)\{k\}_{p-1,1}\\ + \ldots +c_{p-1,d_{p-1}}(\lambda_{p-1}-\lambda_p)\{k\}_{p-1,d_{p-1}}.\end{aligned}$$

Since we have assumed $\{k\}_{1,1}, \ldots, \{k\}_{p,q}$ are linearly independent, we must have

$$c_{1,1}(\lambda_1-\lambda_p)= \ldots =c_{p-1,d_{p-1}}(\lambda_{p-1}-\lambda_p)=0.$$

Hence, since $\lambda_1, \ldots, \lambda_p$ are distinct eigenvalues, we must also have $c_{1,1}= \ldots =c_{p-1,d_{p-1}}=0$. Thus, Eq. (13.2) becomes

$$\{k\}_{p,q+1}=c_{p,1}\{k\}_{p,1}+ \ldots +c_{p,q}\{k\}_{p,q},$$

which says that $\{k\}_{p,1}, \ldots, \{k\}_{p,q+1}$ are linearly dependent. This is contrary to our assumption that $\{k\}_{p,1}, \ldots, \{k\}_{p,d_p}$ are linearly independent eigenvectors associated with λ_p. We have thus arrived at a contradiction by assuming that the result was false and hence the result is established.

Each of the $d_1+ \ldots +d_r$ linearly independent eigenvectors listed in Eq. (13.1) is an element of V_n and in V_n we cannot have more than n linearly independent vectors. Thus we have also proved that *if* $\lambda_1, \ldots, \lambda_r$, $1\leq r\leq n$, *are the distinct eigenvalues of the matrix* $\mathbf{A}\in\mathsf{M}_{n,n}$ *and* d_i, $1\leq i\leq r$, *is the dimension of the solution space of* $(\mathbf{A}-\lambda_i\mathbf{E})\{x\}=0$ *then* $d_1+d_2+ \ldots +d_r\leq n$.

For each eigenvalue λ_i we can find d_i and not more than d_i linearly independent eigenvectors and we have already proved that these $d_1+\ .\ .\ .\ +d_r$ eigenvectors are linearly independent. On the other hand, an n-by-n matrix is diagonalizable if and only if we can find n linearly independent eigenvectors. Thus *if* $\lambda_1,\ .\ .\ .\ ,\ \lambda_r,\ 1\leq r\leq n$, *are the distinct eigenvalues of the matrix* $\mathbf{A}\in \mathsf{M}_{n,n}$ *and* $d_i,\ 1\leq i\leq r$, *is the dimension of the solution space of* $(\mathbf{A}-\lambda_i\mathbf{E})\{x\}=0$ *then the matrix* $\mathbf{A}$ *is diagonalizable if and only if* $d_1+\ .\ .\ .\ +d_n=n$. If we wish to use the above theorem to find whether a matrix $\mathbf{A}$ is diagonalizable we shall have to obtain all distinct eigenvalues λ_i, then determine the dimension d_i of the solution space of each system $(\mathbf{A}-\lambda_i\mathbf{E})\{x\}=0$ and finally check whether $d_1+\ .\ .\ .\ +d_r=n$. This procedure is often simplified by the use of the following theorem which we will not prove (see problem 13.6). *If* λ_i *is an eigenvalue of the matrix* $\mathbf{A}\in \mathsf{M}_{n,n}$, m_i *its multiplicity and* d_i *the dimension of the solution space of* $(\mathbf{A}-\lambda_i\mathbf{E})\{x\}=0$ *then* $d_i\leq m_i$. Since $m_1+\ .\ .\ .\ +m_r=n$ and $d_i\leq m_i$, $1\leq i\leq r$, it follows that $d_1+\ .\ .\ .\ +d_r=n$ if and only if $d_i=m_i,\ 1\leq i\leq r$. Thus we have the following theorem: *If* $\lambda_1,\ .\ .\ .\ ,\ \lambda_r,\ 1\leq r\leq n$, *are the distinct eigenvalues of the matrix* $\mathbf{A}\in \mathsf{M}_{n,n}$, $m_i,\ 1\leq i\leq r$, *is the multiplicity of the root* λ_i *of the characteristic polynomial of* $\mathbf{A}$ *and* d_i *is the dimension of the solution space* $\mathsf{N}(\lambda_i)$ *of* $(\mathbf{A}-\lambda_i\mathbf{E})\{x\}=0$ *then the matrix* $\mathbf{A}$ *is diagonalizable if and only if* $m_i=d_i,\ 1\leq i\leq r$. In order to prove that a matrix is diagonalizable, by the use of the above theorem, we have to make sure that $m_i=d_i$ for *each* distinct root. On the other hand the proof of nondiagonalizability is immediate as soon as we have $d_i<m_i$ for some i.

If $r=n$, that is, if all the roots of the characteristic polynomial are distinct, then the number of linearly independent eigenvectors is n and the n-by-n matrix $\mathbf{A}$ is diagonalizable. Thus *if a matrix* $\mathbf{A}\in \mathsf{M}_{n,n}$ *has n distinct eigenvalues it is diagonalizable.*

The matrix $\mathbf{K}$ that diagonalizes $\mathbf{A}$ is a matrix whose columns are n linearly independent eigenvectors of $\mathbf{A}$. Thus, in constructing the matrix $\mathbf{K}$, all we have to do is to be sure to pick d_i linearly independent vectors from the subspace $\mathsf{N}(\lambda_i)$ that constitutes the solution space of $(\mathbf{A}-\lambda_i\mathbf{E})\times\{k\}=\{0\}$ for each value of i. This is always possible since $d_i=\dim(\mathsf{N}(\lambda_i))$. These d_i linearly independent eigenvectors constitute a basis for $\mathsf{N}(\lambda_i)$.

When $\mathbf{A}$ is diagonalizable, we refer to a matrix $\mathbf{K}$ such that $\mathbf{K}^{-1}\mathbf{A}\mathbf{K}=\mathbf{D}$ as a **matrix of eigenvectors** of $\mathbf{A}$. A matrix $\mathbf{A}$ can have many matrices $\mathbf{K}$ of eigenvectors. For example, we have a new matrix of eigenvectors if we multiply any column of $\mathbf{K}$ by a nonzero number. Thus, we can not speak of *the* matrix of eigenvectors of $\mathbf{A}$ (see problem 13.3 for a systematic method of finding new matrices of eigenvectors from a given one).

As an example of a nondiagonalizable n-by-n matrix, consider

$$\mathbf{A}=\begin{pmatrix} 5 & 1 & & & & 0 \\ & 5 & 1 & & & \\ & & 5 & 1 & & \\ & & & \ddots & \ddots & \\ & & & & 5 & 1 \\ 0 & & & & & 5 \end{pmatrix}, \quad \det(\mathbf{A}-\lambda\mathbf{E})=(5-\lambda)^n,$$

$$\lambda_1=\lambda_2= \ . \ . \ . \ =\lambda_n=5, \qquad m_1=n,$$

$\operatorname{rank}(\mathbf{A}-5\mathbf{E})=n-1$, and we have $d_1=n-\operatorname{rank}(\mathbf{A}-5\mathbf{E})=1$. This n-by-n matrix $\mathbf{A}$ thus has only a one-dimensional space of eigenvectors (i.e., $d_1=\dim(\mathsf{N}(5))=1$ and hence we can find only one linearly independent eigenvector of $\mathbf{A}$.

The matrix

$$\mathbf{A}=\begin{pmatrix} 1 & 1 & 0 & 0 \\ -1 & 1 & 0 & 0 \\ 0 & 0 & 1 & -1 \\ 0 & 0 & 1 & 1 \end{pmatrix}$$

(see page 146) has $m_1=2=d_1$ for $\lambda_1=1+i$ and $m_3=2=d_3$ for $\lambda_3=1-i$, and the matrix is diagonalizable as we have already shown in lecture twelve. If we have

$$\mathbf{A}=\begin{pmatrix} -1 & 1 & 2 \\ -1 & 1 & 1 \\ -2 & 1 & 3 \end{pmatrix}$$

then

$$\mathbf{A}-\lambda\mathbf{E}=\begin{pmatrix} -1-\lambda & 1 & 2 \\ -1 & 1-\lambda & 1 \\ -2 & 1 & 3-\lambda \end{pmatrix}$$

and $p(\lambda)=\det(\mathbf{A}-\lambda\mathbf{E})=(1-\lambda)^3$. Thus $\lambda_1=1$ and $m_1=3$. However,

$$(\mathbf{A}-\lambda_1\mathbf{E})=\begin{pmatrix} -2 & 1 & 2 \\ -1 & 0 & 1 \\ -2 & 1 & 2 \end{pmatrix},$$

so that

$$(\mathbf{A}-\lambda_1\mathbf{E})_R=\begin{pmatrix} 1 & 0 & -1 \\ 0 & 1 & 0 \\ 0 & 0 & 0 \end{pmatrix},$$

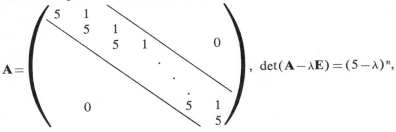

and $d_1=n-\text{rank}(\mathbf{A}-\lambda_1\mathbf{E})=3-2=1$. Thus $m_1=3\neq d_1=1$ and $\mathbf{A}$ is not diagonalizable. The only eigenvectors of $\mathbf{A}$ are

$$\{k\}=\alpha\begin{Bmatrix}1\\0\\1\end{Bmatrix}$$

and $\dim[\mathsf{N}(\lambda_1)]=1$ since $\mathsf{N}(\lambda_1)$ is spanned by $[1, 0, 1]^T$.

The multiplicity of the eigenvalues and the numbers d_i provide a convenient basis for classifying matrices. For example, we can have three basic kinds of matrices for $n=2$:

Type I. Matrices with two distinct eigenvalues and hence two linearly independent eigenvectors, $m_1=d_1=m_2=d_2=1$.

Type II. Matrices with an eigenvalue of multiplicity two and two linearly independent eigenvectors $m_1=2=d_1$ (these matrices are scalar matrices, and hence already diagonal).

Type III. Matrices with an eigenvalue of multiplicity two and with only one linearly independent eigenvector, $m_1=2$, $d_1=1$.

Types I and II are diagonalizable while type III is not. We leave it as an exercise to show that $\begin{pmatrix}1 & 1\\0 & 2\end{pmatrix}$ is of type I and $\begin{pmatrix}5 & 0\\1 & 5\end{pmatrix}$ is of type III.

Problems

13.1. For each of the following matrices $\mathbf{A}$:

(i) Find the characteristic polynomial.

(ii) Compute all distinct eigenvalues λ_i and give their corresponding multiplicities m_i.

(iii) By row-reducing the matrix $(\mathbf{A}-\lambda_i\mathbf{E})$ obtain the dimension d_i of the solution space of $(\mathbf{A}-\lambda_i\mathbf{E})\{x\}=\mathbf{0}$ and give a basis for it.

(iv) State whether $\mathbf{A}$ is diagonalizable. If it is, give two different matrices of eigenvectors $\mathbf{K}_1$, $\mathbf{K}_2$, and write fully the corresponding equations $\mathbf{K}^{-1}\mathbf{AK} = \mathbf{D}(\lambda_1, \ldots, \lambda_n)$.

(a) $\begin{pmatrix}-2 & 1\\-12 & 5\end{pmatrix}$, (b) $\begin{pmatrix}2 & -3\\1 & -2\end{pmatrix}$, (c) $\begin{pmatrix}1 & -1\\1 & 1\end{pmatrix}$,

(d) $\begin{pmatrix}-2 & 2\\-6 & 5\end{pmatrix}$, (e) $\begin{pmatrix}2 & -3\\3 & 8\end{pmatrix}$, (f) $\begin{pmatrix}-2 & 4\\-3 & 5\end{pmatrix}$,

(g) $\begin{pmatrix}-5 & 9\\-3 & 7\end{pmatrix}$, (h) $\begin{pmatrix}2 & 1\\-1 & 2\end{pmatrix}$, (i) $\begin{pmatrix}10 & -4 & 2\\-12 & 8 & -5\\-48 & 24 & -14\end{pmatrix}$,

(j) $\begin{pmatrix} 19 & -8 & -12 \\ 32 & -13 & -24 \\ 8 & -4 & -3 \end{pmatrix}$, (k) $\begin{pmatrix} 10 & -4 & 4 \\ -12 & 8 & -10 \\ -24 & 12 & -14 \end{pmatrix}$,

(l) $\begin{pmatrix} 0 & -1 & 1 \\ 1 & 0 & -1 \\ 0 & 0 & 1 \end{pmatrix}$, (m) $\begin{pmatrix} -5 & 18 & 42 \\ 6 & -17 & -42 \\ -3 & 9 & 22 \end{pmatrix}$,

(n) $\begin{pmatrix} 10 & -8 & 4 \\ -6 & 8 & -5 \\ -24 & 24 & -14 \end{pmatrix}$, (o) $\begin{pmatrix} 3 & -6 & -14 \\ 3 & -8 & -21 \\ -1 & 3 & 8 \end{pmatrix}$,

(p) $\begin{pmatrix} 10 & -2 & 2 \\ -24 & 8 & -10 \\ -48 & 12 & -14 \end{pmatrix}$, (q) $\begin{pmatrix} 1 & -1 & -2 \\ 1 & 1 & -1 \\ 0 & 0 & -1 \end{pmatrix}$,

(r) $\begin{pmatrix} 3 & -20 & -4 & 20 \\ 0 & 3 & 0 & -2 \\ 2 & -10 & -3 & 10 \\ 0 & 4 & 0 & -3 \end{pmatrix}$, (s) $\begin{pmatrix} 3 & -10 & -2 & 10 \\ 0 & 3 & 0 & -2 \\ 4 & -10 & -3 & 10 \\ 0 & 4 & 0 & -3 \end{pmatrix}$,

(t) $\begin{pmatrix} 1 & -2 & 0 & 8 \\ 0 & 1 & 0 & 0 \\ 0 & 3 & 1 & 7 \\ 0 & 6 & 0 & 1 \end{pmatrix}$, (u) $\begin{pmatrix} 3 & -10 & -4 & 20 \\ 0 & 3 & 0 & -4 \\ 2 & -5 & -3 & 10 \\ 0 & 2 & 0 & -3 \end{pmatrix}$.

13.2. Prove that if $(a-d)^2 + 4bc = 0$ and $b^2 + c^2 \neq 0$ the matrix $\begin{pmatrix} a & b \\ c & d \end{pmatrix}$ is not diagonalizable.

13.3. Let **A** be a n-by-n diagonalizable matrix with the distinct eigenvalues λ_1, λ_2 of multiplicities r and s, respectively, and $\mathbf{K} = [\{k\}_{1,1}, \ldots, \{k\}_{1,r}, \{k\}_{2,1}, \ldots, \{k\}_{2,s}]$ a matrix of eigenvectors of **A**. Show that if **G** is a matrix of eigenvectors of **A** then

$$\mathbf{G} = \mathbf{K}\begin{pmatrix} a_{11} & \ldots & a_{1r} & 0 & \ldots & 0 \\ \cdot & \cdots & \cdot & \cdot & \cdots & \cdot \\ a_{r1} & \ldots & a_{rr} & 0 & \ldots & 0 \\ 0 & \ldots & 0 & b_{11} & \ldots & b_{1s} \\ \cdot & \cdots & \cdot & \cdot & \cdots & \cdot \\ 0 & \ldots & 0 & b_{s1} & \ldots & b_{ss} \end{pmatrix}\mathbf{E}(i_1, \ldots, i_n)$$

where

$$\begin{pmatrix} a_{11} & \ldots & a_{1r} \\ \cdot & \cdots & \cdot \\ a_{r1} & \ldots & a_{rr} \end{pmatrix} \quad \text{and} \quad \begin{pmatrix} b_{11} & \ldots & b_{1s} \\ \cdot & \cdots & \cdot \\ b_{s1} & \ldots & b_{ss} \end{pmatrix}$$

are two nonsingular matrices. [See problems 11.13 and 11.15.]

13.4. Let $p(\lambda)$ be the characteristic polynomial of the n-by-n matrix **A**. Show that the characteristic polynomial of the matrix $\mathbf{A} - x\mathbf{E}$ is $p(\lambda + x)$.

13.5. Let λ_1 be an eigenvalue of multiplicity m_1 of the n-by-n matrix **A**. If $p(\lambda)$ is the characteristic polynomial of **A**, show that

(i) $p(\lambda) = (-1)^n(\lambda - \lambda_1)^{m_1}q(\lambda)$, where $q(\lambda_1) \neq 0$.

(ii) The characteristic polynomial of $\mathbf{A} - \lambda_1\mathbf{E}$ is

$$(-1)^n\lambda^{m_1}[\lambda^{n-m_1} + b_1\lambda^{n-m_1-1} + \ . \ . \ . + b_{n-m_1-1}\lambda + q(\lambda_1)].$$

(iii) There is at least one principal minor of order $n - m_1$ of the matrix $\mathbf{A} - \lambda_1\mathbf{E}$ which is different from zero. [Use problems 13.4 and 12.8.]

13.6. Let λ_1 be an eigenvalue of multiplicity m_1 of the n-by-n matrix $\mathbf{A}$. Show that

(i) $\text{rank}(\mathbf{A} - \lambda_1\mathbf{E}) \geq n - m_1$;

(ii) if d_1 is the dimension of the solution space of $(\mathbf{A} - \lambda_1\mathbf{E})\{x\} = 0$, then $d_1 \leq m_1$. This statement is usually referred to as the **rank-multiplicity theorem**. [See problems 11.11 and 13.5.]

13.7 If $\mathbf{A} \in \mathsf{M}_{3,3}$ is a proper orthogonal matrix, then show that its eigenvalues are 1, $\cos\alpha \pm i\sin\alpha$, $0 \leq \alpha \leq \pi$. The *unique* angle α is called the **angle of the proper orthogonal matrix A.**

13.8. A unit eigenvector associated with the eigenvalue 1 of a proper orthogonal matrix is called a **principal eigenvector** of the matrix. Let α be the angle and $\{p\}$ a principal eigenvector of the proper orthogonal matrix $\mathbf{A} \in \mathsf{M}_{3,3}$. If $\mathbf{P}$ is a proper orthogonal matrix, the first column of which is $\{p\}$, then show that

$$\mathbf{A} = \mathbf{P}\mathbf{O}_{1,\psi}\mathbf{P}^T$$

where $\psi = \alpha$ or $2\pi - \alpha$. [Prove $\mathbf{P}^T\mathbf{A}\mathbf{P}\{e\}_1 = \{e\}_1$ and deduce from the orthogonality of $\mathbf{P}^T\mathbf{A}\mathbf{P}$ and the theorem on p. 140 that $\mathbf{P}^T\mathbf{A}\mathbf{P} = \mathbf{O}_{1,\psi}$.]

13.9. Show that the angle ψ in problem 13.8 is uniquely determined by $\mathbf{A}$ and $\{p\}$.

13.10. If $\mathbf{A} \neq \mathbf{E}$ is a proper three-by-three orthogonal matrix, then show that the principal eigenvector of $\mathbf{A}$ is determined to within the factor ± 1. [Apply problem 13.8 to prove that 1 is a simple root. Then use problem 13.6.]

13.11. Let OP be an axis in E_3 with unit vector $\{p\}$. If the point with coordinates x_1, x_2, x_3 is rotated about the axis OP through the angle ψ and y_1, y_2, y_3 are the new coordinates of the point, then show that

(i) $\{y\} = \mathbf{P}\mathbf{O}_{1,\psi}\mathbf{P}^T\{x\}$,

where $\mathbf{P}$ is any proper orthogonal matrix with first column $\{p\}$ and $\mathbf{O}_{1,\psi}$ is the matrix given on page 110.

(ii) the matrix $\mathbf{P}\mathbf{O}_{1,\psi}\mathbf{P}^T$ is proper orthogonal and $\mathbf{P}\mathbf{O}_{1,\psi}\mathbf{P}^T$

$$= \begin{pmatrix} p_1{}^2(1-\cos\psi)+\cos\psi & p_2p_1(1-\cos\psi)-p_3\sin\psi & p_3p_1(1-\cos\psi)+p_2\sin\psi \\ p_1p_2(1-\cos\psi)+p_3\sin\psi & p_2{}^2(1-\cos\psi)+\cos\psi & p_3p_2(1-\cos\psi)-p_1\sin\psi \\ p_1p_3(1-\cos\psi)-p_2\sin\psi & p_2p_3(1-\cos\psi)+p_1\sin\psi & p_3{}^2(1-\cos\psi)+\cos\psi \end{pmatrix}.$$

Deduce that any rotation in E_3 is represented by a proper orthogonal matrix which depends only on the angle of rotation and the direction cosines of the axis of rotation. [Consider orthogonal cartesian axes *OP*, *OQ*, *OR* and use the problems 9.18 and 12.25.]

13.12. $R[\alpha, \mathbf{p}]$ will denote the rotation through an angle α about the axis *OP* with unit vector $\mathbf{p}$. Show that the rotations $R[\alpha, \mathbf{p}]$ and $R[2\pi - \alpha, -\mathbf{p}]$ are the same.

13.13. Let α be the angle and $\{p\}$ a principal eigenvector of the orthogonal matrix $\mathbf{A} \in \mathsf{M}_{3,3}$. Show that $\{y\} = \mathbf{A}\{x\}$ represents *either* the rotation $R[\alpha, \mathbf{p}]$ *or* the rotation $R[\alpha, -\mathbf{p}]$. [Use the problems 13.8 and 13.12.]

13.14. With the rotation $R[\alpha, \mathbf{p}]$, $\alpha \neq \pi$, we associated the **skew-symmetric matrix of** ***R***

$$\mathbf{R}_S = \tan \frac{\alpha}{2} \begin{pmatrix} 0 & p_3 & -p_2 \\ -p_3 & 0 & p_1 \\ p_2 & -p_1 & 0 \end{pmatrix}.$$

Show that for any given skew-symmetric matrix $\mathbf{B}$ the rotation $R(\alpha, \mathbf{p})$ such that $\mathbf{B} = \mathbf{R}_S$ is uniquely determined.

13.15. Let $\mathbf{R}_O$ and $\mathbf{R}_S$ be the proper orthogonal matrix and the skew-symmetric matrix, respectively, of the rotation $R[\alpha, \mathbf{p}]$, $\alpha \neq \pi$. Show that

$$\mathbf{R}_O = (\mathbf{E} - \mathbf{R}_S)(\mathbf{E} + \mathbf{R}_S)^{-1}, \quad \mathbf{R}_S = (\mathbf{E} - \mathbf{R}_O)(\mathbf{E} + \mathbf{R}_O)^{-1}.$$

[Note that the equations are equivalent. To prove the second use problems 13.8 and 9.21.]

13.16. Show that an improper orthogonal matrix represents a reflexion in the origin followed by a rotation. Conversely, a reflexion in the origin followed by a rotation is represented by an orthogonal matrix.

13.17. If $\{k\}_1$ and $\{k\}_2$ are two unit orthogonal vectors in V_3, show that there is one and only one proper orthogonal matrix $\mathbf{A} \in \mathsf{M}_{3,3}$ such that $\{k\}_\alpha = \mathbf{A}\{e\}_\alpha$, $\alpha = 1, 2$. [See problem 12.12.]

13.18. Let a rigid body B move from its initial position B_0 to a final position B in E_3 while its point *O* remains fixed. If x_i and y_i are the initial and final coordinates of a generic point *P* of B with respect to a system of cartesian coordinate axes OX_i, then show that

$$\{y\} = \mathbf{A}\{x\}$$

where $\mathbf{A}$ is a proper orthogonal matrix independent of *P*. [Note that the position of a rigid body is determined when the coordinates of three of its points are known. Use problem 13.17.]

13.19. Let a rigid body B move from an initial position B_0 to a final position B in E_3. The initial and final coordinates of a generic point of B with respect to a given system of orthogonal cartesian coordinates will be denoted by x_i and y_i, respectively. If *Q* is any given point of B with initial and final coordinates p_i and q_i, respectively, then show that there is a proper orthogonal matrix $\mathbf{A}$ such that

$$\{y - q\} = \mathbf{A}\{x - p\}.$$

This expression can also be written in the form

$$\{y\} = \mathbf{A}\{x\} + \{u\}.$$

where $\{u\} = \{q\} - \mathbf{A}\{p\}$ is independent of $\{x\}$.

13.20. Show that any movement of a rigid body B can be considered either as a translation (i.e., shifting of B parallel to itself) superimposed on a rotation or as a rotation superimposed on a translation. [Use problem 13.19 and the solution of $\mathbf{A}\{z\} = \{u\}$.]

13.21. Let a body B be deformed from the initial configuration B_0 to the final configuration B so that if $\{x\}$ and $\{y\}$ are the initial and final positions of a generic point P of B, with respect to a given system of axes OX_i in E_3, then

$$\{y\} = \text{diag}(\lambda_1, \lambda_2, \lambda_3,)\{x\}, \quad \lambda_i > 0.$$

This deformation is a **pure homogeneous strain** referred to its principal axes. Show that in the above deformation

(i) planes and straight lines remain planes and straight lines;

(ii) planes and straight lines initially parallel to the coordinate planes and coordinate axes respectively retain these properties;

(iii) if s_0 and s are the initial and final length of a line segment initially parallel to the OX_i axis then $s/s_0 = \lambda_i$. The ratio $s/s_0 = \lambda_i$ is called the **stretch** in the direction of the OX_i axis.

13.22. In every orthogonal cartesian system in E_3 a **three dimensional cartesian tensor** $\mathbf{T} = \mathbf{T}(\mathbf{z})$ of the second order is represented by a 3-by-3 matrix $\mathbf{A} = \mathbf{A}(\mathbf{z})$, where $\mathbf{z}$ is a point in E_3. A **constant tensor** is a tensor independent of position, i.e., independent of $\mathbf{z}$. This representation is such that if $\mathbf{A}$ and $\mathbf{B}$ represent the same tensor in the two systems of coordinate axes OX_i and OY_i respectively, then $\mathbf{B} = \mathbf{PAP}^T$ where $\mathbf{P}$ is the matrix of the direction cosines of the second system with respect to the first. Show that if the representation of a tensor in any *one* system of coordinates is given, its representation in any other system is determined.

13.23. If for *any given* points X, Y in E_3 the matrix $\mathbf{A}$ is such that $\{x\}^T\mathbf{A}\{y\}$ remains a constant under a change of axes, then show that the matrix $\mathbf{A}$ represents a tensor.

13.24. If for *any given* point X in E_3 the matrix $\mathbf{A}$ is such that $\{x\}^T\mathbf{A}\{x\}$ remains a constant under a change of axes, then show that the matrix $\mathbf{A} + \mathbf{A}^T$ represents a tensor.

13.25. An **isotropic tensor** $\mathbf{T}(\mathbf{z})$ has the same representation in any orthogonal cartesian system. Show that any isotropic tensor is represented by $b\mathbf{E}$, where $b = b(\mathbf{z})$. [Consider two systems of axes such that $\mathbf{P} = [-\{e\}_1, \{e\}_2, \{e\}_3]$ etc.]

13.26. In the following we shall write "the tensor $\mathbf{T}$" instead of "the tensor represented by the matrix $\mathbf{T}$." Show that if a tensor $\mathbf{T}$ is symmetric in any *one* system of coordinates, then it is symmetric in any system of coordinates, i.e., it is a **symmetric tensor.**

13.27. Show that if a tensor **T** is nonsingular in any *one* system of coordinates then it is nonsingular in any system, i.e., it is a **nonsingular tensor**.

13.28. Let **T** be a nonsingular tensor. Show that the matrix $\mathbf{T}^{-1}$ represents also a tensor, the **reciprocal tensor** of **T**.

13.29. Let the deformation of a body B be described by $\{y\} = \mathbf{A}\{x\}$ [see problem 13.21] with respect to a given cartesian system of axes OX_i. Show that in any system OY_i the deformation is $\{y\} = \mathbf{T}\{x\}$ where **T** is a tensor represented by **A** in the coordinate system OX_i.

LECTURE 14

Symmetric Matrices

Reality of eigenvalues of a symmetric matrix • Orthogonality of eigenvectors of a symmetric matrix that are associated with distinct eigenvalues • Diagonalizability of a symmetric matrix • Gram–Schmidt orthogonalization • Existence of an orthogonal matrix of eigenvectors of a symmetric matrix • The transformation $\mathbf{W}^T\mathbf{A}\mathbf{W}=\mathbf{D}(\pm 1, \ldots, \pm 1)$ for symmetric $\mathbf{A}$ • Problems

More often than not, the n-by-n matrices that arise in applications are real symmetric matrices. We shall therefore devote this lecture to the study of the eigenvectors and eigenvalues of real symmetric matrices.

Throughout this lecture, the matrix $\mathbf{A}$ is assumed to be a real symmetric n-by-n matrix:

$$\mathbf{A}^T=\mathbf{A}. \tag{14.1}$$

If $\{x\}$ and $\{y\}$ are arbitrary elements of $\mathsf{M}_{n,1}$, we can form the scalar quantity $\{x\}^T\mathbf{A}\{y\}$. Since $\{x\}^T\mathbf{A}\{y\}$ is a scalar, its transpose is equal to itself; that is

$$\{x\}^T\mathbf{A}\{y\}=(\{x\}^T\mathbf{A}\{y\})^T=\{y\}^T\mathbf{A}^T\{x\}.$$

However, since $\mathbf{A}$ is symmetric, we have

$$\{x\}^T\mathbf{A}\{y\}=\{y\}^T\mathbf{A}\{x\}, \quad \mathbf{A}^T=\mathbf{A}. \tag{14.2}$$

The reason for establishing this result is that it allows us to prove that *all of the eigenvalues of a (real) symmetric matrix are real numbers.* Suppose that $\lambda=\alpha+i\beta$ is an eigenvalue of $\mathbf{A}$, where α and β are real numbers, and let $\{k\}$ be an eigenvector of $\mathbf{A}$ that is associated with λ. Under these conditions, we know from the previous lectures that $\bar{\lambda}=\alpha-i\beta$ is also an eigenvalue of $\mathbf{A}$ and an associated eigenvector is given by $\{\bar{k}\}$. We thus have

$$\mathbf{A}\{k\}=\lambda\{k\}, \qquad \mathbf{A}\{\bar{k}\}=\bar{\lambda}\{\bar{k}\}. \tag{14.3}$$

If we multiply the first of Eqs. (14.3) on the left by $\{\bar{k}\}^T$ and the second of Eqs. (14.3) on the left by $\{k\}^T$, we obtain the pair of results

$$\{\bar{k}\}^T\mathbf{A}\{k\}=\lambda\{\bar{k}\}^T\{k\}, \qquad \{k\}^T\mathbf{A}\{\bar{k}\}=\bar{\lambda}\{k\}^T\{\bar{k}\}. \tag{14.4}$$

We can now use Eq. (14.2) to conclude that $\{\bar{k}\}^T\mathbf{A}\{k\}=\{k\}^T\mathbf{A}\{\bar{k}\}$, since $\mathbf{A}$ is symmetric, and hence Eqs. (14.4) give us

$$\lambda\{\bar{k}\}^T\{k\}=\bar{\lambda}\{k\}^T\{\bar{k}\}.$$

However, $\{\bar{k}\}^T\{k\}=(\{\bar{k}\}^T\{k\})^T=\{k\}^T\{\bar{k}\}$ since $\{\bar{k}\}^T\{k\}=||\{k\}||^2$ is a scalar (see problem 3.1), and we thus have

$$(\lambda-\bar{\lambda})\{\bar{k}\}^T\{k\}=0. \tag{14.5}$$

Setting

$$\{k\}=\{u\}+i\{v\}, \qquad \{\bar{k}\}=\{u\}-i\{v\},$$

where $\{u\}$ and $\{v\}$ are elements of $\mathsf{M}_{n,1}$, we have

$$\begin{aligned}\{\bar{k}\}^T\{k\}&=(\{u\}^T-i\{v\}^T)(\{u\}+i\{v\})\\&=\{u\}^T\{u\}+\{v\}^T\{v\}+i(\{u\}^T\{v\}-\{v\}^T\{u\})\\&=\{u\}^T\{u\}+\{v\}^T\{v\}.\end{aligned}$$

Since an eigenvector is not a zero vector, we must therefore have $\{\bar{k}\}^T\{k\}>0$. Thus, Eq. (14.5) can be satisfied only if we have $\lambda-\bar{\lambda}=0$. However, $\lambda-\bar{\lambda}=(\alpha+i\beta)-(\alpha-i\beta)=2i\beta$. Thus, we must have $\beta=0$, and accordingly $\lambda=\alpha$ so that λ is real.

In addition to guaranteeing that you do not have to worry about complex eigenvalues and complex eigenvectors when you are dealing with a symmetric matrix, the above result also gives another check on whether you have calculated the eigenvalues of a symmetric matrix properly. If you obtain a complex eigenvalue for a symmetric matrix, then you have made a mistake.

The eigenvectors of a symmetric matrix have an important property that we will now establish. Let λ_1 and λ_2 be two distinct eigenvalues of $\mathbf{A}$ and let $\{k\}_1$ and $\{k\}_2$ be eigenvectors associated with these eigenvalues:

$$\mathbf{A}\{k\}_1=\lambda_1\{k\}_1, \qquad \mathbf{A}\{k\}_2=\lambda_2\{k\}_2. \tag{14.6}$$

If we multiply the first of these equations on the left by $\{k\}_2{}^T$ and the second on the left by $\{k\}_1{}^T$, we have

$$\begin{aligned}\{k\}_2{}^T\mathbf{A}\{k\}_1&=\lambda_1\{k\}_2{}^T\{k\}_1,\\\{k\}_1{}^T\mathbf{A}\{k\}_2&=\lambda_2\{k\}_1{}^T\{k\}_2.\end{aligned} \tag{14.7}$$

Since $\mathbf{A}$ is symmetric, Eq. (14.2) shows that the left hand sides of the two equations (14.7) are equal, and we also have $\{k\}_1{}^T\{k\}_2=\{k\}_2{}^T\{k\}_1$ since $\{k\}_1{}^T\{k\}_2$ is a scalar and hence is equal to its own transpose. Thus, Eqs. (14.7) give us

$$(\lambda_1-\lambda_2)\{k\}_1{}^T\{k\}_2=0. \tag{14.8}$$

Since λ_1 and λ_2 were assumed to be distinct eigenvalues of $\mathbf{A}$, $(\lambda_1-\lambda_2)\neq 0$, and hence Eq. (14.8) can be satisfied only if we have $\{k\}_1{}^T\{k\}_2=0$; that is, $\{k\}_1$ and $\{k\}_2$ are orthogonal vectors. We have thus shown that *the eigenvectors of a symmetric matrix that are associated with distinct eigenvalues are mutually orthogonal vectors.*

The next result we shall simply state since its proof requires a bit more machinery than we have available in this set of lectures (see problems). *Every symmetric n-by-n matrix is diagonalizable.* Thus, in particular, *a symmetric* $\mathbf{A} \in \mathsf{M}_{n,n}$ *has n linearly independent eigenvectors,* and *if a symmetric* $\mathbf{A} \in \mathsf{M}_{n,n}$ *has an eigenvalue* λ_i *of multiplicity* m_i *then* $d_i \equiv n - \text{rank}(\mathbf{A} - \lambda_i \mathbf{E}) = m_i$ *and* $\dim(\mathsf{N}(\lambda_i)) = m_i$. This last result simply states that if the multiplicity of λ_i is m_i, then there are always m_i linearly independent eigenvectors of $\mathbf{A}$ associated with λ_i. This result also gives you a check on your calculations, for if you find an eigenvalue of multiplicity m_i for a symmetric matrix, then when you row reduce $(\mathbf{A} - \lambda_i \mathbf{E})$, you should find that there are exactly m_i zero rows of $(\mathbf{A} - \lambda_i \mathbf{E})_R$. If this isn't the case then you have made a mistake.

We have seen that eigenvectors of a symmetric matrix that are associated with distinct eigenvalues are mutually orthogonal, and if there is an eigenvalue λ_i of multiplicity m_i then there are m_i linearly independent eigenvectors associated with λ_i. Each of these m_i linearly independent eigenvectors is orthogonal to all other eigenvectors associated with eigenvalues distinct from λ_i. It will then follow that we can choose all n of the eigenvectors of a symmetric matrix to be orthogonal if we can show the following: *if a system of* m_i *linearly independent vectors spans a subspace of* $\mathsf{M}_{n,1}$ *then we can find a system of* m_i *orthogonal vectors which spans the same subspace.* [Recall that the eigenvectors associated with an eigenvalue of multiplicity $m_i > 1$ are chosen under the sole condition that they constitute a basis for $\mathsf{N}(\lambda_i)$, and hence we can replace them by any other system of vectors that forms a basis for $\mathsf{N}(\lambda_i)$.]

Let $\{k\}_1, \{k\}_2, \ldots, \{k\}_m$ be a system of $m > 1$ linearly independent vectors that spans a subspace N of $\mathsf{M}_{n,1}$ of dimension m. Hence $\|\{k\}_i\| \neq 0$ for $i = 1, \ldots, m$. We then define m new vectors by the relations

$$
\begin{aligned}
\{u\}_1 &= \{k\}_1, \\
\{u\}_2 &= \{k\}_2 - \frac{\{u\}_1^T \{k\}_2}{\|\{u\}_1\|^2} \{u\}_1, \\
\{u\}_3 &= \{k\}_3 - \frac{\{u\}_1^T \{k\}_3}{\|\{u\}_1\|^2} \{u\}_1 - \frac{\{u\}_2^T \{k\}_3}{\|\{u\}_2\|^2} \{u\}_2, \\
&\ \ \vdots \\
\{u\}_m &= \{k\}_m - \frac{\{u\}_1^T \{k\}_m}{\|\{u\}_1\|^2} \{u\}_1 - \cdots - \frac{\{u\}_{m-1}^T \{k\}_m}{\|\{u\}_{m-1}\|^2} \{u\}_{m-1}.
\end{aligned}
\tag{14.9}
$$

It is a straightforward matter of direct calculation to show that the vectors $\{u\}_1, \ldots, \{u\}_m$ are nonzero and mutually orthogonal, that is $\{u\}_i^T\{u\}_j = 0$ if $i \neq j$. Further, $\{u\}_1, \ldots, \{u\}_m$ belong to N since they are linear combinations of vectors that form a basis of N. We know (see problem 5.10) that m orthogonal vectors, none of which is the zero vector, are linearly independent. Thus, all we have to do is to show that none of the vectors defined by Eqs. (14.9) is the zero vector and we are finished. Suppose that $\{u\}_r = \{0\}$, then Eqs. (14.9) show that we have a linear combination of the first r vectors $\{k\}_1, \ldots, \{k\}_r$ equal to the zero vector. This would say that $\{k\}_1, \ldots, \{k\}_r$ are linearly dependent, which is a contradiction since $\{k\}_1, \ldots, \{k\}_m$ are linearly independent. Hence, *the set of m vectors* $\{u\}_1, \ldots, \{u\}_m$ *is a mutually orthogonal system of vectors that spans the subspace* N *that is spanned by the m linearly independent vectors* $\{k\}_1, \ldots, \{k\}_m$. Stated another way, *a basis for a subspace can always be replaced by a mutually orthogonal basis for the subspace.* The process given by Eqs. (14.9) for generating a mutually orthogonal basis for a subspace is known as the **Gram-Schmidt orthogonalization process.**

If the basis for each subspace of eigenvectors of a symmetric matrix that is associated with each eigenvalue of multiplicity $m > 1$ is replaced by an orthogonal basis, then this orthogonal basis for the subspace is also comprised of eigenvectors. Since eigenvectors corresponding to distinct eigenvalues of a symmetric matrix are mutually orthogonal, we then have that *all of the eigenvectors of a symmetric matrix can be chosen in such a way that they are mutually orthogonal.* We know that eigenvectors are only determined to within arbitrary nonzero multiples, and hence we can multiply each of the mutually orthogonal eigenvectors of a symmetric matrix by nonzero numbers and obtain another system of n mutually orthogonal eigenvectors. In particular, we can multiply the ith eigenvector by the nonzero number $\|\{k\}_i\|^{-1}$, in which case, each of the new eigenvectors will be a unit vector. It thus follows that we can choose the eigenvectors of a symmetric matrix so that they satisfy

$$\{k\}_i^T\{k\}_j = \begin{cases} 1 & \text{if} \quad i=j \\ 0 & \text{if} \quad i \neq j \end{cases}. \tag{14.10}$$

The matrix $\mathbf{K}$ that is defined by $\mathbf{K} = [\{k\}_1, \ldots, \{k\}_n]$ has the property that $\mathbf{K}^{-1}\mathbf{A}\,\mathbf{K} = \mathbf{D}(\lambda_1, \ldots, \lambda_n)$, and in addition, the columns of $\mathbf{K}$ are mutually orthogonal unit vectors. Thus, since a matrix whose columns are mutually orthogonal unit vectors is an orthogonal matrix, we have shown that *a symmetric matrix possesses an orthogonal matrix of eigenvectors.* Further, since $\mathbf{K}^{-1}\mathbf{A}\,\mathbf{K} = \mathbf{D}(\lambda_1, \ldots, \lambda_n)$, we have

$$\mathbf{K}^T = \mathbf{K}^{-1} \quad \text{and} \quad \mathbf{K}^T\mathbf{A}\,\mathbf{K} = \mathbf{D}(\lambda_1, \ldots, \lambda_n). \tag{14.11}$$

Thus, for the case of symmetric matrices, we can replace the equation

$$\mathbf{K}^{-1}\mathbf{A}\,\mathbf{K}=\mathbf{D}(\lambda_1,\ .\ .\ .\ ,\ \lambda_n) \tag{14.12}$$

by the equations

$$\mathbf{K}^T\mathbf{A}\,\mathbf{K}=\mathbf{D}(\lambda_1,\ .\ .\ .\ ,\ \lambda_n),\ \mathbf{K}^T\mathbf{K}=\mathbf{E} \tag{14.13}$$

The utility of replacing Eq. (14.12) by Eqs. (14.13) is most easily seen by the following problem. Find a nonsingular matrix $\mathbf{W}$ such that $\mathbf{W}^T\mathbf{A}\,\mathbf{W}=\mathbf{D}(\pm 1,\ \pm 1,\ .\ .\ .\ ,\ \pm 1)$ when $\mathbf{A}$ is a nonsingular symmetric matrix. Since $\mathbf{A}$ is symmetric, we know that there exists an orthogonal matrix $\mathbf{K}$ such that

$$\mathbf{K}^T\mathbf{A}\,\mathbf{K}=\mathbf{D}(\lambda_1,\ .\ .\ .\ ,\ \lambda_n). \tag{14.14}$$

Now $\det(\mathbf{K}^T\mathbf{A}\,\mathbf{K})=\det(\mathbf{K}^{-1}\mathbf{A}\,\mathbf{K})$, since $\mathbf{K}$ is orthogonal, and hence Eq. (14.14) gives $\det(\mathbf{K}^T\mathbf{A}\,\mathbf{K})=\det(\mathbf{A})=\det(\mathbf{D}(\lambda_1,\ .\ .\ .\ ,\ \lambda_n))=\lambda_1\lambda_2\cdots\lambda_n$ (Thus, $\mathbf{A}$ *is nonsingular if and only if none of its eigenvalues are equal to zero.* We leave it to the student as an exercise to show that this result is true whether or not $\mathbf{A}$ is a symmetric matrix.) Since none of the λ's are zero, the matrix

$$\mathbf{U}=\mathbf{D}\left(\frac{1}{\sqrt{|\lambda_1|}},\frac{1}{\sqrt{|\lambda_2|}},\ .\ .\ .\ ,\frac{1}{\sqrt{|\lambda_n|}}\right) \tag{14.15}$$

is well defined and has the property that

$$\mathbf{U}^T\mathbf{D}(\lambda_1,\ .\ .\ .\ ,\ \lambda_n)\mathbf{U}=\mathbf{D}\left(\frac{\lambda_1}{|\lambda_1|},\frac{\lambda_2}{|\lambda_2|},\ .\ .\ .\ ,\frac{\lambda_n}{|\lambda_n|}\right), \tag{14.16}$$

and hence $\mathbf{U}^T\mathbf{D}(\lambda_1,\ .\ .\ .\ ,\ \lambda_n)\mathbf{U}=\mathbf{D}(\pm 1,\ .\ .\ .\ ,\ \pm 1)$. Thus, if we multiply Eq. (14.14) on the left by $\mathbf{U}^T$ and on the right by $\mathbf{U}$, we have

$$\mathbf{U}^T\mathbf{K}^T\mathbf{A}\,\mathbf{K}\,\mathbf{U}=\mathbf{D}(\pm 1,\ .\ .\ .\ ,\ \pm 1). \tag{14.17}$$

The matrix $\mathbf{W}$ which satisfies $\mathbf{W}^T\mathbf{A}\,\mathbf{W}=\mathbf{D}(\pm 1,\ .\ .\ .\ ,\pm 1)$ is thus given by $\mathbf{W}=\mathbf{K}\,\mathbf{U}$. Thus, *if* $\mathbf{A}$ *is a nonsingular symmetric matrix with eigenvalues* $\lambda_1,\ .\ .\ .\ ,\ \lambda_n$ *and if* $\mathbf{K}$ *is an associated orthogonal matrix of eigenvectors of* $\mathbf{A}$*, then* $\mathbf{W}=\mathbf{K}\,\mathbf{U}$ *satisfies*

$$\mathbf{W}^T\mathbf{A}\,\mathbf{W}=\mathbf{D}(\pm 1,\ .\ .\ .\ ,\ \pm 1), \tag{14.18}$$

if $\mathbf{U}$ *is defined by Eq.* (14.15). In addition to being an interesting application of the fact that a symmetric matrix possesses an orthogonal matrix of eigenvectors, the above result is an essential ingredient in studying problems that demand the simplification of more than one quadratic form. Some of the results that we shall obtain in lecture sixteen depend heavily on the statement derived above.

Problems

14.1. For each of the following sets of vectors:

(i) Use the Gram-Schmidt orthogonalization process to find a set of mutually orthogonal vectors spanning the same subspace S spanned by the given set.

(ii) Obtain a set of orthonormal vectors spanning S.

(a) $\left\{\begin{matrix}1\\0\end{matrix}\right\}, \left\{\begin{matrix}3\\4\end{matrix}\right\}$; (b) $\left\{\begin{matrix}3\\-4\end{matrix}\right\}, \left\{\begin{matrix}0\\9\end{matrix}\right\}$; (c) $\left\{\begin{matrix}1\\2\end{matrix}\right\}, \left\{\begin{matrix}0\\4\end{matrix}\right\}$;

(d) $\left\{\begin{matrix}3\\0\\4\end{matrix}\right\}, \left\{\begin{matrix}0\\2\\3\end{matrix}\right\}$; (e) $\left\{\begin{matrix}1\\2\\-1\end{matrix}\right\}, \left\{\begin{matrix}0\\4\\0\end{matrix}\right\}$; (f) $\left\{\begin{matrix}3\\1\\0\end{matrix}\right\}, \left\{\begin{matrix}2\\0\\3\end{matrix}\right\}$.

14.2. For each of the following matrices $\mathbf{A}$:

(i) Find a matrix $\mathbf{K}_1$ such that $\mathbf{K}_1^{-1}\,\mathbf{A}\,\mathbf{K}_1 = \mathbf{D}(\lambda_1, \ldots, \lambda_n)$.

(ii) Obtain a matrix $\mathbf{K}_2$ the columns of which are mutually orthogonal vectors such that $\mathbf{K}_2^{-1}\,\mathbf{A}\,\mathbf{K}_2 = \mathbf{D}(\lambda_1, \ldots, \lambda_n)$.

(iii) Derive an orthogonal matrix $\mathbf{K}_3$ such that $\mathbf{K}_3^T\,\mathbf{A}\,\mathbf{K}_3 = \mathbf{D}(\lambda_1, \ldots, \lambda_n)$.

(iv) Is the matrix $\mathbf{A}$ nonsingular? If it is find a matrix $\mathbf{W}$ such that $\mathbf{W}^T\mathbf{A}\,\mathbf{W} = \mathbf{D}(\pm 1, \ldots, \pm 1)$.

(a) $\begin{pmatrix}7 & 4\\4 & 1\end{pmatrix}$, (b) $\begin{pmatrix}2 & 4\\4 & 8\end{pmatrix}$, (c) $\begin{pmatrix}5 & 2\\2 & 2\end{pmatrix}$, (d) $\begin{pmatrix}5 & -2 & -4\\-2 & 8 & -2\\-4 & -2 & 5\end{pmatrix}$,

(e) $\begin{pmatrix}5 & 10 & 8\\10 & 2 & -2\\8 & -2 & 11\end{pmatrix}$, (f) $\begin{pmatrix}1 & -2 & -1\\-2 & 4 & 2\\-1 & 2 & 1\end{pmatrix}$.

14.3. Show that the vectors $\{u\}_1, \ldots, \{u\}_m$ in the Gram-Schmidt orthogonalization process (14.9) are nonzero and mutually orthogonal.

14.4. For $\{k\}_i \in \mathsf{M}_{3,1}$ $i = 1, 2, 3$ give a geometric meaning to the Gram-Schmidt orthogonalization process.

14.5. Prove that if a symmetric matrix has only one distinct root then it is a diagonal matrix.

14.6. Show that the eigenvectors of a real symmetric matrix are real.

14.7. Show that any two-by-two real symmetric matrix is similar to a diagonal matrix.

14.8. Let $\{k\}$ be a unit eigenvector corresponding to the eigenvalue λ_1 of the real symmetric matrix $\mathbf{A} \in \mathsf{M}_{n,n}$. If $\mathbf{S}$ is an orthogonal matrix with $\{k\}$ as its first column, then show that

$$\mathbf{S}^{-1}\mathbf{A}\,\mathbf{S} = \begin{pmatrix}\lambda_1 & \mathbf{0}_{1,\,n-1}\\ \mathbf{0}_{n-1,\,1} & \mathbf{B}_{n-1,\,n-1}\end{pmatrix},$$

where $\mathbf{B}$ is a real symmetric matrix and $\mathbf{0}$ a zero matrix. [Use indicial notation.]

14.9. Show that

$$\begin{pmatrix} 1 & \mathbf{0}_{1,\,n-1} \\ \mathbf{0}_{n-1,\,1} & \mathbf{C}_{n-1,\,n-1} \end{pmatrix} \begin{pmatrix} \lambda_1 & \mathbf{0}_{1,\,n-1} \\ \mathbf{0}_{n-1,\,1} & \mathbf{B}_{n-1,\,n-1} \end{pmatrix} \begin{pmatrix} 1 & \mathbf{0}_{1,\,n-1} \\ \mathbf{0}_{n-1,\,1} & \mathbf{D}_{n-1,\,n-1} \end{pmatrix}$$

$$= \begin{pmatrix} \lambda_1 & \mathbf{0}_{1,\,n-1} \\ \mathbf{0}_{n-1,\,1} & (\mathbf{CBD})_{n-1,\,n-1} \end{pmatrix}.$$

[See problem 4.28.]

14.10. Prove that a real symmetric matrix is similar to a diagonal matrix. [Use induction and the problems 14.7, 14.8 and 14.9.]

14.11. If $\mathbf{A}$ is a real symmetric matrix, λ_1 one of its eigenvalues of multiplicity m_1 and d_1 the dimension of the solution space of $(\mathbf{A} - \lambda_1\mathbf{E})\{x\} = 0$, then show that $m_1 = d_1$. [See problem 14.10.]

14.12. Two matrices $\mathbf{A}$ and $\mathbf{B}$ are called **similar under the (proper) orthogonal group** if $\mathbf{A} = \mathbf{P}^{-1}\mathbf{BP}$ where $\mathbf{P}$ is a (proper) orthogonal matrix. Show that a real symmetric matrix is similar to a real diagonal matrix under the proper orthogonal group. [Use the theorem in p. 14.7.]

14.13. Show that if a matrix $\mathbf{A}$ is similar to a (real) diagonal matrix $\mathbf{D}$ under the orthogonal group, then $\mathbf{A}$ is a (real) symmetric matrix.

14.14. Let $\mathbf{A}$ be similar to a diagonal matrix $\mathbf{D}$. Show that

(i) $\mathbf{A}^k$, where k is a positive integer, is similar to $\mathbf{D}^k$.

(ii) If $\mathbf{A}$ is nonsingular, then $\mathbf{A}^k$, where k is a positive or negative integer, is similar to $\mathbf{D}^k$.

14.15. If $\mathbf{A}$ is similar to a diagonal matrix and $\mathbf{A}^n = \mathbf{0}$, where n is a positive integer, then show that $\mathbf{A} = \mathbf{0}$.

14.16. Show that if two diagonalizable matrices have the same eigenvalues, then they are similar.

14.17. Show that if two diagonalizable matrices $\mathbf{A}$ and $\mathbf{B}$ have the same eigenvalues, then there exist matrices $\mathbf{X}$ and $\mathbf{Y}$, not both singular, such that $\mathbf{A} = \mathbf{XY}$, $\mathbf{B} = \mathbf{YX}$.

14.18. The matrix $\mathbf{A}$ is called **hermitian** if $\mathbf{A}^T = \overline{\mathbf{A}}$, and **skew-hermitian** if $\mathbf{A}^T = -\overline{\mathbf{A}}$. In particular, a real symmetric matrix is hermitian and a real skew-symmetric matrix is skew-hermitian. Show that

(i) $\mathbf{A}$ is a hermitian matrix if and only if $\mathbf{A} = \mathbf{A}_1 + \mathbf{i}\mathbf{A}_2$ where the uniquely determined real matrices $\mathbf{A}_1$, $\mathbf{A}_2$ are symmetric and skew-symmetric, respectively.

(ii) $\mathbf{A}$ is a skew-hermitian matrix if and only if $\mathbf{A} = \mathbf{A}_1 + \mathbf{i}\mathbf{A}_2$ where the uniquely determined real matrices $\mathbf{A}_1$, $\mathbf{A}_2$ are skew-symmetric and symmetric, respectively.

(iii) $\mathbf{A}$ is a hermitian matrix if and only if $\mathbf{iA}$ is a skew-hermitian matrix.

14.19. Show that the diagonal elements of a hermitian or a skew-hermitian matrix are real or pure imaginary, respectively.

14.20. Show that any matrix $\mathbf{A}$ can be written in the form $\mathbf{A} = \mathbf{B} + \mathbf{C}$ where the uniquely determined matrices **B** and **C** are hermitian and skew-hermitian, respectively.

14.21. Show that the eigenvalues of a hermitian matrix (and in particular of a real symmetric matrix) are real. [Proof similar to the one for real matrices.]

14.22. Show that the eigenvalues of a skew-hermitian matrix **A** (and in particular of a real skew-symmetric matrix) are purely imaginary. [Write $|\mathbf{A} - \lambda\mathbf{E}| = 0$ and use $\mathbf{A} = i\mathbf{B}$ where **B** is hermitian.]

14.23. Show that two eigenvectors of a hermitian matrix (and in particular of a real symmetric matrix) corresponding to distinct eigenvalues are orthogonal.

14.24. Show that there is a coordinate system OY_i in which the symmetric tensor **T** is diagonal. The diagonal elements of **T** are the **eigenvalues of the tensor** and the direction of the axes OY_i the **principal directions of the tensor.** Show that a tensor determines uniquely its principal directions and eigenvalues.

14.25. Let **A** and **B** be two reciprocal tensors ($\mathbf{A} = \mathbf{B}^{-1}$). Show that

(i) **A** and **B** have the same principal directions.
(ii) The eigenvalues of **A** are the inverses of the eigenvalues of **B**.

14.26. Show that if the matrices **A** and **B** represent tensors, so does the matrix **AB**. The tensor **AB** is called the **product** of the tensors **A** and **B**.

14.27. Show that the trace of the product of two tensors is an **invariant**, i.e., it does not change if we change the coordinate system. Deduce that, if **T** is a tensor and n is a positive integer, then $\mathrm{tr}(\mathbf{T}^n)$ is an invariant.

14.28. Let the deformation of a body B be $\{y\} = \mathbf{T}\{x\}$ where **T** is a symmetric tensor with positive eigenvalues. Show that a suitable choice of axes reduces this deformation to the form $\{y\} = \mathbf{D}(\lambda_1, \lambda_2, \lambda_3)\{x\}$, $\lambda_i > 0$. [See problem 14.24.]

LECTURE 15

Properties of Matrices and Their Eigenvectors

Eigenvalues and eigenvectors of a positive definite matrix • Families of positive definite matrices • Families of diagonalizable matrices which commute • Families of symmetric matrices whose products are symmetric matrices • The polar decomposition theorem • The Cayley–Hamilton theorem • Problems

The simplest applications of eigenvectors and eigenvalues is to use them to characterize different kinds of matrices. According to the definition given in lecture 9, a matrix **A** is *positive definite* if and only if **A** is symmetric and

$$\{x\}^T\mathbf{A}\{x\}>0, \tag{15.1}$$

for all $\{x\}\in \mathsf{M}_{n,1}$ such that $\|\{x\}\|\neq 0$. Since **A** is symmetric, its eigenvalues are real and it has n linearly independent mutually orthogonal eigenvectors. If we denote such a set of eigenvectors of **A** by $\{k\}_1, \ldots,$ $\{k\}_n$, then for any $\{x\}\in \mathsf{M}_{n,1}$ we have

$$\{x\}=c_1\{k\}_1+c_2\{k\}_2+\ \ldots\ +c_n\{k\}_n, \tag{15.2}$$

since any system of n linearly independent vectors is a basis for $\mathsf{M}_{n,1}$. When Eq. (15.2) is substituted into the left-hand side of Eq. (15.1) and we use the fact that the vectors $\{k\}_i$ are a mutually orthogonal set, we have

$$\begin{aligned}\{x\}^T\mathbf{A}\{x\}&=\sum_{i=1}^{n}\sum_{j=1}^{n} c_i\{k\}_i^T(\mathbf{A}c_j\{k\}_j)=\sum_{i=1}^{n}\sum_{j=1}^{n}c_ic_j\{k\}_i^T\mathbf{A}\{k\}_j\\&=\sum_{i=1}^{n}\sum_{j=1}^{n} c_ic_j\{k\}_i^T\lambda_j\{k\}_j=\sum_{i=1}^{n}\sum_{j=1}^{n}c_ic_j\lambda_j\{k\}_i^T\{k\}_j\\&=\sum_{i=1}^{n} c_i^2\{k\}_i^T\{k\}_i\lambda_i,\end{aligned}$$

because $\{k\}_i^T\{k\}_j=0$ if $i\neq j$. Since $\|\{x\}\|^2=\sum_{i,j=1}^{n}c_ic_j\{k\}_i^T\{k\}_j=\sum_{i=1}^{n}c_i^2\cdot$ $\{k\}_i^T\{k\}_i$, the requirement that Eq. (15.1) hold for all $\{x\}\in \mathsf{M}_{n,1}$ such that

$||\{x\}||^2 > 0$ is equivalent to the requirement that

$$\sum_{i=1}^{n} c_i^2 \{k\}_i^T \{k\}_i \lambda_i > 0, \tag{15.3}$$

for all numbers $c_1, \ldots, c_n$ such that

$$\sum_{i=1}^{n} c_i^2 \{k\}_i^T \{k\}_i > 0.$$

If we note that $\{k\}_i^T\{k\}_i > 0$ we easily see that if any one of the numbers λ_i is zero or negative, then we can choose numbers $c_1, \ldots, c_n$ so as to violate the inequality (15.3) while

$$\sum_{i=1}^{n} c_i^2 \{k\}_i^T \{k\}_i > 0.$$

An n-by-n symmetric matrix is positive definite if and only if each of the eigenvalues of **A** *is a positive number.* We can thus construct positive definite matrices in the following manner. We first write $\mathbf{K}^{-1}\mathbf{A}\,\mathbf{K} = \mathbf{D}(\lambda_1, \ldots, \lambda_n)$. Now, **K** can be taken to be orthogonal since $\mathbf{A}^T = \mathbf{A}$ is assumed to hold, and hence we have

$$\mathbf{A} = \mathbf{K}\,\mathbf{D}(\lambda_1, \ldots, \lambda_n)\mathbf{K}^{-1} = \mathbf{K}\,\mathbf{D}(\lambda_1, \ldots, \lambda_n)\mathbf{K}^T, \quad \mathbf{K}^T\mathbf{K} = \mathbf{E}. \tag{15.4}$$

The above result tells us that if we take the numbers $\lambda_1, \ldots, \lambda_n$ to be any positive real numbers and if we take **K** to be any orthogonal n-by-n matrix, then the matrix **A** defined by (15.4) is positive definite. *All matrices of the form*

$$\mathbf{A} = \mathbf{K}\,\mathbf{D}(\lambda_1, \ldots, \lambda_n)\mathbf{K}^T, \quad \mathbf{K}\,\mathbf{K}^T = \mathbf{E}, \tag{15.5}$$

are positive definite whenever all of the numbers $\lambda_1, \ldots, \lambda_n$ *are positive.*

As an example of this process of constructing positive definite matrices, we start with the orthogonal matrix

$$\mathbf{K} = \frac{1}{3}\begin{pmatrix} 2 & 1 & 2 \\ -2 & 2 & 1 \\ -1 & -2 & 2 \end{pmatrix}$$

We then form the product

$$\begin{aligned}
\mathbf{A}(\alpha, \beta, \gamma) &= \mathbf{K}\,\mathbf{D}(\alpha, \beta, \gamma)\mathbf{K}^T \\
&= \frac{1}{9}\begin{pmatrix} 2 & 1 & 2 \\ -2 & 2 & 1 \\ -1 & -2 & 2 \end{pmatrix}\begin{pmatrix} \alpha & 0 & 0 \\ 0 & \beta & 0 \\ 0 & 0 & \gamma \end{pmatrix}\begin{pmatrix} 2 & -2 & -1 \\ 1 & 2 & -2 \\ 2 & 1 & 2 \end{pmatrix} \\
&= \frac{1}{9}\begin{pmatrix} 4\alpha+\beta+4\gamma & -4\alpha+2\beta+2\gamma & -2\alpha-2\beta+4\gamma \\ -4\alpha+2\beta+2\gamma & 4\alpha+4\beta+\gamma & 2\alpha-4\beta+2\gamma \\ -2\alpha-2\beta+4\gamma & 2\alpha-4\beta+2\gamma & \alpha+4\beta+4\gamma \end{pmatrix}
\end{aligned} \tag{15.6}$$

The theory tells us that each of the three-parameter family of matrices $\mathbf{A}(\alpha, \beta, \gamma)$ with $\alpha>0$, $\beta>0$, $\gamma>0$ is a positive definite matrix.

Let **A** be a diagonalizable square matrix of rank r. We then know that $\mathbf{A}\{x\}=\{0\}$ has a solution space of dimension $n-r$. On the other hand, $\mathbf{A}\{x\}=\{0\}$ can be read as $\mathbf{A}\{x\}=0\{x\}$, and hence every solution of $\mathbf{A}\{x\}=\{0\}$ is an eigenvector of **A** with zero as the associated eigenvalue. We thus conclude that *an n-by-n diagonalizable matrix* **A** *has rank r if and only if zero is an eigenvalue of* **A** *with multiplicity* $m=n-r$.

Quantum mechanics and many other physical disciplines require solutions to the following problem. Find a diagonalizable matrix **B** such that **AB**=**BA**, where **A** is a given diagonalizable matrix (that is; **A** and **B** are required to commute). Since **B** is assumed to be diagonalizable, we can write

$$\mathbf{B}=\mathbf{K}\,\mathbf{D}(\alpha_1, \ldots, \alpha_n)\mathbf{K}^{-1}, \tag{15.7}$$

where **K** is a matrix of eigenvectors of **B**. Then, since $\mathbf{AB}=\mathbf{AKDK}^{-1}$ and $\mathbf{BA}=\mathbf{KDK}^{-1}\mathbf{A}$, the condition **AB**=**BA** becomes

$$\mathbf{AKDK}^{-1}=\mathbf{KDK}^{-1}\mathbf{A}. \tag{15.8}$$

If we multiply Eq. (15.8) on the left by $\mathbf{K}^{-1}$ and on the right by **K**, we then have

$$(\mathbf{K}^{-1}\mathbf{AK})\mathbf{D}=\mathbf{D}(\mathbf{K}^{-1}\mathbf{AK}). \tag{15.9}$$

If **K** is also a matrix of eigenvectors of **A**, then $\mathbf{K}^{-1}\mathbf{AK}=\mathbf{D}^*$ where $\mathbf{D}^* =\mathbf{D}(\lambda_1, \ldots, \lambda_n)$ and λ_i is the corresponding eigenvalue of **A**. It then follows that Eq. (15.9) reduces to $\mathbf{D}^*\mathbf{D}=\mathbf{D}\,\mathbf{D}^*$ which is always true since both **D** and $\mathbf{D}^*$ are diagonal matrices. Thus, *if* **A** *is a given diagonalizable matrix, then* **B** *is a diagonalizable matrix which commutes with* **A** *if a matrix of eigenvectors of* **B** *is also a matrix of eigenvectors of* **A**. Since **A** is assumed given and diagonalizable, we can find a matrix **K** of eigenvectors of **A**. It then follows that $\mathbf{B}=\mathbf{K}\,\mathbf{D}(\alpha_1, \ldots, \alpha_n)\mathbf{K}^{-1}$ commutes with **A** for every choice of the numbers $\alpha_1, \ldots, \alpha_n$. Thus, for each matrix **K** of eigenvectors of **A**, we can construct not just one such matrix **B**, but rather an n parameter family of matrices **B** which commute with the given matrix **A**.

As an example, let

$$\mathbf{A}=\begin{pmatrix} -31 & 18 \\ -54 & 32 \end{pmatrix},$$

then $\lambda_1=5$, $\lambda_2=-4$ and a matrix of eigenvectors of **A** is given by $\mathbf{K}=\begin{pmatrix} -2 & 2 \\ -4 & 3 \end{pmatrix}$. We then form the two-parameter family of matrices

$\mathbf{B}(\alpha_1, \alpha_2)$ by the prescription

$$\begin{aligned}\mathbf{B}(\alpha_1, \alpha_2) &= \mathbf{K}\,\mathbf{D}(\alpha_1, \alpha_2)\mathbf{K}^{-1}\\ &= \begin{pmatrix} -2 & 2 \\ -4 & 3 \end{pmatrix}\begin{pmatrix} \alpha_1 & 0 \\ 0 & \alpha_2 \end{pmatrix}\begin{pmatrix} 3/2 & -1 \\ 2 & -1 \end{pmatrix}\\ &= \begin{pmatrix} -3\alpha_1+4\alpha_2 & 2\alpha_1-2\alpha_2 \\ -6\alpha_1+6\alpha_2 & 4\alpha_1-3\alpha_2 \end{pmatrix}.\end{aligned}$$

We then have $\mathbf{A}\,\mathbf{B}(\alpha_1, \alpha_2)=\mathbf{B}(\alpha_1, \alpha_2)\mathbf{A}$ for every choice of α_1 and α_2. Note also that $\mathbf{B}(5, -4)=\mathbf{A}$.

As an example of the use of the result concerning commuting matrices, consider the following problem which arises in certain numerical computations. Let $\mathbf{A}$ and $\mathbf{C}$ be given matrices with $\mathbf{A}$ diagonalizable. Find a matrix $\mathbf{B}$ such that

$$\mathbf{AB}\{x\}=\mathbf{C}\{x\} \tag{15.10}$$

implies that $\mathbf{A}\{x\}=\{0\}$ and $\mathbf{C}\{x\}=\{0\}$ are equivalent systems. Since $\mathbf{A}$ is diagonalizable, we find a nonsingular matrix $\mathbf{B}$ such that $\mathbf{AB}=\mathbf{BA}$; that is, use Eq. (15.7) where $\mathbf{K}$ is a matrix of eigenvectors of $\mathbf{A}$ and α_i are chosen so that $\alpha_i \neq 0$. We then have $\mathbf{AB}\{x\}=\mathbf{BA}\{x\}$ and hence Eq. (15.10) becomes

$$\mathbf{BA}\{x\}=\mathbf{C}\{x\}, \quad \text{or} \quad \mathbf{A}\{x\}=\mathbf{B}^{-1}\mathbf{C}\{x\}.$$

Since $\mathbf{B}$ is nonsingular, every $\{x\} \in \mathsf{M}_{n,1}$ which satisfies $\mathbf{C}\{x\}=\{0\}$ also satisfies $\mathbf{A}\{x\}=\{0\}$ and conversely; that is, the subspaces of $\mathsf{M}_{n,1}$ that satisfy $\mathbf{A}\{x\}=\{0\}$ and $\mathbf{C}\{x\}=\{0\}$ are identical whenever $\mathbf{AB}\{x\}=\mathbf{C}\{x\}$ and $\mathbf{AB}=\mathbf{BA}$, $\det(\mathbf{B}) \neq 0$.

Although the above example is occasionally useful in solving specific problems, it involves answering a question which the student may not have encountered at this point in his education. A simpler and more direct question is the following: if $\mathbf{A}$ and $\mathbf{B}$ are symmetric n-by-n matrices, when is their product $\mathbf{AB}$ a symmetric matrix? If $\mathbf{AB}$ is to be a symmetric matrix, we must have

$$\mathbf{AB}=(\mathbf{AB})^T=\mathbf{B}^T\mathbf{A}^T.$$

Since $\mathbf{A}$ and $\mathbf{B}$ are symmetric, we have $\mathbf{A}^T=\mathbf{A}$, $\mathbf{B}^T=\mathbf{B}$, so that the above condition becomes

$$\mathbf{AB}=\mathbf{BA}.$$

Thus, *the product of two symmetric n-by-n matrices is a symmetric matrix if and only if the two matrices commute.* Since symmetric matrices are diagonalizable, we can actually construct a family of symmetric matrices such that the product of any two matrices of the family is a symmetric matrix. Let $\mathbf{A}$ be a given symmetric matrix and let $\mathbf{K}$ be an orthogonal matrix of eigenvectors of $\mathbf{A}$. We then have $\mathbf{K}^{-1}\mathbf{A}\,\mathbf{K}=\mathbf{D}(\lambda_1, \ldots, \lambda_n)$ and hence $\mathbf{A}=\mathbf{K}\,\mathbf{D}(\lambda_1, \ldots, \lambda_n)\mathbf{K}^{-1}=\mathbf{K}\,\mathbf{D}(\lambda_1, \ldots, \lambda_n)\mathbf{K}^T$ since $\mathbf{K}$ is orthogonal. Our results concerning commuting matrices tell us that the family B of matrices defined by

$$\mathbf{B}=\mathbf{K}\,\mathbf{D}(\alpha_1, \ldots, \alpha_n)\mathbf{K}^{-1}=\mathbf{K}\,\mathbf{D}(\alpha_1, \ldots, \alpha_n)\mathbf{K}^T \qquad (15.11)$$

for all real numbers $\alpha_1, \ldots, \alpha_n$ commute with the matrix $\mathbf{A}$; that is $\mathbf{AB}=\mathbf{BA}$. Further, for the choice $\alpha_i=\lambda_i$, (15.11) gives $\mathbf{B}=\mathbf{A}$ and hence the family B contains the matrix $\mathbf{A}$ that we started with. It now follows from Eq. (15.11) that

$$\mathbf{B}^T=(\mathbf{K}\,\mathbf{D}(\alpha_1, \ldots, \alpha_n)\mathbf{K}^T)^T=\mathbf{K}\,\mathbf{D}(\alpha_1, \ldots, \alpha_n)\mathbf{K}^T=\mathbf{B};$$

that is, the family B is a family of symmetric matrices. We have thus established that *the family of n-by-n matrices* B *that is defined by*

$$\mathbf{B}=\mathbf{K}\,\mathbf{D}(\alpha_1, \ldots, \alpha_n)\mathbf{K}^T, \quad \mathbf{K}^T\mathbf{K}=\mathbf{E},$$

where $\alpha_1, \ldots, \alpha_n$ *range over the real numbers, is a family of symmetric commuting matrices.* Thus, in particular, we have that *any finite number of products of matrices from the family* B *is a symmetric matrix.* We leave it to you as an exercise to show that products of matrices from the family B have the property that $\mathbf{ABC}=\mathbf{BAC}=\mathbf{BCA}=\mathbf{CAB}$, and so forth for products four at a time, five at a time, etc.

The family of matrices

$$\mathbf{A}(\alpha,\beta,\gamma)=\frac{1}{9}\begin{pmatrix} 4\alpha+\beta+4\gamma & -4\alpha+2\beta+2\gamma & -2\alpha-2\beta+4\gamma \\ -4\alpha+2\beta+2\gamma & 4\alpha+4\beta+\gamma & 2\alpha-4\beta+2\gamma \\ -2\alpha-2\beta+4\gamma & 2\alpha-4\beta+2\gamma & \alpha+4\beta+4\gamma \end{pmatrix}$$

that we constructed earlier in this lecture came from $\mathbf{A}(\alpha,\beta,\gamma)=\mathbf{K}\,\mathbf{D}(\alpha,\beta,\gamma)\mathbf{K}^T$, $\mathbf{K}^T\mathbf{K}=\mathbf{E}$. Thus this family is a family of symmetric commuting matrices for all values of α, β and γ. If we restrict the parameters by $\alpha>0$, $\beta>0$, $\gamma>0$, then the family is a family of positive definite commuting matrices.

Next, we establish the following basic result. *If* $\mathbf{A}$ *is a nonsingular matrix, then there exists an orthogonal matrix* $\mathbf{O}$ *and positive definite matrices* $\mathbf{P}$ *and* $\tilde{\mathbf{P}}$ *such that*

$$\mathbf{A}=\mathbf{O}\,\mathbf{P}=\tilde{\mathbf{P}}\,\mathbf{O}. \qquad (15.12)$$

(We note that the matrices $\mathbf{P}$, $\tilde{\mathbf{P}}$, and $\mathbf{O}$ are unique for given $\mathbf{A}$.) This result is often referred to as the **polar decomposition** theorem. The demonstration of Eq. (15.12) starts by noting that $\mathbf{A}^T\mathbf{A}$ is a positive definite matrix. This was shown in lecture nine since $\mathbf{A}$ is assumed to be a nonsingular matrix. Thus, $\mathbf{A}^T\mathbf{A}$ is diagonalizable and we have

$$\mathbf{A}^T\mathbf{A}=\mathbf{K}\,\mathbf{D}(\lambda_1, \ldots, \lambda_n)\,\mathbf{K}^T, \tag{15.13}$$

where $\mathbf{K}$ is an orthogonal matrix of eigenvectors of $\mathbf{A}^T\mathbf{A}$ and $\lambda_1, \ldots, \lambda_n$ are the eigenvalues of $\mathbf{A}^T\mathbf{A}$. Since the eigenvalues of a positive definite matrix are positive numbers, the matrix

$$\mathbf{P}=\mathbf{K}\,\mathbf{D}(\sqrt{\lambda_1}, \ldots, \sqrt{\lambda_n})\mathbf{K}^T \tag{15.14}$$

is a positive definite (symmetric) matrix (see Eq. (15.5)). This matrix has the property that

$$\begin{aligned}\mathbf{P}^2=\mathbf{P}\,\mathbf{P}&=\mathbf{K}\mathbf{D}(\sqrt{\lambda_1}, \ldots, \sqrt{\lambda_n})\,\mathbf{K}^T\mathbf{K}\mathbf{D}(\sqrt{\lambda_1}, \ldots, \sqrt{\lambda_n})\,\mathbf{K}^T\\ &=\mathbf{K}\mathbf{D}(\lambda_1, \ldots, \lambda_n)\,\mathbf{K}^T=\mathbf{A}^T\mathbf{A},\end{aligned} \tag{15.15}$$

as follows from Eq. (15.13) and $\mathbf{K}^T\mathbf{K}=\mathbf{E}$. Since $\mathbf{P}$ is nonsingular, the equation $\mathbf{A}=\mathbf{O}\,\mathbf{P}$ yields $\mathbf{O}=\mathbf{A}\,\mathbf{P}^{-1}$ and the result will follow if we can show that $\mathbf{O}$ is an orthogonal matrix. We have

$$\mathbf{O}^T\mathbf{O}=(\mathbf{P}^{-1})^T\mathbf{A}^T\mathbf{A}\,\mathbf{P}^{-1}=\mathbf{P}^{-1}(\mathbf{A}^T\mathbf{A})\,\mathbf{P}^{-1},$$

since $\mathbf{P}$ is symmetric $[(\mathbf{P}^{-1})^T=(\mathbf{P}^T)^{-1}=(\mathbf{P})^{-1}=\mathbf{P}^{-1}]$. However, when Eq. (15.15) is used, we then have

$$\mathbf{O}^T\mathbf{O}=\mathbf{P}^{-1}\mathbf{P}^2\mathbf{P}^{-1}=\mathbf{E}$$

and thus $\mathbf{O}$ is an orthogonal matrix. We have now established $\mathbf{A}=\mathbf{O}\,\mathbf{P}$. We now wish to show that $\mathbf{A}=\tilde{\mathbf{P}}\,\mathbf{O}$ where $\tilde{\mathbf{P}}$ is positive definite. We thus have to solve $\mathbf{O}\,\mathbf{P}=\tilde{\mathbf{P}}\,\mathbf{O}$ since $\mathbf{A}=\mathbf{O}\,\mathbf{P}$. This gives $\tilde{\mathbf{P}}=\mathbf{O}\,\mathbf{P}\,\mathbf{O}^T$ and hence $\tilde{\mathbf{P}}$ is positive definite. We finally note that $\mathbf{A}=\tilde{\mathbf{P}}\,\mathbf{O}$ implies

$$\mathbf{A}\,\mathbf{A}^T=\tilde{\mathbf{P}}\,\mathbf{O}\,\mathbf{O}^T\tilde{\mathbf{P}}=\tilde{\mathbf{P}}^2, \tag{15.16}$$

while $\tilde{\mathbf{P}}=\mathbf{O}\,\mathbf{P}\,\mathbf{O}^T$ gives

$$\tilde{\mathbf{P}}^2=\mathbf{O}\,\mathbf{P}^2\mathbf{O}^T \quad\text{or}\quad \begin{aligned}\mathbf{A}\,\mathbf{A}^T&=\mathbf{O}\,\mathbf{A}^T\mathbf{A}\,\mathbf{O}^T\\ &=(\mathbf{A}\,\mathbf{O}^T)^T(\mathbf{A}\,\mathbf{O}^T).\end{aligned} \tag{15.17}$$

If $\mathbf{A}$ is a given n-by-n matrix, we can form the matrices $\mathbf{A}^2=\mathbf{A}\mathbf{A}$, $\mathbf{A}^3=\mathbf{A}\mathbf{A}^2=\mathbf{A}\mathbf{A}\mathbf{A}$, $\mathbf{A}^p=\mathbf{A}\mathbf{A}^{p-1}$. In addition, we define $\mathbf{A}^0=\mathbf{E}$. The following result we state without proof. The proof is beyond the scope of these lectures, but the result is used so often in applications that the student should be familiar with it. The **Cayley-Hamilton theorem** states that *any n-by-n matrix satisfies its own characteristic equation* $p(\mathbf{A})=\mathbf{0}$ (see problems for the proof). Thus, since the characteristic polynomial of $\mathbf{A}$ is given by $p(\lambda)=\det(\mathbf{A}-\lambda\mathbf{E})$, we then have

$$\begin{aligned}p(\lambda)&=a_0(-\lambda)^0+a_1(-\lambda)+a_2(-\lambda)^2\\ &\quad+\ldots+a_{n-1}(-\lambda)^{n-1}+(-\lambda)^n.\end{aligned} \tag{15.18}$$

The matrix **A** thus satisfies

$$a_0\mathbf{E}+a_1(-\mathbf{A})+a_2(-\mathbf{A})^2+\ .\ .\ .\ +a_{n-1}(-\mathbf{A})^{n-1}+(-\mathbf{A})^n=\mathbf{0}. \qquad (15.19)$$

For example, the characteristic polynomial of

$$\mathbf{A}=\begin{pmatrix}-31 & 18\\ -54 & 32\end{pmatrix} \text{ is } p(\lambda)=(\lambda-5)(\lambda+4)=\lambda^2-\lambda-20.$$

We thus have the identity

$$\begin{pmatrix}-31 & 18\\ -54 & 32\end{pmatrix}^2-\begin{pmatrix}-31 & 18\\ -54 & 32\end{pmatrix}-20\begin{pmatrix}1 & 0\\ 0 & 1\end{pmatrix}=\begin{pmatrix}0 & 0\\ 0 & 0\end{pmatrix}.$$

If $\mathbf{A}\in\mathsf{M}_{n,n}$ is a nonsingular matrix, then we can use Eq. (15.19) to compute $\mathbf{A}^{-1}$ in terms of $\mathbf{E}$, $\mathbf{A}$, $\mathbf{A}^2$, . . . , $\mathbf{A}^{n-1}$. This is easily seen by multiplying Eq. (15.19) by $\mathbf{A}^{-1}$:

$$a_0\mathbf{A}^{-1}-a_1\mathbf{E}-a_2(-\mathbf{A})-\ .\ .\ .\ -a_{n-1}(-\mathbf{A})^{n-2}-(-\mathbf{A})^{n-1}=\mathbf{0}\ .$$

Since a_0 is not zero if $\det(\mathbf{A})\neq 0$ [i.e., $p(0)=\det(\mathbf{A}-0\mathbf{E})=\det(\mathbf{A})=a_0$ when we use Eq. (15.18)], we have

$$\mathbf{A}^{-1}=\frac{1}{a_0}(a_1\mathbf{E}+a_2(-\mathbf{A})+\ .\ .\ .\ +a_{n-1}(-\mathbf{A})^{n-2}+(-\mathbf{A})^{n-1}).$$

The importance of the Cayley-Hamilton theorem is that it tells us that *any polynomial in an n-by-n matrix* **A**, *such as*

$$\mathbf{P}(\mathbf{A})=\sum_{i=0}^{N}a_i(\mathbf{A})^i$$

is equal to a polynomial in **A** *whose degree is always less than n.* First off, since **A** satisfies its own characteristic equation $p(\mathbf{A})=\mathbf{0}$ and this equation is a polynomial of degree n in **A**, we accordingly have (see Eq. (15.19))

$$(-\mathbf{A})^n=-a_0\mathbf{E}-a_1(-\mathbf{A})-a_2(-\mathbf{A})^2-\ .\ .\ .\ -a_{n-1}(-\mathbf{A})^{n-1}. \qquad (15.20)$$

Thus the nth power of **A** can be written in terms of **E** and the first $(n-1)$th powers of **A**. If we multiply Eq. (15.20) by $-\mathbf{A}$, the left-hand side becomes $(-\mathbf{A})^{n+1}$ and the right-hand side becomes a polynomial of degree n in $(-\mathbf{A})$. We can eliminate the term on the right-hand side that involves $(-\mathbf{A})^n$ by use of Eq. (15.20). Thus, $(-\mathbf{A})^{n+1}$ can be written in terms of a polynomial of degree $n-1$ in **A**. If we then just continue this procedure, all powers of $-\mathbf{A}$ higher than the $(n-1)$th can be written in terms of the first $(n-1)$ powers of **A** and the result is established.

We end this lecture by establishing the results

$$\mathrm{tr}(\mathbf{A}^p)=\sum_{i=1}^{n}\lambda_i^p, \quad p=1,\ 2,\ .\ .\ .\ , \qquad (15.21)$$

for diagonalizable matrices $\mathbf{A} \in \mathsf{M}_{n,n}$. Since $\mathbf{A}$ is diagonalizable, we have $\mathbf{K}^{-1}\mathbf{A}\,\mathbf{K}=\mathbf{D}(\lambda_1, \ldots, \lambda_n)$ and hence

$$\mathbf{A}=\mathbf{K}\,\mathbf{D}(\lambda_1, \ldots, \lambda_n)\,\mathbf{K}^{-1}. \tag{15.22}$$

Thus

$$\begin{aligned}\mathbf{A}^2 &= \mathbf{K}\,\mathbf{D}(\lambda_1, \ldots, \lambda_n)\,\mathbf{K}^{-1}\mathbf{K}\,\mathbf{D}(\lambda_1, \ldots, \lambda_n)\,\mathbf{K}^{-1}\\ &= \mathbf{K}\,\mathbf{D}(\lambda_1^2, \ldots, \lambda_n^2)\,\mathbf{K}^{-1},\end{aligned}$$

and

$$\mathbf{A}^p=\mathbf{K}\,\mathbf{D}(\lambda_1^p, \ldots, \lambda_n^p)\mathbf{K}^{-1}. \tag{15.23}$$

Now, $\mathrm{tr}(\mathbf{RST})=\mathrm{tr}(\mathbf{TRS})$, and hence Eq. (15.23) gives

$$\begin{aligned}\mathrm{tr}(\mathbf{A}^p) &= \mathrm{tr}[\mathbf{K}\,\mathbf{D}(\lambda_1^p, \ldots, \lambda_n^p)\,\mathbf{K}^{-1}]=\mathrm{tr}[\mathbf{K}^{-1}\mathbf{K}\,\mathbf{D}(\lambda_1^p, \ldots, \lambda_n^p)]\\ &= \mathrm{tr}[\mathbf{D}(\lambda_1^p, \ldots, \lambda_n^p)]=\sum_{i=1}^{n}\lambda_i^p.\end{aligned}$$

The formula (15.21) is often useful in writing the coefficients of the characteristic polynomial of $\mathbf{A}$ in terms of $\mathrm{tr}(\mathbf{A})$, $\mathrm{tr}(\mathbf{A}^2)$, $\mathrm{tr}(\mathbf{A}^3)$, ..., (see problems).

Problems

15.1. A quadratic form $\{x\}^T\mathbf{A}\{x\}$, $\mathbf{A}=\mathbf{A}^T$, and the symmetric matrix $\mathbf{A}$ are called **positive definite (negative definite)** if $\{x\}^T\mathbf{A}\{x\} > 0$ (< 0) for all $\{x\} \neq 0$. If $\{x\}^T\mathbf{A}\{x\} \geq 0$ (≤ 0) for all $\{x\} \neq 0$ the form and the matrix are called **positive (negative) semidefinite**. Finally, if the quadratic form can take both negative and positive values, the matrix and the form are called **indefinite**.

Characterize the following forms (see problem 15.7):

(a) $6x_1^2 + 4x_1x_2 + 9x_3^2$, (b) $-28x_1^2 + 12x_1x_2 - 12x_2^2$,
(c) $23x_1^2 + 24x_1x_2 + 2x_2^2$, (d) $12x_1^2 - 12x_1x_2 + 3x_2^2$,
(e) $-9x_1^2 + 24x_1x_2 - 16x_2^2$,
(f) $18x_1^2 + 15x_2^2 + 21x_3^2 + 12x_1x_2 + 12x_1x_3$,
(g) $x_1^2 + 7x_2^2 + x_3^2 - 8x_1x_2 - 8x_2x_3 - 16x_3x_1$,
(h) $-53x_1^2 - 58x_2^2 - 85x_3^2 + 12x_1x_2 + 36x_2x_3 - 24x_3x_1$,
(i) $126x_1^2 + 84x_2^2 + 35x_3^2 + 84x_2x_3 - 84x_3x_1$,
(j) $-10x_1^2 - 16x_2^2 - 10x_3^2 + 8x_1x_2 + 8x_2x_3 + 16x_3x_1$.

15.2. For each of the following forms determine a so that the form belongs to each one of the five classes described in problem 15.1:

(a) $(5a-1)x_1^2 - 4x_1x_2 + (5a-4)x_2^2$,
(b) $(10a-19)x_1^2 + 6x_1x_2 + (10a-11)x_2^2$,
(c) $3(1-a)x_1^2 + (2-3a)_2^2 + (4-3a)x_3^2 + 4x_1x_2 + 4x_3x_1$,
(d) $(5a+1)x_1^2 + (5a+4)x_2^2 + (5a+6)x_3^2 + (5a-1)x_4^2$
$+ 4x_1x_2 - 24x_3x_4$.

15.3. For each of the following diagonalizable matrices **A** find a 3-parameter family of diagonalizable matrices **B** which commute with **A**:

$$\text{(a)} \begin{pmatrix} -3 & -\frac{1}{2} & 1 \\ 12 & 4 & -6 \\ 4 & 2 & -3 \end{pmatrix}, \quad \text{(b)} \begin{pmatrix} -1 & 0 & 0 \\ \frac{1}{2} & 0 & -1 \\ 1 & 2 & -3 \end{pmatrix}, \quad \text{(c)} \begin{pmatrix} 0 & 2 & 1 \\ 0 & 2 & 0 \\ 4 & -4 & 0 \end{pmatrix},$$

$$\text{(d)} \begin{pmatrix} -10 & 4 & -2 \\ 12 & -8 & 5 \\ 48 & -24 & 14 \end{pmatrix}, \quad \text{(e)} \begin{pmatrix} -19 & 8 & 12 \\ -32 & 13 & 24 \\ -8 & 4 & 3 \end{pmatrix},$$

$$\text{(f)} \begin{pmatrix} 5 & -18 & -42 \\ -6 & 17 & 42 \\ 3 & -9 & -22 \end{pmatrix}.$$

15.4. For each of the matrices **A** given in problem 14.2 find a two- or three-parameter family of symmetric matrices **B** which commute with **A**.

15.5. For each of the following matrices **A**, calculate **O**, **P**, $\tilde{\mathbf{P}}$ of the polar decomposition $\mathbf{A} = \mathbf{OP} = \tilde{\mathbf{P}}\mathbf{O}$

$$\text{(a)} \begin{pmatrix} 1 & \frac{3}{2} \\ 0 & 1 \end{pmatrix}, \quad \text{(b)} \begin{pmatrix} 1 & \frac{8}{3} \\ 0 & 1 \end{pmatrix}, \quad \text{(c)} \begin{pmatrix} \sqrt{3} & 1 & 0 \\ 0 & 2 & 0 \\ 0 & 0 & 1 \end{pmatrix}.$$

15.6. For each of the matrices **A** in problem 9.1:

(a) Express $\mathbf{A}^3$ and $\mathbf{A}^4$ in terms of **E**, **A**, $\mathbf{A}^2$.

(b) Find two polynomials of the second order in **A** equal respectively to

$$f_1(\mathbf{A}) = \mathbf{E} + 2\mathbf{A} - \mathbf{A}^2 + \mathbf{A}^3,$$
$$f_2(\mathbf{A}) = 2\mathbf{E} - \mathbf{A} + 2\mathbf{A}^2 - \mathbf{A}^3 + \mathbf{A}^4.$$

15.7. Prove that a symmetric matrix **A** is

(a) positive semidefinite if and only if it has nonnegative eigenvalues;

(b) negative definite (semidefinite) if and only if it has negative (nonpositive) eigenvalues;

(c) indefinite if and only if it has both positive and negative eigenvalues.

15.8. Let **K** be a given orthogonal matrix. Show that the product of a finite number of matrices of the form $\mathbf{B} = \mathbf{KD}(\alpha_1, \ldots, \alpha_n)\mathbf{K}^T$, where $\alpha_1, \ldots, \alpha_n$ are any real numbers, is independent of the order of its factors.

15.9. Let **A** be a positive semidefinite matrix. Obtain a matrix **P** such that $\mathbf{P}^m = \mathbf{A}$, where m is a positive integer.

15.10. Let **A** be symmetric. Obtain a matrix **P** such that $\mathbf{P}^{(2m+1)} = \mathbf{A}$, where m is a positive integer.

15.11. A **polynomial in x with matrix coefficients** is a matrix $\mathbf{F}(x)$ of the form

$$\mathbf{F}(x) = \mathbf{F}_0 + \mathbf{F}_1 x + \ldots + \mathbf{F}_p x^p,$$

where $\mathbf{F}_0, \mathbf{F}_1, \ldots, \mathbf{F}_p$ are n-by-n matrices and the positive integer p is the degree of the polynomial. For any n-by-n matrix **A**, $\mathbf{F}(\mathbf{A})$ will denote the matrix

$$\mathbf{F}(\mathbf{A}) = \mathbf{F}_0 + \mathbf{F}_1\mathbf{A} + \ldots + \mathbf{F}_p\mathbf{A}^p.$$

Show, by way of example, that if $\mathbf{A}(x)$, $\mathbf{B}(x)$, and $\mathbf{C}(x)$ are three polynomials with matrix coefficients such that $\mathbf{A}(x) = \mathbf{B}(x)\mathbf{C}(x)$ for all x, then it is not in general true that $\mathbf{A}(\mathbf{Y}) = \mathbf{B}(\mathbf{Y})\mathbf{C}(\mathbf{Y})$.

15.12. Let $\mathbf{F}(x)$, $\mathbf{G}(x)$ be two given polynomials with matrix coefficients and $\mathbf{A}$ a given matrix such that $\mathbf{G}(x) = \mathbf{F}(x)(\mathbf{A} - x\mathbf{E})$ for all x. Show that $\mathbf{G}(\mathbf{A}) = \mathbf{0}$. [Write $\mathbf{F}(x)$ in polynomial form, calculate $\mathbf{G}(x) = \mathbf{F}(x)(\mathbf{A} - x\mathbf{E})$, then $\mathbf{G}(\mathbf{A})$.]

15.13. Let the elements a_{ij} of a square matrix $\mathbf{A}$ be (algebraic) polynomials in x of degree $\leqq p$. Show that $\mathbf{A}$ can be written as a polynomial in x with matrix coefficients and degree $\leqq p$.

15.14. If $\mathbf{A}$ is an n-by-n matrix, then show that

(i) The adjugate matrix $(\mathbf{A} - \lambda\mathbf{E})^*$ of $(\mathbf{A} - \lambda\mathbf{E})$ can be written as a matrix polynomial in λ of degree $\leqq n - 1$.

(ii) $\mathbf{E}(-\lambda)^n + \mathbf{E}a_{n-1}(-\lambda)^{n-1} + \ldots + \mathbf{E}a_0 = (\mathbf{A} - \lambda\mathbf{E})^*(\mathbf{A} - \lambda\mathbf{E})$, where $(-\lambda)^n + a_{n-1}(-\lambda)^{n-1} + \ldots + a_0$ is the characteristic polynomial of $\mathbf{A}$.

From the above two statements deduce the Cayley-Hamilton theorem. [Use problem 11.7.]

15.15. If $s_m = x_1^m + x_2^m + \ldots + x_n^m$, where m is a positive integer $\leqq n$, then for the polynomial

$$f(x) = (x - x_1)(x - x_2) \ldots (x - x_n) = x^n + p_1 x^{n-1} + \ldots + p_{n-1}x + p_n,$$

we have the **Newton's formulae**

$$\begin{aligned}
&s_1 + p_1 = 0\\
&s_2 + p_1 s_1 + 2p_2 = 0\\
&s_3 + p_1 s_2 + p_2 s_1 + 3p_3 = 0\\
&\cdot\\
&\cdot\\
&\cdot\\
&s_n + p_1 s_{n-1} + p_2 s_{n-2} + \ldots + p_{n-1}s_1 + np_n = 0.
\end{aligned}$$

Use these formulae to prove that the characteristic polynomial of an n-by-n matrix $\mathbf{A}$ can be expressed in terms of $\mathrm{tr}(\mathbf{A})$, $\mathrm{tr}(\mathbf{A}^2)$, . . . , $\mathrm{tr}(\mathbf{A}^n)$.

15.16. Let the deformation of a body B be $\{y\} = \mathbf{A}\{x\}$ where $\mathbf{A}$ is a nonsingular matrix. Show that this deformation can be considered as a pure homogeneous strain superimposed on a rotation or as the same rotation superimposed on a pure homogeneous strain. [Use the polar decomposition theorem].

LECTURE 16

Quadratic Forms

Quadratic forms • Diagonalization of a quadratic form • Simultaneous diagonalization of two quadratic forms • Simplification of Lagrange's equations • Problems

As usual, we use $\{x\}$ to denote an arbitrary element of $\mathsf{M}_{n,1}$. A scalar function $\Phi(\{x\})$ of the n variables $x_1, \ldots, x_n$ that comprise $\{x\}$ is said to be a **quadratic form** with coefficient matrix $\mathbf{A} \in \mathsf{M}_{n,n}$ if it can be written in the form

$$\Phi(\{x\}) = \{x\}^T\mathbf{A}\{x\}. \tag{16.1}$$

For $n=2$, $a_{11}(x_1)^2 + a_{12}x_1x_2 + a_{21}x_2x_1 + a_{22}(x_2)^2 = a_{11}(x_1)^2 + (a_{12}+a_{21})x_1x_2 + a_{22}(x_2)^2$ is a quadratic form whose coefficient matrix $\mathbf{A}$ is given by $\mathbf{A} \equiv (a_{ij})$. Similarly, for $n=3$, $a_{11}(x_1)^2 + a_{22}(x_2)^2 + a_{33}(x_3)^2 + (a_{12}+a_{21})x_1x_2 + (a_{13}+a_{31})x_1x_3 + (a_{23}+a_{32})x_2x_3$ is a quadratic form. These examples show that the coefficient of x_ix_j is given by $(a_{ij}+a_{ji})$ when $i \neq j$. If $a_{ij} = -a_{ji}$, for $i \neq j$, the coefficient of x_ix_j would be zero. The requirement $a_{ij} = -a_{ji}$ for $i \neq j$ is very close to the requirement that the coefficient matrix be skewsymmetric. We may thus expect that there will be some simplification of a quadratic form in terms of the symmetry properties of its coefficient matrix.

Let $\mathbf{V}$ be a skewsymmetric matrix so that $\mathbf{V}^T = -\mathbf{V}$. If we construct a quadratic form with $\mathbf{V}$ as the coefficient matrix, we have $\Phi(\{x\}) = \{x\}^T\mathbf{V}\{x\}$. Since Φ is a scalar, it is equal to its own transpose, and hence we have

$$\begin{aligned}\Phi(\{x\}) &= \{x\}^T\mathbf{V}\{x\} = (\{x\}^T\mathbf{V}\{x\})^T = \{x\}^T\mathbf{V}^T\{x\} \\ &= -\{x\}^T\mathbf{V}\{x\} = -\Phi(\{x\}).\end{aligned}$$

Since the only function which is equal to its negative for all values of its arguments is the identically zero function, we have

$$\Phi(\{x\}) = \{x\}^T\mathbf{V}\{x\} = 0, \quad \text{when} \quad \mathbf{V}^T = -\mathbf{V}; \tag{16.2}$$

a quadratic form with a skewsymmetric coefficient matrix vanishes identically.

The above result allows us to simplify quadratic forms in a very important way. We saw in lecture 9 that any n-by-n matrix $\mathbf{A}$ can be uniquely decomposed into the sum of a symmetric matrix and a skewsymmetric matrix:

$$\mathbf{A}=\mathbf{U}+\mathbf{V}, \quad \mathbf{U}^T=\mathbf{U}, \quad \mathbf{V}^T=-\mathbf{V}, \tag{16.3}$$

where

$$\mathbf{U}=\frac{1}{2}(\mathbf{A}+\mathbf{A}^T), \quad \mathbf{V}=\frac{1}{2}(\mathbf{A}-\mathbf{A}^T). \tag{16.4}$$

If $\mathbf{A}$ is the coefficient matrix of a quadratic form Φ, then Eq. (16.3) gives

$$\Phi(\{x\})=\{x\}^T\mathbf{A}\{x\}=\{x\}^T\mathbf{U}\{x\}+\{x\}^T\mathbf{V}\{x\}.$$

The quadratic form $\{x\}^T\mathbf{V}\{x\}$ vanishes identically, however, since $\mathbf{V}$ is skewsymmetric. We thus have

$$\Phi(\{x\})=\{x\}^T\mathbf{A}\{x\}=\{x\}^T\mathbf{U}\{x\}, \quad \mathbf{U}=\frac{1}{2}(\mathbf{A}+\mathbf{A}^T). \tag{16.5}$$

Thus, *the coefficient matrix of a quadratic form can be replaced by its symmetric part without altering the values of the quadratic form for any* $\{x\}\in \mathsf{M}_{n,1}$. For example, if

$$\mathbf{A}=\begin{pmatrix} 1 & -2 \\ 3 & -5 \end{pmatrix},$$

then

$$\mathbf{A}^T=\begin{pmatrix} 1 & 3 \\ -2 & -5 \end{pmatrix}, \quad \mathbf{U}=\frac{1}{2}(\mathbf{A}+\mathbf{A}^T)=\begin{pmatrix} 1 & \tfrac{1}{2} \\ \tfrac{1}{2} & -5 \end{pmatrix},$$

and $\{x\}^T\mathbf{A}\{x\}=(x_1)^2+(-2+3)x_1x_2-5(x_2)^2$, so that $\{x\}^T\mathbf{U}\{x\}=(x_1)^2+(\tfrac{1}{2}+\tfrac{1}{2})x_1x_2-5(x_2)^2=\{x\}^T\mathbf{A}\{x\}$. In particular, we are free to take the coefficient matrix of a quadratic form as a symmetric matrix, for if it is not symmetric, we can replace it by a symmetric matrix with no change in the quadratic form. From now on we shall assume that the coefficient matrix of any quadratic form is symmetric:

$$\Phi(\{x\})=\{x\}^T\mathbf{A}\{x\}, \quad \mathbf{A}^T=\mathbf{A}.$$

In general, a quadratic form can be fairly complicated since it will involve products of the form x_ix_j for each value of i and j:

$$\Phi(\{x\})=\{x\}^T\mathbf{A}\{x\}=\sum_{i=1}^{n}\sum_{j=1}^{n} a_{ij}x_ix_j. \tag{16.6}$$

We would thus like to simplify such an expression if at all possible. Since the coefficient matrix of a quadratic form is given, we can not change this.

Thus the only thing that we can do is to try to find another collection of independent variables which will replace the x's and which will yield the desired simplification. If **K** is an n-by-n nonsingular matrix, we try the substitution

$$\{x\}=\mathbf{K}\{y\}, \quad \{y\}=\mathbf{K}^{-1}\{x\}. \tag{16.7}$$

Since $\{x\}^T=(\mathbf{K}\{y\})^T=\{y\}^T\mathbf{K}^T$, the substitution of (16.7) into Eq. (16.6) gives us

$$\Phi(\{x\})=\Phi(\mathbf{K}\{y\})=\{y\}^T\mathbf{K}^T\mathbf{A}\,\mathbf{K}\,\{y\}. \tag{16.8}$$

Thus, if we define the new quadratic form in the variables $\{y\}$ by

$$\Phi^*(\{y\})=\{y\}^T\mathbf{K}^T\mathbf{A}\,\mathbf{K}\{y\}, \tag{16.9}$$

we have

$$\Phi(\{x\})=\Phi^*(\{y\})=\{y\}^T\mathbf{K}^T\mathbf{A}\,\mathbf{K}\{y\} \text{ for } \{x\}=\mathbf{K}\{y\}. \tag{16.10}$$

The equality $\Phi(\{x\})=\Phi^*(\{y\})$ tells us that we can replace one quadratic form $\Phi(\{x\})$ by the new quadratic form $\Phi^*(\{y\})$ provided we retain the relation $\{x\}=\mathbf{K}\{y\}$. The coefficient matrix of Φ^* is $\mathbf{K}^T\mathbf{AK}$, however. Thus, since **K** was an arbitrary nonsingular matrix, the possibility presents itself to choose the matrix **K** so that the new coefficient matrix $\mathbf{K}^T\mathbf{AK}$ is "simpler" than the coefficient matrix **A** of the original quadratic form. The notion of simplicity should reflect the use that is to be made of the matrix $\mathbf{K}^T\mathbf{AK}$, namely the coefficient matrix of a quadratic form, and hence we want to choose **K** so that $\{y\}^T\mathbf{K}^T\mathbf{A}\,\mathbf{K}\{y\}$ is as simple as possible. The simplest quadratic form is a sum of squares, and hence we are lead to ask whether we can choose **K** so that we have

$$\mathbf{K}^T\mathbf{A}\,\mathbf{K}=\mathbf{D}, \tag{16.11}$$

where **D** is a diagonal matrix. If Eq. (16.11) is satisfied, then Eq. (16.10) gives $\Phi^*(\{y\})=\{y\}^T\mathbf{D}\{y\}$, which is indeed a sum of squares: $\Phi^*(\{y\})=\alpha_1(y_1)^2+\alpha_2(y_2)^2+\ .\ .\ .\ +\alpha_n(y_n)^2$ where $\mathbf{D}=\mathbf{D}(\alpha_1,\ .\ .\ .\ ,\ \alpha_n)$.

Our search for simplification of a quadratic form with coefficient matrix **A** has been reduced to the search for nonsingular matrices **K** such that

$$\mathbf{K}^T\mathbf{A}\,\mathbf{K}=\mathbf{D}. \tag{16.12}$$

Since **K** is still arbitrary to within the constraint $\det(\mathbf{K})\neq 0$, we certainly can take **K** to be an orthogonal matrix, in which case we have

$$\mathbf{K}^T=\mathbf{K}^{-1}. \tag{16.13}$$

Under these conditions, Eq. (16.12) becomes

$$\mathbf{K}^{-1}\mathbf{A}\,\mathbf{K}=\mathbf{D}. \tag{16.14}$$

Now, **A** is the coefficient matrix of a quadratic form, and hence **A** is a symmetric matrix. Thus, **A** is diagonalizable and possesses an orthogonal matrix of eigenvectors. If **K** is thus chosen to be an orthogonal matrix of eigenvectors of **A**, then Eq. (16.14) is satisfied if we take $\mathbf{D}=\mathbf{D}(\lambda_1, \ldots, \lambda_n)$ where the λ's are the eigenvalues of **A** that are associated with the eigenvectors that constitute the columns of **K**. We thus have the following result. *If* **A** *is a (symmetric) coefficient matrix of a quadratic form* $\Phi(\{x\})$, *then the substitution* $\{x\}=\mathbf{K}\{y\}$ *reduces* $\Phi(\{x\})$ *to the equivalent quadratic form* $\Phi(\{x\})=\Phi^*(\{y\})=\{y\}^T\mathbf{D}(\lambda_1, \ldots, \lambda_n)\{y\}$ *if* **K** *is an orthogonal matrix of eigenvectors of* **A** *with associated eigenvalues* $\lambda_1, \ldots, \lambda_n$.

The process whereby we reduce a quadratic form to a sum of squares by a substitution $\{x\}=\mathbf{K}\{y\}$ is called **diagonalization** of a quadratic form. The above result states that a quadratic form is diagonalized by finding an orthogonal matrix **K** of eigenvectors of the coefficient matrix **A** of $\{x\}^T\mathbf{A}\{x\}$, in which case we have $\{x\}^T\mathbf{A}\{x\}=\{y\}^T\mathbf{D}(\lambda_1, \ldots, \lambda_n)\{y\}$ $=\lambda_1(y_1)^2+\ldots+\lambda_n(y_n)^2$, where $\{x\}=\mathbf{K}\{y\}$.

If we only have to diagonalize one quadratic form, then the above method will always work; that is, we do not have to look for more general matrices **K** than the one we construct from a system of n mutually orthogonal unit eigenvectors of **A**. There are important situations, however, in which we have to diagonalize two quadratic forms by the single substitution $\{x\}=\mathbf{T}\{r\}$. Suppose that the two quadratic forms are

$$\Phi(\{x\})=\{x\}^T\mathbf{A}\{x\}, \qquad \Psi(\{x\})=\{x\}^T\mathbf{B}\{x\}, \tag{16.15}$$

and that the coefficient matrix **A** is positive definite. If we make the substitution $\{x\}=\mathbf{K}\{y\}$, where **K** is an orthogonal matrix of eigenvectors of **A**,

$$\mathbf{K}^{-1}\mathbf{A}\,\mathbf{K}=\mathbf{D}(\lambda_1, \ldots, \lambda_n), \quad \mathbf{K}^{-1}=\mathbf{K}^T, \tag{16.16}$$

then

$$\Phi(\{x\})=\{y\}^T\mathbf{D}(\lambda_1, \ldots, \lambda_n)\{y\}, \tag{16.17}$$

and

$$\Psi(\{x\})=\{y\}^T\mathbf{K}^T\mathbf{B}\,\mathbf{K}\{y\}. \tag{16.18}$$

Since $\lambda_1, \ldots, \lambda_n$ are the eigenvalues of **A** and **A** is positive definite, we have $\lambda_i>0$, and hence the matrix

$$\mathbf{P}=\mathbf{D}(\lambda_1^{-1/2}, \lambda_2^{-1/2}, \ldots, \lambda_n^{-1/2}) \tag{16.19}$$

is a real matrix with the properties

$$\mathbf{P}=\mathbf{P}^T, \qquad \mathbf{P}^T\mathbf{D}(\lambda_1, \ldots, \lambda_n)\mathbf{P}=\mathbf{E}. \tag{16.20}$$

Thus, if we make the further substitution $\{y\}=\mathbf{P}\{z\}$, then Eqs. (16.17) and (16.18) become

$$\Phi(\{x\})=\{z\}^T\mathbf{P}^T\mathbf{D}(\lambda_1, \ldots, \lambda_n)\mathbf{P}\{z\}=\{z\}^T\{z\}, \tag{16.21}$$

$$\Psi(\{x\})=\{z\}^T\mathbf{P}^T\mathbf{K}^T\mathbf{B}\,\mathbf{K}\,\mathbf{P}\{z\}, \tag{16.22}$$

where

$$\{x\}=\mathbf{K}\{y\}=\mathbf{K}\,\mathbf{P}\{z\}. \tag{16.23}$$

The result given by Eqs. (16.21) and (16.23) are the key to the problem. Equations (16.21) and (16.23) actually just restate the result we obtained in lecture 14 to the effect that we can find a matrix $\mathbf{U}=\mathbf{KP}$ such that $\mathbf{U}^T\mathbf{A}\,\mathbf{U}=\mathbf{D}(\pm 1, \ldots, \pm 1)$. Since $\mathbf{A}$ is positive definite, and $\mathbf{U}^T\mathbf{A}\,\mathbf{U}=\mathbf{D}(\lambda_1/|\lambda_1|, \ldots, \lambda_n/|\lambda_n|)$, we have $\mathbf{U}^T\mathbf{A}\,\mathbf{U}=\mathbf{D}(1, \ldots, 1)=\mathbf{E}$ and $\{z\}^T\mathbf{U}^T\mathbf{A}\,\mathbf{U}\{z\}=\{z\}^T\mathbf{E}\{z\}=\{z\}^T\{z\}$.

Now, $\mathbf{P}^T\mathbf{K}^T\mathbf{B}\,\mathbf{K}\,\mathbf{P}$ is a symmetric matrix, and hence we can find an orthogonal matrix $\mathbf{W}$ such that

$$\mathbf{W}^T(\mathbf{P}^T\mathbf{K}^T\mathbf{B}\,\mathbf{K}\,\mathbf{P})\mathbf{W}=\mathbf{D}(\alpha_1, \ldots, \alpha_n), \quad \mathbf{W}^T\mathbf{W}=\mathbf{E}; \tag{16.24}$$

that is, $\mathbf{W}$ is an orthogonal matrix of eigenvectors of the symmetric matrix $\mathbf{P}^T\mathbf{K}^T\mathbf{B}\,\mathbf{K}\,\mathbf{P}$ and $\alpha_1, \ldots, \alpha_n$ are the associated eigenvalues of this matrix. Thus, if we make the further substitution $\{z\}=\mathbf{W}\{r\}$, Eqs. (16.21) and (16.22) give the **simultaneous diagonalization**

$$\Phi(\{x\})=\{r\}^T\mathbf{W}^T\mathbf{W}\{r\}=\{r\}^T\{r\}, \tag{16.25}$$

$$\Psi(\{x\})=\{r\}^T\mathbf{W}^T\mathbf{P}^T\mathbf{K}^T\mathbf{B}\,\mathbf{K}\,\mathbf{P}\,\mathbf{W}\{r\}=\{r\}^T\mathbf{D}(\alpha_1, \ldots, \alpha_n)\{r\}, \tag{16.26}$$

where

$$\{x\}=\mathbf{K}\{y\}=\mathbf{K}\,\mathbf{P}\{z\}=\mathbf{K}\,\mathbf{P}\,\mathbf{W}\{r\}. \tag{16.27}$$

The reason why this procedure works is because the substitution $\{z\}=\mathbf{W}\{r\}$ leaves the quadratic form $\{z\}^T\{z\}$ diagonalized since $\mathbf{W}$ is orthogonal: $\{z\}^T\{z\}=\{r\}^T\mathbf{W}^T\mathbf{W}\{r\}=\{r\}^T\{r\}$ (an orthogonal substitution $\{z\}=\mathbf{W}\{r\}$ leaves the norm $||\{z\}||^2=\{z\}^T\{z\}$ unchanged).

It is worth putting all of this into words. *If* $\mathbf{A}$ *and* $\mathbf{B}$ *are coefficient matrices of two quadratic forms* $\Phi(\{x\})$ *and* $\Psi(\{x\})$ *and if* $\mathbf{A}$ *is positive definite, then there exists a matrix* $\mathbf{T}$ *such that the substitution*

$$\{x\}=\mathbf{T}\{r\} \tag{16.28}$$

diagonalizes both of the quadratic forms $\Phi(\{x\})$ *and* $\Psi(\{x\})$. *The matrix* $\mathbf{T}$ *is given by*

$$\mathbf{T}=\mathbf{K}\,\mathbf{P}\,\mathbf{W}, \tag{16.29}$$

where

$$\mathbf{K}^{-1}\mathbf{A}\,\mathbf{K}=\mathbf{D}(\lambda_1, \ldots, \lambda_n), \qquad \mathbf{K}^{-1}=\mathbf{K}^T, \tag{16.30}$$

$$\mathbf{P}^{-1}=\mathbf{D}(\sqrt{\lambda_1}, \ldots, \sqrt{\lambda_n}), \tag{16.31}$$

$$\mathbf{W}^{-1}(\mathbf{P}^T\mathbf{K}^T\mathbf{B}\,\mathbf{K}\,\mathbf{P})\mathbf{W}=\mathbf{D}(\alpha_1, \ldots, \alpha_n), \qquad \mathbf{W}^{-1}=\mathbf{W}^T, \tag{16.32}$$

and we have

$$\Phi(\{x\})=\{x\}^T\mathbf{A}\{x\}=\{r\}^T\{r\}, \tag{16.33}$$

$$\Psi(\{x\})=\{x\}^T\mathbf{B}\{x\}=\{r\}^T\mathbf{D}\,(\alpha_1, \ldots, \alpha_n)\{r\}, \tag{16.34}$$

under the substitution $\{x\}=\mathbf{T}\{r\}$.

Let $\{x\}=\{x(t)\}$ be an n-tuple of functions of the variable t and let $\{\dot{x}\}=d\{x(t)\}/dt$ be the n-tuple of functions that is obtained from $\{x\}$ by differentiation with respect to the variable t. We assume that **A** and **B** are constant n-by-n symmetric matrices with **A** being positive definite. We can then define the scalar function $L(\{x\}, \{\dot{x}\})$ by the relation

$$L(\{x\}, \{\dot{x}\})=\frac{1}{2}\{\dot{x}\}^T\mathbf{A}\{\dot{x}\}-\frac{1}{2}\{x\}^T\mathbf{B}\{x\}. \tag{16.35}$$

Thus $2L$ is the difference of the two quadratic forms $\{\dot{x}\}^T\mathbf{A}\{\dot{x}\}$ and $\{x\}^T\mathbf{B}\{x\}$. If we define $\{r\}=\{r(t)\}$ by the relation

$$\{x(t)\}=\mathbf{T}\{r(t)\}, \tag{16.36}$$

where **T** is a matrix of constants that is defined by Eqs. (16.29) through (16.32), then we have ($\{\dot{x}\}=\mathbf{T}\{\dot{r}\}$)

$$\begin{aligned} L(\{\dot{x}\}, \{x\}) &= L(\mathbf{T}\{\dot{r}\}, \mathbf{T}\{r\})=L^*(\{\dot{r}\}, \{r\}) \\ &= \frac{1}{2}\{\dot{r}\}^T\{\dot{r}\}-\frac{1}{2}\{r\}^T\mathbf{D}(\alpha_1, \ldots, \alpha_n)\{r\}, \end{aligned} \tag{16.37}$$

when Eqs. (16.33) and (16.34) are used. Thus the diagonalization of two quadratic forms allows us to reduce the function L to a sum of squares in the arguments $\dot{r}_1, \ldots, \dot{r}_n, r_1, \ldots, r_n$. The importance of being able to do this lies in the fact that a great many problems in the physical world satisfy differential equations that are obtained according to the prescription (Lagrange's equations)

$$\frac{d}{dt}\left\{\frac{\partial L}{\partial \dot{x}}\right\}-\left\{\frac{\partial L}{\partial x}\right\}=\{0\}, \tag{16.38}$$

where the notation $\{\partial L/\partial x\}$ is that introduced in lecture 9. Since **A** and **B** are symmetric, Eq. (16.35) gives

$$\left\{\frac{\partial L}{\partial \dot{x}}\right\}=\mathbf{A}\{\dot{x}\}, \quad \left\{\frac{\partial L}{\partial x}\right\}=-\mathbf{B}\{x\}, \quad \frac{d}{dt}\left\{\frac{\partial L}{\partial \dot{x}}\right\}=\mathbf{A}\ddot{x},$$

and so Eq. (16.38) gives

$$\mathbf{A}\{\ddot{x}\}+\mathbf{B}\{x\}=0. \tag{16.39}$$

If we make the transformation $\{x\}=\mathbf{T}\{r\}$, $L(\{\dot{x}\}, \{x\})=L^*(\{\dot{r}\}, \{r\})$

and the system (16.38) becomes

$$\frac{d}{dt}\left\{\frac{\partial L^*}{\partial \dot{r}}\right\}-\left\{\frac{\partial L^*}{\partial r}\right\}=\{0\}.$$

Since $\{\partial L^*/\partial \dot{r}\}=\{\dot{r}\}$, $\{\partial L^*/\partial r\}=-\mathbf{D}(\alpha_1, \ldots, \alpha_n)\{r\}$, we thus have

$$\{\ddot{r}\}+\mathbf{D}(\alpha_1, \ldots, \alpha_n)\{r\}=\{0\}, \qquad (16.40)$$

that is

$$\ddot{r}_i+\alpha_i r_i=0, \qquad i=1, \ldots, n, \qquad (16.41)$$

which is a significant simplification over Eq. (16.39) even when we write Eq. (16.39) in the equivalent form

$$\{\ddot{x}\}+\mathbf{A}^{-1}\mathbf{B}\{x\}=\{0\},$$

since $\mathbf{A}^{-1}\mathbf{B}$ is not symmetric, in general. Once we have solved each of the n independent equations (16.41) for $\{r_i(t)\}$ we can then find $\{x(t)\}$ by $\{x(t)\}=\mathbf{T}\{r(t)\}$. The general solution of Eqs. (16.41) is given by

$$r_i(t)=F_i\cos(\alpha_i t)+G_i\sin(\alpha_i t),$$

where F_i and G_i are constants. The function $r_i(t)$ is a periodic function of t with period $2\pi/\alpha_i$ and frequency α_i. Thus, the numbers $\alpha_i, \ldots, \alpha_n$ that we obtain in the simultaneous diagonalization process give us the frequencies of $\{r(t)\}$ and hence of $\{x(t)\}$ directly. The equations (16.39) describe what is called a system of coupled linear oscillators. The physical world being what it is, these equations arise at one time or another in almost every branch of the quantified sciences. It is primarily for this reason that we have included the problem of simultaneous diagonalization of two quadratic forms, since neglecting it would leave the student with a definite handicap.

Problems

16.1. Diagonalize the following quadratic forms:

(a) $19x_1^2+11x_2^2-6x_1x_2$, (b) $-3x_1^2+3x_2^2+8x_1x_2$,
(c) $9x_1^2+16x_2^2+24x_1x_2$, (d) $2x_1^2-7x_2^2-12x_1x_2$,
(e) $41x_1^2+31x_2^2-23x_3^2+24x_1x_2-48x_1x_3+72x_2x_3$,
(f) $2x_1^2+11x_2^2+5x_3^2-4x_1x_2-20x_1x_3-16x_2x_3$,
(g) $-19x_1^2+50x_2^2+67x_3^2+36x_1x_2+96x_1x_3-60x_2x_3$.

16.2. Diagonalize simultaneously the following pairs of quadratic forms:

(a) $\frac{1}{5}(17x_1^2+8x_2^2-12x_1x_2)$, $\frac{1}{10}(-16x_1^2+16x_2^2-24x_1x_2)$;

(b) $5x_1^2 + 5x_2^2 - 8x_1x_2, \quad \frac{1}{10}(99x_1^2 + 75x_2^2 - 150x_1x_2);$

(c) $\frac{1}{9}(21x_1^2 + 12x_2^2 + 21x_3^2 + 12x_1x_2 + 24x_1x_3 + 12x_2x_3),$

$\frac{1}{81}(-12x_1^2 + 96x_2^2 - 165x_3^2 + 24x_1x_2 - 96x_1x_3 - 12x_2x_3).$

16.3. Reduce each of the following systems of equations to the form $\ddot{r}_i + \alpha_i r_i = 0, \quad i = 1, 2, \ldots$:

(a) $\frac{37}{10}\ddot{x}_1 + \frac{9}{10}\ddot{x}_2 + \frac{6}{5}x_1 - \frac{8}{5}x_2 = 0,$

$\frac{9}{10}\ddot{x}_1 + \frac{13}{10}\ddot{x}_2 - \frac{8}{5}x_1 - \frac{6}{5}x_2 = 0;$

(b) $\frac{17}{5}\ddot{x}_1 - \frac{6}{5}\ddot{x}_2 - \frac{16}{10}x_1 - \frac{12}{10}x_2 = 0,$

$-\frac{6}{5}\ddot{x}_1 + \frac{8}{5}\ddot{x}_2 - \frac{12}{10}x_1 + \frac{16}{10}x_2 = 0;$

(c) $\frac{41}{5}\ddot{x}_1 + \frac{12}{5}\ddot{x}_2 - \frac{9}{5}x_1 + \frac{12}{5}x_2 = 0,$

$\frac{12}{5}\ddot{x}_1 + \frac{9}{5}\ddot{x}_2 + \frac{12}{5}x_1 + \frac{9}{5}x_2 = 0;$

(d) $5\ddot{x}_1 - 4\ddot{x}_2 + \frac{99}{10}x_1 - \frac{75}{10}x_2 = 0,$

$-4\ddot{x}_1 + 5\ddot{x}_2 - \frac{75}{10}x_1 + \frac{75}{10}x_2 = 0;$

(e) $\frac{7}{3}\ddot{x}_1 + \frac{2}{3}\ddot{x}_2 + \frac{4}{3}\ddot{x}_3 - \frac{4}{27}x_1 + \frac{4}{27}x_2 - \frac{16}{27}x_3 = 0,$

$\frac{2}{3}\ddot{x}_1 + \frac{4}{3}\ddot{x}_2 + \frac{2}{3}\ddot{x}_3 + \frac{4}{27}x_1 + \frac{32}{27}x_2 - \frac{2}{27}x_3 = 0,$

$\frac{4}{3}\ddot{x}_1 + \frac{2}{3}\ddot{x}_2 + \frac{7}{3}\ddot{x}_3 - \frac{16}{27}x_1 - \frac{2}{27}x_2 - \frac{55}{27}x_3 = 0.$

16.4. Let $\Phi(\{z\}) = \{z\}^T\mathbf{A}\{z\}$, $\mathbf{A} = \mathbf{A}^T$. Prove that

$$\left\{\frac{\partial\Phi}{\partial z}\right\} = 2\mathbf{A}\{z\}.$$

16.5. Let $\Phi(\{z\}) = \{z\}^T\mathbf{A}\{z\}$, where $\mathbf{A} = \mathbf{A}^T$, $\{z\} = \mathbf{B}\{y\}$ and $\Phi(\mathbf{B}\{y\}) = \Phi^*(\{y\})$. Prove that

$$\left\{\frac{\partial\Phi}{\partial z}\right\} = (\mathbf{B}^T)^{-1}\left\{\frac{\partial\Phi^*}{\partial y}\right\}.$$

16.6. Let $L(\{\dot{x}\}, \{x\}) = \{\dot{x}\}^T\mathbf{A}\{\dot{x}\} - \{x\}^T\mathbf{B}\{x\}$ where $\mathbf{A}$ and $\mathbf{B}$ are symmetric matrices. If $\{x\} = \mathbf{T}\{r\}$ and $L^*(\{\dot{r}\}, \{r\}) = L(\mathbf{T}\{\dot{r}\}, \mathbf{T}\{r\})$ show that

$$\frac{d}{dt}\left\{\frac{\partial L}{\partial \dot{x}}\right\} - \left\{\frac{\partial L}{\partial x}\right\} = (\mathbf{T}^T)^{-1}\left(\frac{d}{dt}\left\{\frac{\partial L^*}{\partial \dot{r}}\right\} - \left\{\frac{\partial L^*}{\partial r}\right\}\right).$$

16.7. The determinant of the matrix

$$\mathbf{\Delta} = \begin{pmatrix} \mathbf{A} & \{b\} \\ \{b\}^T & d \end{pmatrix}$$

is called the **discriminant** of

$$\Phi(\{x\}) = \{x\}^T\mathbf{A}\{x\} + 2\{x\}^T\{b\} + d$$

where $\mathbf{A}^T = \mathbf{A} \in \mathsf{M}_{n,n}$ and $\{b\} \in \mathsf{M}_{n,1}$. Show that

$$\Phi[\mathbf{P}(\{x\} + \{w\})] = \{x\}^T\mathbf{P}^T\mathbf{A}\mathbf{P}\{x\} + 2\{x\}^T(\mathbf{P}^T\mathbf{A}\mathbf{P}\{w\} + \mathbf{P}^T\{b\}) + (\{w\}^T\mathbf{P}^T\mathbf{A}\mathbf{P}\{w\} + 2\{w\}^T\mathbf{P}^T\{b\} + d),$$

and deduce that

(i) the discriminant $|\mathbf{\Delta}|$ is **invariant** under rotations, translations and reflections, i.e. the discriminants of $\Phi(\{x\})$ and $\Phi[\mathbf{P}(\{x\} + \{w\})]$ are the same if $\{w\} \in \mathsf{M}_{n,1}$ and $\mathbf{P} \in \mathsf{M}_{n,n}$ is an orthogonal matrix;
(ii) if $\text{rank}(\mathbf{A}) = n$ then $|\mathbf{\Delta}| = |\mathbf{A}|[d - \{b\}^T\mathbf{A}^{-1}\{b\}]$;
(iii) if $\text{rank}(\mathbf{A}) < n - 1$ then $|\mathbf{\Delta}| = 0$.

[Use the problems 11.3, 11.11, 11.16 and 11.17.]

16.8. Let $|\mathbf{\Delta}|$ be the discriminant of

$$\Phi(\{x\}) = \{x\}^T\mathbf{D}\{x\} + 2\{x\}^T\{b\} + d,$$

where $\text{rank}(\mathbf{D}) = r \leqq n$ and $\mathbf{D} = \mathbf{D}(\lambda_1, \ldots, \lambda_r, 0, \ldots, 0)$.
Show that

(i) if $\text{rank}(\mathbf{D}) = n$ then $|\mathbf{\Delta}| = \lambda_1 \cdots \lambda_n[d - \sum_{n=1}^{n} (b_i^2/\lambda_i)]$;
(ii) if $\text{rank}(\mathbf{D}) = n - 1$ then $|\mathbf{\Delta}| = -b_n^2\lambda_1 \cdots \lambda_{n-1}$.

[Use problems 11.3 and 16.7.]

16.9. We use the notation of problem 16.7. If $|\mathbf{A}| \neq 0$ and $\{p\}_i$ is the unit eigenvector which corresponds to the eigenvector λ_i of $\mathbf{A}$, then show that there is a unique vector $\{w\} = -\mathbf{P}^T\mathbf{A}^{-1}\{b\}$ such that

$$\Phi[\mathbf{P}(\{y\} + \{w\})] = \sum_{i=1}^{n} \lambda_i y_i^2 + \frac{|\mathbf{\Delta}|}{\lambda_1 \cdots \lambda_n},$$

where $\mathbf{P}$ is the orthogonal matrix $\mathbf{P} = [\{p\}_1, \ldots, \{p\}_n]$.

16.10. We use the notation of the problem 16.7. If $\text{rank}(\mathbf{A}) = r < n$ and $\{p\}_i$, $i = 1, \ldots, r$, are the unit eigenvectors of $\mathbf{A}$ corresponding to its nonzero eigenvalues $\lambda_1, \ldots, \lambda_r$, then show that

$$\Phi[\mathbf{P}(\{x\} + \{w\})] = \sum_{s=1}^{r} \lambda_i x_i^2 + 2 \sum_{s=r+1}^{n} \{p\}_s^T\{b\}x_s + \left[-\sum_{s=1}^{r} \frac{1}{\lambda_s}(\{p\}_s^T\{b\})^2 + 2 \sum_{s=r+1}^{n} w_s\{p\}_s^T\{b\} + d \right],$$

where $w_s = -\dfrac{1}{\lambda_s}\{p\}_s^T\{b\}$, $s = 1, \ldots, r$, and $\mathbf{P} = [\{p\}_1, \ldots, \{p\}_n]$ is an orthogonal matrix. Deduce that if $|\boldsymbol{\Delta}| \neq 0$ then $r = n - 1$ and there is a unique vector $\{w\}$, where

$$w_s = -\frac{1}{\lambda_s}\{p\}_s^T\{b\}, \quad s = 1, \ldots, n-1, \quad w_n = -\frac{1}{2}\frac{d}{\{p\}_n^T\{b\}},$$

such that

$$\Phi[\mathbf{P}(\{x\} + \{w\})] = \sum_{s=1}^{n-1} \lambda_s y_s^2 + 2\left(-\frac{|\boldsymbol{\Delta}|}{\lambda_1 \cdots \lambda_{n-1}}\right)^{\frac{1}{2}} y_n.$$

[Use problems 16.7 and 16.8.]

16.11. Let OX_i be a system of orthogonal cartesian axes in E_a. The set of all points $\{x\}$ in E_a such that

$$\Phi(\{x\}) = \{x\}^T\mathbf{A}\{x\} + 2\{x\}^T\{b\} + d = 0,$$

where $\mathbf{A} = \mathbf{A}^T \in \mathsf{M}_{a,a}$ is called a **conic** or a **quadric** if $a = 2$ or $a = 3$, respectively. Let $|\boldsymbol{\Delta}|$ denote the discriminant of $\Phi(\{x\})$, $\{p\}_i$ be the unit eigenvector of $\mathbf{A}$ which corresponds to its eigenvalue λ_i and OY_i the system of orthogonal cartesian axes with matrix of direction cosines $\mathbf{P} = [\{p\}_1, \ldots, \{p\}_a]$. Show that if $\Phi(\{x\})$ is referred to the axes OY_i and then translated through the vector $-\{c\} = \mathbf{P}^T\mathbf{A}^{-1}\{b\}$, then its equation is reduced to

$$\Phi[\mathbf{P}(\{y\} + \{c\})] = \sum_{s=1}^{a} \lambda_s y_s^2 + \frac{|\boldsymbol{\Delta}|}{\lambda_1 \cdots \lambda_a} = 0.$$

Deduce that

(i) the conic $\Phi(\{x\}) = 0$ represents the ellipse or hyperbola $\lambda_1 y_1^2 + \lambda_2 y_2^2 + (|\boldsymbol{\Delta}|/\lambda_1\lambda_2) = 0$ if $|\mathbf{A}| \neq 0$, $|\boldsymbol{\Delta}| \neq 0$ or the two lines $\lambda_1^2 y_1^2 + \lambda_2^2 y_2^2 = 0$ if $|\mathbf{A}| \neq 0$, $|\boldsymbol{\Delta}| = 0$.

(ii) the quadric $\Phi(\{x\}) = 0$ represents the ellipsoid or hyperboloid $\lambda_1 y_1^2 + \lambda_2 y_2^2 + \lambda_3 y_3^2 + (|\boldsymbol{\Delta}|/\lambda_1\lambda_2\lambda_3) = 0$ if $|\mathbf{A}| \neq 0$, $|\boldsymbol{\Delta}| \neq 0$ or the cone $\lambda_1 y_1^2 + \lambda_2 y_2^2 + \lambda_3 y_3^2 = 0$ if $|\mathbf{A}| \neq 0$, $|\boldsymbol{\Delta}| = 0$.

[Use problem 16.9.]

16.12. We use the notation of problem 16.11. Let $|\mathbf{A}| = 0$, $|\boldsymbol{\Delta}| \neq 0$, and $\{p\}_i$, $i = 1, \ldots, \alpha - 1$, be the unit eigenvectors of $\mathbf{A}$ which correspond to its nonzero eigenvalues $\lambda_1, \ldots, \lambda_{\alpha-1}$. Show that if $\Phi(\{x\})$ is referred to the orthogonal cartesian axes OY_i and then translated through the vector $-\{c\}$ where

$$c_s = -(1/\lambda_s)\{p\}_s^T\{b\}, s = 1, \ldots, \alpha - 1, \qquad c_\alpha = -(d/2\{p\}_\alpha^T\{b\})$$

then its equation is reduced to

$$\Phi[\mathbf{P}(\{y\} + \{c\})] = \sum_{s=1}^{\alpha-1} \lambda_s y_s^2 + 2\left(-\frac{|\boldsymbol{\Delta}|}{\lambda_1 \cdots \lambda_{\alpha-1}}\right)^{\frac{1}{2}} y_\alpha = 0.$$

Deduce that if $|\mathbf{A}| = 0$, $|\boldsymbol{\Delta}| \neq 0$,

(i) the conic $\Phi(\{x\}) = 0$ represents the parabola

$$\lambda_1 y_1^2 + 2\sqrt{-\frac{|\boldsymbol{\Delta}|}{\lambda_1}}\, y_2 = 0;$$

(ii) the quadric $\Phi(\{x\}) = 0$ represents the paraboloid

$$\lambda_1 y_1^2 + \lambda_2 y_2^2 + 2\sqrt{-\frac{|\boldsymbol{\Delta}|}{\lambda_1\lambda_2}}\, y_3 = 0.$$

16.13. We use the notation of problem 16.11. Let $|\mathbf{A}| = |\boldsymbol{\Delta}| = 0$ and $\{p\}_1$, $\{p\}_2$ be the unit eigenvectors of $\mathbf{A} \in \mathsf{M}_{2,2}$ which correspond to its eigenvalues $\lambda_1 \neq 0$, $\lambda_2 = 0$. Show that if the conic $\Phi(\{x\}) = 0$ is referred to the axes OY_i and then translated through the vector $-\{c\}$, where $c_1 = -(\{p\}_1^T\{b\})/\lambda_1$ then its equation is reduced to

$$\lambda_1 y_1^2 + d - \frac{(\{p\}_1^T\{b\})^2}{\lambda_1} = 0.$$

Deduce that if $|\mathbf{A}| = |\boldsymbol{\Delta}| = 0$ then the conic represents two parallel or coincident lines.

16.14. We use the notation of problem 16.11 and assume that $\operatorname{rank}(\mathbf{A}) = 1$ in the quadric $\Phi(\{x\}) = 0$. Let $\{p\}_i$, $i = 1, 2, 3$ be eigenvectors of $\mathbf{A}$ such that $\{p\}_1$ corresponds to its nonzero eigenvalue λ_1. Show that

(i) $\{p\}_2$ can be chosen so that $\{p\}_2^T\{b\} = 0$;

(ii) if the quadric $\Phi(\{x\}) = 0$ is referred to the axes OY_i with matrix of direction cosines $P = [\{p\}_1, \{p\}_2, \{p\}_3]$ and then translated through the vector $-\{c\}$ where $c_1 = -\{p\}_1^T\{b\}/\lambda_1$ then its equation is reduced to

$$\lambda_1 y_1^2 + 2\{p\}_3^T\{b\}y_3 + [2\{p\}_3^T\{b\}c_3 + d - (\{p\}_1^T\{b\})^2/\lambda_1] = 0.$$

Deduce that if the $\{p\}_1$ and $\{b\}$ are parallel vectors the quadric represents the two parallel planes

$$\lambda_1 y_1^2 + d - \|\{b\}\|^2/\lambda_1 = 0,$$

otherwise the quadric is the parabolic cylinder

$$\lambda_1 y_1^2 + 2\{p\}_3^T\{b\}y_3 = 0,$$

when

$$c_3 = -\frac{\lambda_1 d - (\{p\}_1^T\{b\})^2}{2\lambda_1\{p\}_3^T\{b\}}.$$

LECTURE 17

Homogeneous Systems of Differential Equations

First-order, linear, homogeneous systems of differential equations with constant coefficients • The coefficient matrix • Closure of solutions under addition and multiplication by numbers • Simplification by the substitution $\{y(t)\} = \mathbf{K}\{z(t)\}$ • The reduced system • Solution of the reduced system • Solution of the original system • Representation of the general solution in terms of the eigenvalues and the eigenvectors of the coefficient matrix • Representation of the solution by matrix multiplication • A basis for the solution space • The initial value problem • Solution of the initial value problem • Problems

We introduced the notion of diagonalizability of a matrix in lecture twelve by asking what simplifications could we make in systems of linear first-order differential equations with constant coefficients. The remaining lectures will be devoted to a study of such systems.

The first thing we need to do is to introduce a system of notation which will assist us in using the algebraic results we have already obtained. Let $x_1(t), x_2(t), \ldots, x_n(t)$ be a n-tuple of functions of the independent variable t. If we arrange these functions in a column, then for each value of the independent variable t, $\{x(t)\}$ is an n-tuple of real numbers. We can accordingly define addition and multiplication by numbers for each value of t and hence we obtain $\{x(t)\} \in \mathsf{M}_{n,1}$ for each value of t with

$$\{x(t)\} + \{y(t)\} \equiv \begin{Bmatrix} x_1(t) + y_1(t) \\ \cdot \\ \cdot \\ \cdot \\ x_n(t) + y_n(t) \end{Bmatrix}, \qquad a\{x(t)\} \equiv \begin{Bmatrix} ax_1(t) \\ \cdot \\ \cdot \\ \cdot \\ ax_n(t) \end{Bmatrix}.$$

Similarly, we can construct the full matrix algebra of functions with the definition $\mathbf{C}(t) = \mathbf{A}(t)\mathbf{B}(t)$, $c_{ij}(t) = \sum_k a_{ik}(t) b_{kj}(t)$. Further, since we require the processes of differentiation and integration, we make the following definitions:

$$\frac{d}{dt}\{x(t)\} \equiv \begin{Bmatrix} \dfrac{dx_1(t)}{dt} \\ \cdot \\ \cdot \\ \cdot \\ \dfrac{dx_n(t)}{dt} \end{Bmatrix}, \quad \int x(t)\,dt \equiv \begin{Bmatrix} \int x_1(t)\,dt \\ \cdot \\ \cdot \\ \cdot \\ \int x_n(t)\,dt \end{Bmatrix},$$

$$\int_a^b \{x(\gamma)\}\,d\gamma \equiv \begin{Bmatrix} \int_a^b x_1(\gamma)\,d\gamma \\ \cdot \\ \cdot \\ \cdot \\ \int_a^b x_n(\gamma)\,d\gamma \end{Bmatrix},$$

where the limits of integration, a and b, may be functions of the independent variable t.

Let $\mathbf{A}$ be a given constant n-by-n matrix. If we are given the system of *first-order, linear, homogeneous differential equations*

$$\frac{d}{dt}\{x(t)\} = \mathbf{A}\{x(t)\}, \tag{17.1}$$

then the matrix $\mathbf{A}$ is said to be the **coefficient matrix** of the system (17.1). The reason for laying stress on the coefficient matrix of the system (17.1) is that this matrix determines all of the solutions of the given system of differential equations, as we shall see.

Our task is to find *all* n-tuples of functions $x_1(t), \ldots, x_n(t)$ that satisfy the given system of first-order, linear, homogeneous differential equations (17.1).

The requirement that we find all solutions of the system (17.1) is very reminiscent of the requirement that we find all solutions of the linear homogeneous algebraic system $\mathbf{A}\{y\} = \{0\}$. In fact, the linearity and homogeneity of the system (17.1) allows us to establish the following result: *if* $\{u(t)\}$ *and* $\{v(t)\}$ *are two solutions of Eq.* (17.1), *then all linear combinations* $a\{u(t)\} + b\{v(t)\}$ *with constant coefficients a and b are solutions of Eq.* (17.1); *that is, the solutions of Eq.* (17.1) *are closed under addition and multiplication by constants.* The statements that $\{u(t)\}$ and $\{v(t)\}$ are solutions of Eq. (17.1) are

$$\frac{d}{dt}\{u(t)\} = \mathbf{A}\{u(t)\}, \quad \frac{d}{dt}\{v(t)\} = \mathbf{A}\{v(t)\}. \tag{17.2}$$

Since a and b are constants, we have

$$\frac{d}{dt}(a\{u(t)\} + b\{v(t)\}) = a\frac{d}{dt}\{u(t)\} + b\frac{d}{dt}\{v(t)\}. \tag{17.3}$$

When we substitute from Eqs. (17.2) into Eq. (17.3), we then have

$$\frac{d}{dt}(a\{u(t)\}+b\{v(t)\}) = a\,\mathbf{A}\{u(t)\}+b\,\mathbf{A}\{v(t)\}$$
$$= \mathbf{A}(a\{u(t)\}+b\{v(t)\}),$$

and the result is established.

The closure property of solutions of the system (17.1) tells us that *the solutions form a subspace with respect to the operations of addition and multiplication by numbers.* The solutions of (17.1) are n-tuples of functions of the independent variable t, rather than just n-tuples of numbers, however. Thus, all solutions of (17.1) form a subspace of the linear space of all n-tuples of functions of the independent variable t. Now, a linear space of functions is much "larger" and more unwieldy than the simple linear spaces of n-tuples of numbers and this additional size and complexity requires significantly more machinery than we have developed in these lectures. We shall therefore approach the problem of solving systems of linear homogeneous differential equations with constant coefficients directly by using the algebraic methods we have developed in the previous lectures. When we are finished, we will then be able to exhibit what each reader should be expecting: a basis for the solution space of Eq. (17.1).

The method outlined at the beginning of lecture twelve gave a reasonable approach to solving Eq. (17.1), so let us proceed along these lines. The key to the method is to introduce a new n-tuple of dependent functions by the substitution

$$\{x(t)\}=\mathbf{K}\{z(t)\},\quad \{z(t)\}=\mathbf{K}^{-1}\{x(t)\},\tag{17.4}$$

where $\mathbf{K}$ is an n-by-n, nonsingular, constant matrix. Since $\mathbf{K}$ is a constant matrix, we have

$$\frac{d}{dt}(\mathbf{K}\{z(t)\})=\mathbf{K}\frac{d}{dt}\{z(t)\},$$

and hence the substitution of Eq. (17.4) into Eq. (17.1) gives

$$\mathbf{K}\frac{d}{dt}\{z(t)\}=\mathbf{A}\,\mathbf{K}\{z(t)\}.$$

Thus, since $\mathbf{K}$ is nonsingular, we have the new system

$$\frac{d}{dt}\{z(t)\}=\mathbf{K}^{-1}\mathbf{A}\,\mathbf{K}\{z(t)\}.\tag{17.5}$$

We now make the one assumption that is essential in this approach to the problem: *we assume that the matrix* $\mathbf{A}$ *is a diagonalizable matrix.* If $\lambda_1, \ldots, \lambda_n$ are the eigenvalues of $\mathbf{A}$ and $\{k\}_1, \ldots, \{k\}_n$ are a system of linearly independent eigenvectors of $\mathbf{A}$ that are associated with the eigenvalues $\lambda_1, \ldots, \lambda_n$, then we can take $\mathbf{K}=[\{k\}_1, \ldots, \{k\}_n]$, in which case we have $\mathbf{K}^{-1}\mathbf{A}\,\mathbf{K}=\mathbf{D}(\lambda_1, \ldots, \lambda_n)$. With this choice of the matrix $\mathbf{K}$, the system (17.5) becomes

$$\frac{d}{dt}\{z(t)\}=\mathbf{D}(\lambda_1, \ldots, \lambda_n)\{z(t)\}. \tag{17.6}$$

This new system (17.6), called the **reduced system**, is given explicitly by

$$\frac{d}{dt}z_i(t)=\lambda_i\, z_i(t), \quad i=1, \ldots, n; \tag{17.7}$$

the equation which $z_i(t)$ satisfies involves only $z_i(t)$ and not the rest of the n-tuple of functions $\{z(t)\}$. It is an easy matter to solve each of the differential equations (17.7). *All* solutions of Eq. (17.7) are given by

$$z_i(t)=c_i\, e^{\lambda_i t}=c_i \exp(\lambda_i t), \tag{17.8}$$

where c_i is an arbitrary constant. The **general solution** of Eq. (17.6), i.e., a solution which involves n arbitrary constants is thus given by

$$\{z(t)\}=\begin{Bmatrix} c_1 \exp(\lambda_1 t) \\ c_2 \exp(\lambda_2 t) \\ \cdot \\ \cdot \\ \cdot \\ c_n \exp(\lambda_n t) \end{Bmatrix}. \tag{17.9}$$

Now that we know $\{z(t)\}$, the original unknowns $\{x(t)\}$ are given by Eqs. (17.4), that is

$$\{x(t)\}=\mathbf{K}\{z(t)\}=\mathbf{K}\begin{Bmatrix} c_1 \exp(\lambda_1 t) \\ \cdot \\ \cdot \\ \cdot \\ c_n \exp(\lambda_n t) \end{Bmatrix}. \tag{17.10}$$

However, $\mathbf{K}$ is a matrix of eigenvectors $\{k\}_1, \ldots, \{k\}_n$ of $\mathbf{A}$. When this is used in Eq. (17.10) and we recall that

$$[\{k\}_1, \ldots, \{k\}_n]\begin{Bmatrix} u_1 \\ \cdot \\ \cdot \\ \cdot \\ u_n \end{Bmatrix}=u_1\{k\}_1+ \ldots +u_n\{k\}_n,$$

we finally have

$$\{x(t)\}=c_1 \exp(\lambda_1 t)\{k\}_1+ \ldots +c_n \exp(\lambda_n t)\{k\}_n.$$

We have thus established the following result. *Let* $\mathbf{A}$ *be a diagonalizable matrix and let* $\{k\}_1, \ldots, \{k\}_n$ *be a system of linearly independent eigenvectors of* $\mathbf{A}$ *with associated eigenvalues* $\lambda_1, \ldots, \lambda_n$. *For each choice of the n constants* $c_1, \ldots, c_n$,

$$\{x(t)\} = c_1 \exp(\lambda_1 t)\{k\}_1 + \ldots + c_n \exp(\lambda_n t)\{k\}_n \tag{17.11}$$

satisfies the system of differential equations

$$\frac{d}{dt}\{x(t)\} = \mathbf{A}\{x(t)\}. \tag{17.12}$$

The form of the solution given by Eq. (17.11) suggests that the n vectors $\exp(\lambda_1 t)\{k\}_1, \ldots, \exp(\lambda_n t)\{k\}_n$ form a basis for the solution space of Eq. (17.12). This is indeed the case, as we shall establish in the following two steps. The first thing we note is that Eq. (17.8) gives all solutions of Eqs. (17.7), and hence Eq. (17.9) gives all solutions of the system (17.6). Once we know all $\{z(t)\}$, then we know all $\{x(t)\}$ by the relation $\{x(t)\} = \mathbf{K}\{z(t)\}$. Thus, *the n vectors* $\exp(\lambda_1 t)\{k\}_1, \ldots, \exp(\lambda_n t)\{k\}_n$ *span the solution space of the system of differential equations* (17.12) since every solution of Eq. (17.12) is thus expressible in the form (17.11) for suitable choices of the constants $c_1, \ldots, c_n$. We now have to show that the spanning set $\exp(\lambda_1 t)\{k\}_1, \ldots, \exp(\lambda_n t)\{k\}_n$ is linearly independent.

The definition of linear independence for numerical vectors in $\mathsf{M}_{n,1}$ is

$$c_1\{u\}_1 + \ldots + c_n\{u\}_n = \{0\}, \tag{17.13}$$

if and only if $c_1 = c_2 = \ldots = c_n = 0$. For **vector functions** $\{u(t)\}_i$ whose entries are functions of the independent variable t, the definition of **linear independence** is

$$c_1\{u(t)\}_1 + \ldots + c_n\{u(t)\}_n = \{0\}, \tag{17.14}$$

for all t within an interval $a \leq t \leq b$ if and only if $c_1 = c_2 = \ldots = c_n = 0$. Consequently, if the vector functions $\{u(t)\}_i$ are linearly independent for a specific value $t_0 \in (a,b)$, then they are linearly independent on (a,b). Thus, the vector functions $\exp(\lambda_1 t)\{k\}_1, \ldots, \exp(\lambda_n t)\{k\}_n$ are linearly independent, since $\exp(\lambda_1 t_0)\{k\}_1, \ldots, \exp(\lambda_n t_0)\{k\}_n$ are linearly independent. We summarize our results in the following statement:

Let $\mathbf{A}$ *be a diagonalizable matrix with eigenvalues* $\lambda_1, \ldots, \lambda_n$ *and an associated matrix of eigenvectors* $\mathbf{K}$. *Every solution of the system of differential equations* $d\{x(t)\}/dt = \mathbf{A}\{x(t)\}$ *is of the form*

$$\begin{aligned}\{x(t)\} &= c_1 \exp(\lambda_1 t)\{k\}_1 + \ldots + c_n \exp(\lambda_n t)\{k\}_n \\ &= \mathbf{K}\,\mathbf{D}(\exp(\lambda_1 t), \ldots, \exp(\lambda_n t))\{c\},\end{aligned} \tag{17.15}$$

where $c_1, \ldots, c_n$ *are constants,* $\{c\}=[c_1, \ldots, c_n]^T$ *and*

$$\exp(\lambda_1 t)\{k\}_1, \ldots, \exp(\lambda_n t)\{k\}_n \tag{17.16}$$

is a basis for the solution space.

So far no restriction was imposed on the eigenvalues of the real matrix $\mathbf{A}$ some or all of which may be complex. If $\lambda_i=a+ib$ is an eigenvalue so is $\bar{\lambda}_i=a-ib$ and the corresponding eigenvectors are also complex conjugates. Thus, if the complex vector $\mathbf{w}$ belongs to the basis (17.16) so does $\bar{\mathbf{w}}$ and consequently, see problem 17.6, the real and imaginary parts of the vectors (17.16) are a set of n linearly independent vectors. Moreover, if $\mathbf{x}(t)$ is a real solution, because of Eq. (17.15) and problem 17.6, $\mathbf{x}(t)$ is a linear combination of the real and imaginary components of the vectors of the basis (17.16). Thus, we have proved the following theorem: *The real and imaginary components of the vectors* (17.16) *form a real basis for the real solution space of* $d\{x(t)\}/dt=\mathbf{A}\{x\}$. Obviously, this real basis and Eq. (17.15) coincide if the matrix $\mathbf{A}$ has real eigenvalues.

At this point it is worth considering a few examples. Let $n=2$ and

$$\mathbf{A}=\begin{pmatrix} 3 & 1 \\ -6 & -4 \end{pmatrix}.$$

The linear homogeneous system of first-order differential equations with coefficient matrix $\mathbf{A}$ is

$$\frac{d}{dt}\{x(t)\}=\begin{pmatrix} 3 & 1 \\ -6 & -4 \end{pmatrix}\{x\};$$

that is,

$$\frac{dx_1}{dt}=3x_1+x_2, \qquad \frac{dx_2}{dt}=-6x_1-4x_2.$$

We have already calculated the eigenvalues and eigenvectors of

$$\begin{pmatrix} 3 & 1 \\ -6 & -4 \end{pmatrix}$$

in lecture 12, and so we can simply state the results

$$\lambda_1=2, \quad \lambda_2=-3,$$

$$k_1=\begin{Bmatrix} 1 \\ -1 \end{Bmatrix}, \quad k_2=\begin{Bmatrix} -1 \\ 6 \end{Bmatrix}, \quad \mathbf{K}=\begin{Bmatrix} 1 & -1 \\ -1 & 6 \end{Bmatrix}.$$

Thus, the substitution

$$\{x\}=\begin{pmatrix} 1 & -1 \\ -1 & 6 \end{pmatrix}\{z\}$$

reduces the original system of differential equations to

$$\frac{d}{dt}\{z(t)\}=\mathbf{D}(2,\ -3)\{z\},$$

that is,

$$\frac{dz_1}{dt}=2z_1, \qquad \frac{dz_2}{dt}=-3z_2.$$

The solutions of these equations are

$$z_1(t)=c_1e^{2t}, \qquad z_2(t)=c_2e^{-3t}$$

and hence

$$\{z(t)\}=\begin{Bmatrix} c_1e^{2t} \\ c_2e^{-3t} \end{Bmatrix}.$$

We thus have

$$\{x(t)\}=\mathbf{K}\{z\}=\begin{pmatrix} 1 & -1 \\ -1 & 6 \end{pmatrix}\begin{Bmatrix} c_1e^{2t} \\ c_2e^{-3t} \end{Bmatrix}=\begin{Bmatrix} c_1e^{2t}-\ c_2e^{-3t} \\ -c_1e^{2t}+6c_2e^{-3t} \end{Bmatrix}$$

$$=c_1e^{2t}\begin{Bmatrix} 1 \\ -1 \end{Bmatrix}+c_2e^{-3t}\begin{Bmatrix} -1 \\ 6 \end{Bmatrix}=c_1e^{\lambda_1 t}\{k\}_1+c_2e^{\lambda_2 t}\{k\}_2.$$

The coefficient matrix for the next example is

$$\mathbf{A}=\begin{pmatrix} 8 & 56 & -8 & -20 \\ 0 & -7 & 0 & 5 \\ 4 & 25 & -4 & -7 \\ 0 & -10 & 0 & 8 \end{pmatrix},$$

and its eigenvalues and eigenvectors have been calculated in lecture 12:

$$\lambda_1=4,\ \lambda_2=-2,\ \lambda_3=0,\ \lambda_4=3,$$

$$\{k\}_1=\begin{Bmatrix} 2 \\ 0 \\ 1 \\ 0 \end{Bmatrix},\ \{k\}_2=\begin{Bmatrix} -6 \\ 1 \\ -3 \\ 1 \end{Bmatrix},\ \{k\}_3=\begin{Bmatrix} 1 \\ 0 \\ 1 \\ 0 \end{Bmatrix},\ \{k\}_4=\begin{Bmatrix} -8 \\ 1 \\ -3 \\ 2 \end{Bmatrix}.$$

The system

$$\frac{d}{dt}\{x(t)\}=\mathbf{A}\{x(t)\}$$

is reduced to the system

$$\frac{d}{dt}\{z(t)\}=\mathbf{D}(4,\ -2, 0, 3)\{z(t)\}$$

by the substitution

$$\{x(t)\}=\mathbf{K}\{z(t)\}=\begin{pmatrix}2 & -6 & 1 & -8\\ 0 & 1 & 0 & 1\\ 1 & -3 & 1 & -3\\ 0 & 1 & 0 & 2\end{pmatrix}\{z(t)\}.$$

We thus have

$$z_1(t)=c_1e^{4t},\ z_2(t)=c_2e^{-2t},\ z_3(t)=c_3,\ z_4(t)=c_4e^{3t},$$

and hence the general solution of the original problem is given by

$$\{x(t)\}=\mathbf{K}\{z(t)\}=c_1e^{4t}\begin{Bmatrix}2\\0\\1\\0\end{Bmatrix}+c_2e^{-2t}\begin{Bmatrix}-6\\1\\-3\\1\end{Bmatrix}+c_3\begin{Bmatrix}1\\0\\1\\0\end{Bmatrix}+c_4e^{3t}\begin{Bmatrix}-8\\1\\-3\\2\end{Bmatrix}.$$

The next example has the coefficient matrix

$$\mathbf{A}=\begin{pmatrix}1 & 1 & 0 & 0\\ -1 & 1 & 0 & 0\\ 0 & 0 & 1 & -1\\ 0 & 0 & 1 & 1\end{pmatrix}.$$

The following results were obtained in lecture 12:

$$\lambda_1=1+i,\ \lambda_2=1+i,\ \lambda_3=1-i,\ \lambda_4=1-i,$$

$$\{k\}_1=\begin{Bmatrix}-i\\1\\0\\0\end{Bmatrix},\ \{k\}_2=\begin{Bmatrix}0\\0\\i\\1\end{Bmatrix},\ \{k\}_3=\begin{Bmatrix}i\\1\\0\\0\end{Bmatrix},\ \{k\}_4=\begin{Bmatrix}0\\0\\-i\\1\end{Bmatrix}.$$

Thus, the system of differential equations

$$\frac{d}{dt}\{x(t)\}=\mathbf{A}\{x(t)\}$$

has the general solution

$$\{x(t)\}=c_1e^{(1+i)t}\begin{Bmatrix}-i\\1\\0\\0\end{Bmatrix}+c_2e^{(1+i)t}\begin{Bmatrix}0\\0\\i\\1\end{Bmatrix}+c_3e^{(1-i)t}\begin{Bmatrix}i\\1\\0\\0\end{Bmatrix}+c_4e^{(1-i)t}\begin{Bmatrix}0\\0\\-i\\1\end{Bmatrix}.$$

Since the eigenvalues and eigenvectors of **A** are complex, this solution is a complex vector function of t, and the constants c_1, c_2, c_3, c_4 are complex numbers, in general. We usually need a basis for the *real* solution space.

Since

$$e^{(1+i)t}\begin{Bmatrix}-i\\1\\0\\0\end{Bmatrix}=e^{t+it}\begin{Bmatrix}-i\\1\\0\\0\end{Bmatrix}=(e^t\cos t+ie^t\sin t)\left(\begin{Bmatrix}0\\1\\0\\0\end{Bmatrix}+i\begin{Bmatrix}-1\\0\\0\\0\end{Bmatrix}\right)$$

$$=e^t\cos t\begin{Bmatrix}0\\1\\0\\0\end{Bmatrix}-e^t\sin t\begin{Bmatrix}-1\\0\\0\\0\end{Bmatrix}+i\left(e^t\cos t\begin{Bmatrix}-1\\0\\0\\0\end{Bmatrix}+e^t\sin t\begin{Bmatrix}0\\1\\0\\0\end{Bmatrix}\right)$$

$$=e^t\begin{Bmatrix}\sin t\\\cos t\\0\\0\end{Bmatrix}+ie^t\begin{Bmatrix}-\cos t\\\sin t\\0\\0\end{Bmatrix},$$

$$e^{(1-i)t}\begin{Bmatrix}i\\1\\0\\0\end{Bmatrix}=e^t\begin{Bmatrix}\sin t\\\cos t\\0\\0\end{Bmatrix}-ie^t\begin{Bmatrix}-\cos t\\\sin t\\0\\0\end{Bmatrix},$$

$$e^{(1+i)t}\begin{Bmatrix}0\\0\\i\\1\end{Bmatrix}=e^{t+it}\begin{Bmatrix}0\\0\\i\\1\end{Bmatrix}=(e^t\cos t+ie^t\sin t)\left(\begin{Bmatrix}0\\0\\0\\1\end{Bmatrix}+i\begin{Bmatrix}0\\0\\0\\1\end{Bmatrix}\right)$$

$$=e^t\cos t\begin{Bmatrix}0\\0\\0\\1\end{Bmatrix}-e^t\sin t\begin{Bmatrix}0\\0\\1\\0\end{Bmatrix}+i\left(e^t\cos t\begin{Bmatrix}0\\0\\1\\0\end{Bmatrix}+e^t\sin t\begin{Bmatrix}0\\0\\0\\\sin t\end{Bmatrix}\right)$$

$$=e^t\begin{Bmatrix}0\\0\\-\sin t\\\cos t\end{Bmatrix}+ie^t\begin{Bmatrix}0\\0\\\cos t\\\sin t\end{Bmatrix},$$

$$e^{(1-i)t}\begin{Bmatrix}0\\0\\-i\\1\end{Bmatrix}=e^t\begin{Bmatrix}0\\0\\-\sin t\\\cos t\end{Bmatrix}-ie^t\begin{Bmatrix}0\\0\\\cos t\\\sin t\end{Bmatrix}.$$

The basis for the *real* solution space is

$$e^t\begin{Bmatrix}\sin t\\\cos t\\0\\0\end{Bmatrix},\quad e^t\begin{Bmatrix}0\\0\\-\sin t\\\cos t\end{Bmatrix},\quad e^t\begin{Bmatrix}-\cos t\\\sin t\\0\\0\end{Bmatrix},\quad e^t\begin{Bmatrix}0\\0\\\cos t\\\sin t\end{Bmatrix},$$

and every *real* solution $x(t)$ is given by

$$x(t)=e^t\left(a_1\begin{Bmatrix}\sin t\\ \cos t\\ 0\\ 0\end{Bmatrix}+a_2\begin{Bmatrix}0\\ 0\\ -\sin t\\ \cos t\end{Bmatrix}+a_3\begin{Bmatrix}-\cos t\\ \sin t\\ 0\\ 0\end{Bmatrix}+a_4\begin{Bmatrix}0\\ 0\\ \cos t\\ \sin t\end{Bmatrix}\right),$$

where $a_1, \ldots, a_4$ are real numbers.

For each choice of the constants $c_1, \ldots, c_n$, Eq. (17.15) gives us a solution of the system of differential equations (17.12). We thus have not just one solution, but rather an n-fold infinity of solutions of the system (17.12) that is obtained by allowing the constants $c_1, \ldots, c_n$ to range over all numbers. In most applications, the solution of Eq. (17.12) has to satisfy additional conditions which select one or more solutions from among all of the solutions of (17.12). Usually, such additional conditions are what are termed *initial conditions*: we require $\{x(t)\}$ to satisfy $\{x(\alpha)\} = \{w\}$, where $\{w\}$ is a given column matrix of numbers and α is a given number. The number α is referred to as the *initial time* and the numbers $w_1, \ldots, w_n$ are referred to as the *initial values*. We thus want to solve the *initial value problem*

$$\frac{d}{dt}\{x(t)\}=\mathbf{A}\{x(t)\}, \tag{17.17}$$

$$\{x(\alpha)\}=\{w\}. \tag{17.18}$$

As usual, we assume that $\mathbf{A}$ is diagonalizable. Our previous results tell us that the general solution of Eq. (17.17) is given by

$$\{x(t)\}=\mathbf{K}\,\mathbf{D}(\exp(\lambda_1 t), \ldots, \exp(\lambda_n t))\{c\}, \tag{17.19}$$

and hence we have

$$\{x(\alpha)\}=\mathbf{K}\,\mathbf{D}(\exp(\lambda_1 \alpha), \ldots, \exp(\lambda_n \alpha))\{c\}. \tag{17.20}$$

When Eq. (17.20) is substituted into the initial condition (17.18), we then obtain the following equation for the determination of $\{c\}$:

$$\{w\}=\mathbf{K}\,\mathbf{D}(\exp(\lambda_1 \alpha), \ldots, \exp(\lambda_n \alpha))\{c\}. \tag{17.21}$$

We thus find that

$$\{c\}=\mathbf{D}[\exp(-\lambda_1 \alpha), \ldots, \exp(-\lambda_n \alpha)]\mathbf{K}^{-1}\{w\}. \tag{17.22}$$

When we substitute this expression for $\{c\}$ back into Eq. (17.19), *the solution of the initial value problem* (17.17), (17.18) *is given by*

$$\{x(t)\}=\mathbf{K}\,\mathbf{D}(\exp(t-\alpha)\lambda_1, \ldots, \exp(t-\alpha)\lambda_n)\mathbf{K}^{-1}\{w\}, \tag{17.23}$$

on noting that

$$\mathbf{D}[\exp(\lambda_1 t), \ldots, \exp(\lambda_n t)]\,\mathbf{D}[\exp(-\lambda_1\alpha), \ldots, \exp(-\lambda_n\alpha)] = \mathbf{D}[\exp(t-\alpha)\lambda_1, \ldots, \exp(t-\alpha)\lambda_n].$$

Thus, the solution of the initial value problem (17.17), (17.18) is uniquely determined in terms of the eigenvalues and a matrix of eigenvectors of the given coefficient matrix **A** and the given initial data (α, $\{w\}$).

We note that if the general solution (17.15) involves complex quantities and we are interested, as we usually are, in a particular *real* solution, we can solve much simpler the initial value problem (17.17), (17.18) if we use a procedure similar to the above but based on the basis for the space of the *real* solutions of the system (17.17).

We now consider initial value problems associated with the first two examples given above: For the first example, we have

$$\frac{d}{dt}\{x(t)\} = \begin{pmatrix} 3 & 1 \\ -6 & -4 \end{pmatrix}\{x\}, \qquad \{x(7)\} = \begin{Bmatrix} 4 \\ -9 \end{Bmatrix},$$

and hence

$$\{x(t)\} = \mathbf{K}\{z(t)\} = \begin{pmatrix} 1 & -1 \\ -1 & 6 \end{pmatrix}\mathbf{D}(e^{2t}, e^{-3t})\{c\}.$$

Thus,

$$\begin{Bmatrix} 4 \\ -9 \end{Bmatrix} = \{x(7)\} = \begin{pmatrix} 1 & -1 \\ -1 & 6 \end{pmatrix}\mathbf{D}(e^{14}, e^{-21})\{c\},$$

so that

$$\{c\} = \mathbf{D}(e^{-14}, e^{21})\begin{pmatrix} 1 & -1 \\ -1 & 6 \end{pmatrix}^{-1}\begin{Bmatrix} 4 \\ -9 \end{Bmatrix}$$

$$= \mathbf{D}(e^{-14}, e^{21})\frac{1}{5}\begin{pmatrix} 6 & 1 \\ 1 & 1 \end{pmatrix}\begin{Bmatrix} 4 \\ -9 \end{Bmatrix}$$

and we have

$$\{x(t)\} = \frac{1}{5}\begin{pmatrix} 1 & -1 \\ -1 & 6 \end{pmatrix}\mathbf{D}(e^{2t}, e^{-3t})\mathbf{D}(e^{-14}, e^{21})\begin{pmatrix} 6 & 1 \\ 1 & 1 \end{pmatrix}\begin{Bmatrix} 4 \\ -9 \end{Bmatrix}$$

$$= \frac{1}{5}\begin{pmatrix} 1 & -1 \\ -1 & 6 \end{pmatrix}\mathbf{D}(e^{2(t-7)}, e^{-3(t-7)})\begin{pmatrix} 6 & 1 \\ 1 & 1 \end{pmatrix}\begin{Bmatrix} 4 \\ -9 \end{Bmatrix}$$

$$= \begin{Bmatrix} 3e^{2(t-7)} + e^{-3(t-7)} \\ -3e^{2(t-7)} - 6e^{-3(t-7)} \end{Bmatrix}.$$

For the second example, we have

$$\frac{d}{dt}\{x(t)\} = \begin{pmatrix} 8 & 56 & -8 & -20 \\ 0 & -7 & 0 & 5 \\ 4 & 25 & -4 & -7 \\ 0 & -10 & 0 & 8 \end{pmatrix}\{x(t)\}, \quad \{x(-1)\} = \begin{Bmatrix} 0 \\ 1 \\ 0 \\ -1 \end{Bmatrix}.$$

Our previous results give

$$\mathbf{K}=\begin{pmatrix} 2 & -6 & 1 & -8 \\ 0 & 1 & 0 & 1 \\ 1 & -3 & 1 & -3 \\ 0 & 1 & 0 & 2 \end{pmatrix}, \quad \begin{matrix} \lambda_1=4, & \lambda_2=-2, \\ \lambda_3=0, & \lambda_4=3, \end{matrix}$$

$$\mathbf{K}^{-1}=\begin{pmatrix} 1 & 1 & -1 & 2 \\ 0 & 2 & 0 & -1 \\ -1 & 2 & 2 & -2 \\ 0 & -1 & 0 & 1 \end{pmatrix}.$$

Equation (17.22) thus gives

$$\{x(t)\}=\begin{pmatrix} 2 & -6 & 1 & -8 \\ 0 & 1 & 0 & 1 \\ 1 & -3 & 1 & -3 \\ 0 & 1 & 0 & 2 \end{pmatrix}\mathbf{D}(e^{4(t+1)}, e^{-2(t+1)}, 1, e^{3(t+1)})\cdot$$

$$\cdot\begin{pmatrix} 1 & 1 & -1 & 2 \\ 0 & 2 & 0 & -1 \\ -1 & 2 & 2 & -2 \\ 0 & -1 & 0 & 1 \end{pmatrix}\begin{Bmatrix} 0 \\ 1 \\ 0 \\ -1 \end{Bmatrix},$$

so that

$$\{x(t)\}= -e^{4(t+1)}\begin{Bmatrix} 2 \\ 0 \\ 1 \\ 0 \end{Bmatrix} + 3e^{-2(t+1)}\begin{Bmatrix} -6 \\ 1 \\ -3 \\ 1 \end{Bmatrix}$$

$$+4\begin{Bmatrix} 1 \\ 0 \\ 1 \\ 0 \end{Bmatrix} - 2e^{3(t+1)}\begin{Bmatrix} -8 \\ 1 \\ -3 \\ 2 \end{Bmatrix}.$$

Problems

17.1. For $z = x + iy$ we define the **exponential function**

$$\exp(z) = e^z = e^{x+iy} = e^x(\cos y + i \sin y),$$

where y is treated as the measure in radians of an angle for the calculation of $\cos y$ and $\sin y$. Thus $\exp(z)$ is defined for any z and $e^z = e^x$ for real $z = x + i0$.

It can be easily proved that $\exp(z)$ can take any value $w \neq 0$ for an appropriate value of z, also that $\exp(z) \neq 0$.

If $z_j = x_j + iy_j$, $j = 1, 2$, use the definition of the exponential function to show that

(i) $(\overline{e^{z}}) = e^{\bar{z}}$, $|e^{z_1}| = e^{x_1}$, $\arg(e^{z_1}) = y_1 + 2k\pi$, where $k = 0, \pm 1, \ldots$

(ii) $e^{z_1} = e^{z_2}$ if and only if $z_2 = z_1 + 2k\pi i$, $k = 0, \pm 1, \ldots$; that is e^z is *periodic with period* $2\pi i$.

(iii) If A is a real number and $w \neq 0$ a complex number, the equation $e^z = w$ for z has one and only one solution with $A < \text{Im}(z) \leq A + 2\pi$, i.e., within the **period strip** $A < \text{Im}(z) \leq A + 2\pi$ the exponential function admits only once any value different from zero. The strip $-\pi < \text{Im}(z) \leq \pi$ is called the **fundamental strip.**

(iv) $z = |z|e^{i \arg(z)}$.

(v) $e^{z_1}e^{z_2} = e^{z_1+z_2}$, $e^{z_1}/e^{z_2} = e^{z_1-z_2}$, $(e^z)^n = e^{nz}$, $n = 0, \pm 1, \ldots$

17.2. Verify that

(a) $e^{1+i} + e^{1-i} = 2e\cos(1)$, $e^{2+i\frac{\pi}{16}} + e^{2-i\frac{\pi}{16}} = 2e^2 \cos\dfrac{\pi}{16}$;

(b) $e^{\pm 2\pi i} = 1$, $e^{\pm\pi i} = -1$, $e^{\pm\frac{\pi}{2}i} = \pm i$;

(c) $e^{3+i\frac{\pi}{8}} = e^{3+i\frac{17\pi}{8}}$, $e^{2+i\frac{\pi}{3}} = e^{2+i\frac{13\pi}{3}}$;

(d) $1 + i\sqrt{3} = 2e^{i\frac{\pi}{3}}$, $1 - i\sqrt{3} = 2e^{i\frac{5\pi}{3}}$;

(e) $e^{1+i\frac{\pi}{3}}\left\{\begin{matrix} 1+i \\ 2 \end{matrix}\right\} = \dfrac{e}{2}\left\{\begin{matrix} 1-\sqrt{3} \\ 2 \end{matrix}\right\} + i\dfrac{e}{2}\left\{\begin{matrix} 1+\sqrt{3} \\ 2 \end{matrix}\right\}$;

(f) $e^{1+i\frac{\pi}{4}}\left\{\begin{matrix} 2-i \\ 3+2i \end{matrix}\right\} = \dfrac{e\sqrt{2}}{2}\left\{\begin{matrix} 3 \\ 1 \end{matrix}\right\} + i\dfrac{e\sqrt{2}}{2}\left\{\begin{matrix} 1 \\ 5 \end{matrix}\right\}$;

(g) $e^{2+i\frac{2\pi}{3}}\left\{\begin{matrix} 2+3i \\ 1-2i \\ 4i \end{matrix}\right\} = -\dfrac{e^2}{2}\left\{\begin{matrix} 2+3\sqrt{3} \\ 1-2\sqrt{3} \\ 4\sqrt{3} \end{matrix}\right\} + i\dfrac{e^2}{2}\left\{\begin{matrix} 2\sqrt{3}-3 \\ 2+\sqrt{3} \\ 4 \end{matrix}\right\}$.

17.3. Write the following systems in the form

$$\frac{d}{dt}\{x(t)\} = \mathbf{A}\{x(t)\}:$$

(a) $x_1' = 3x_1 + 5x_2$, $x_2' = 2x_1 + 3x_2$;

(b) $x_1' = -x_1 + 2x_2$, $x_2' = 4x_1 - x_2$;

(c) $x_1' + 3x_2 + 5x_3 = 0$, $x_1' + x_2' + 3x_2 = 0$;

(d) $2x_1' + 3x_2' + x_1 + 4x_2 = 0$, $5x_1' + 3x_2' - x_1 = 0$;

(e) $x_1' = x_2 - 3x_3$,
$x_2' = 2x_1 - 4x_3$,
$x_3' = x_1 - x_2 - 8x_3$;

(f) $x_1' + x_2' + 2x_3' + x_1 + 7x_2 = 0$,
$2x_2' - x_3' + 2x_1 - 6x_2 + x_3 = 0$,
$2x_1' + 3x_3 + x_1 - x_2 - 8x_3 = 0$.

17.4. For each of the systems $\frac{d}{dt}\{x(t)\} = \mathbf{A}\{x\}$ where the matrix $\mathbf{A}$ is given in example 12.1,

(i) write the system fully;

(ii) give the eigenvalues λ_i of the matrix $\mathbf{A}$, their multiplicity m_i, and the dimension d_i of the solution space $\mathsf{N}(\lambda_i)$ of the corresponding algebraic system $(\mathbf{A} - \lambda_i\mathbf{E})\{y\} = \{0\}$;

(iii) state whether the matrix $\mathbf{A}$ is diagonalizable; if it is give a matrix $\mathbf{K}$ of eigenvectors and obtain the general solution to the system;

(iv) Give a basis for the real solution space and the general real solution.

17.5. (i) Obtain the general solution,

(ii) give a basis for the real solution space and

(iii) determine the solution $\{x(t)\}$ which is such that $\{x(1)\} = \{c\}$ for the systems $\frac{d}{dt}\{x(t)\} = \mathbf{A}\{x\}$, where $\mathbf{A}$ and $\{c\}$ are, respectively, as follows:

$$\text{(a)} \begin{pmatrix} 2 & -3 \\ 1 & -2 \end{pmatrix}, \begin{Bmatrix} 1 \\ -1 \end{Bmatrix}; \quad \text{(b)} \begin{pmatrix} 1 & -1 \\ 1 & 1 \end{pmatrix}, \begin{Bmatrix} 0 \\ 3 \end{Bmatrix};$$

$$\text{(c)} \begin{pmatrix} 8 & -4 & -6 \\ 10 & -5 & -12 \\ 8 & -4 & -3 \end{pmatrix}, \begin{Bmatrix} 1 \\ 2 \\ 3 \end{Bmatrix}; \quad \text{(d)} \begin{pmatrix} 3 & -6 & -14 \\ -2 & 7 & 14 \\ 1 & -3 & -6 \end{pmatrix}, \begin{Bmatrix} 0 \\ 1 \\ 2 \end{Bmatrix};$$

$$\text{(e)} \begin{pmatrix} 0 & -1 & 1 \\ 1 & 0 & -1 \\ 0 & 0 & 1 \end{pmatrix}, \begin{Bmatrix} 1 \\ -1 \\ 1 \end{Bmatrix}; \quad \text{(f)} \begin{pmatrix} 1 & -1 & 0 \\ 1 & 1 & -1 \\ 0 & 0 & 1 \end{pmatrix}, \begin{Bmatrix} 1 \\ 2 \\ 3 \end{Bmatrix}.$$

17.6. Let $\mathbf{w}_j(t) = \mathbf{u}_j(t) + i\mathbf{v}_j(t)$, $j = 1, \ldots, r$, be r complex vector functions. If the $n + r$ vector functions

$$\mathbf{w}_1(t), \quad \overline{\mathbf{w}}_1(t), \ldots, \mathbf{w}_r(t), \quad \overline{\mathbf{w}}_r(t), \quad \mathbf{k}_{r+1}(t), \ldots, \mathbf{k}_n(t),$$

where $\mathbf{k}_{r+1}(t), \ldots, \mathbf{k}_n(t)$ are real vector functions, are linearly independent in the space of complex vectors show that

(i) The $n + r$ real vector functions

$$\mathbf{u}_1(t), \ldots, \mathbf{u}_r(t), \quad \mathbf{v}_1(t), \ldots, \mathbf{v}_r(t), \quad \mathbf{k}_{r+1}(t), \ldots, \mathbf{k}_n(t)$$

are linearly independent in the space of real vectors.
[Prove that if $\mathbf{u}_1, \ldots, \mathbf{k}_n$ are linearly dependent, so are $\mathbf{w}_1, \overline{\mathbf{w}}_1, \ldots, \mathbf{k}_n$.]

(ii) If $x(t)$ is a *real* vector function and

$$\mathbf{x}(t) = a_1\mathbf{w}_1(t) + b_1\overline{\mathbf{w}}_1(t) + \ldots + a_r\mathbf{w}_r(t) + b_r\overline{\mathbf{w}}_r(t) + c_{r+1}\mathbf{k}_{r+1}(t) + \ldots + c_n\mathbf{k}_n(t)$$

where a_i, b_i, c_i are complex constants, then there exist $n + r$ *real* constants $d_1, \ldots, d_r, p_1, \ldots, p_r, q_{r+1}, \ldots, q_n$ such that

$$\mathbf{x}(t) = d_1\mathbf{u}_1(t) + p_1\mathbf{v}_1(t) + \ldots + d_r\mathbf{u}_r(t) + p_r\mathbf{v}_r(t) + q_{r+1}\mathbf{k}_{r+1}(t) + \ldots + q_n\mathbf{k}_n(t).$$

17.7. Let the **complex vector function** $\{u(t)\} + i\{v(t)\}$ be a solution to the system $\frac{d}{dt}\{x(t)\} = \mathbf{A}\{x(t)\}$, where $\mathbf{A}$ is a real (not necessarily constant) matrix.

Prove that the real vector functions $\{u(t)\}$ and $\{v(t)\}$ are solutions to the same system.

17.8. Let $\{u(t)\}_1, \ldots, \{u(t)\}_n$ be the solutions of $\frac{d}{dt}\{x(t)\} = \mathbf{A}\{x(t)\}$ such that $\{u(t_0)\}_j = \{e\}_j$, $j = 1, \ldots, n$. Show that the solution to the initial value problem

$$\frac{d}{dt}\{x(t)\} = \mathbf{A}\{x(t)\}, \quad \{x(t_0)\} = \{k\},$$

is $[\{u(t)\}_1, \ldots, \{u(t)\}_n]\{k\}$.

17.9. If $\mathbf{A}(t) = [a_{ij}(t)] \in \mathsf{M}_{m,n}$, then its **derivative** is defined by $\frac{d}{dt}\mathbf{A}(t) = \mathbf{A}'(t) = \left(\frac{d}{dt}a_{ij}(t)\right)$. Show that if c is a constant, $f(t)$ a function of t and $\mathbf{B}(t) \in \mathsf{M}_{n,p}$, then

$$[c\mathbf{A}(t)]' = c\mathbf{A}'(t), \quad [f(t)\mathbf{A}(t)]' = f'(t)\mathbf{A}(t) + f(t)\mathbf{A}'(t),$$
$$[\mathbf{A}(t)\mathbf{B}(t)]' = \mathbf{A}'(t)\mathbf{B}(t) + \mathbf{A}(t)\mathbf{B}'(t).$$

Give a formula for $[\mathbf{A}_1(t) \cdots \mathbf{A}_p(t)]'$, where $\mathbf{A}_i(t) \in \mathsf{M}_{n,n}$.

17.10. Show that if $\frac{d}{dt}\mathbf{A}(t) = 0$, then $\mathbf{A}(t)$ is independent of t.

17.11. We define the **norm** $||\mathbf{A}||$ of a not necessarily real m-by-n matrix $\mathbf{A} = (a_{ij})$ to be

$$||\mathbf{A}|| = \max|a_{ij}|, \quad i = 1, \ldots, m, \quad j = 1, \ldots, n.$$

If c is any real or imaginary number, then show that

(i) $||c\mathbf{A}|| = |c| \cdot ||\mathbf{A}||$
(ii) $||\mathbf{A} + \mathbf{B}|| \leq ||\mathbf{A}|| + ||\mathbf{B}||$

[See problem 1.1.]

17.12. If $\mathbf{A} \in \mathsf{M}_{m,n}$, $\mathbf{B} \in \mathsf{M}_{n,p}$, where $\mathbf{A}$ and $\mathbf{B}$ may be complex, then show that $||\mathbf{AB}|| \leq n||\mathbf{A}|| \cdot ||\mathbf{B}||$. Deduce that if $\mathbf{A} \in \mathsf{M}_{n,n}$ and k is a positive integer, then

$$||\mathbf{A}^k|| \leq n^{k-1}||\mathbf{A}||^k.$$

[Calculate the (i, j) element of $\mathbf{AB}$ and use problem 1.1.]

17.13. We define the m-by-n matrix $\mathbf{A} = (a_{ij})$ to be the sum of a convergent series of m-by-n matrices $\mathbf{A}_1 + \cdots + \mathbf{A}_k + \cdots$, where $\mathbf{A}_k = (a_{ij}^{(k)})$, and we write

$$\mathbf{A} = \sum_{k=1}^{\infty} \mathbf{A}_k \quad \text{if} \quad a_{ij} = \sum_{k=1}^{\infty} a_{ij}^{(k)}, \quad i = 1, \ldots, m, \quad j = 1, \ldots, n.$$

Let the m-by-n matrices $\mathbf{B}_k = (b_{ij}^{(k)})$ have nonnegative elements. If $|a_{ij}^{(k)}| \leq b_{ij}^{(k)}$, then show that the series $\sum_{k=1}^{\infty} \mathbf{A}_k$ converges if the series $\sum_{k=1}^{\infty} \mathbf{B}_k$ converges. [Note that $|\sum_{k=1}^{p} a_{ij}^{(k)}| \leq \sum_{k=1}^{p} b_{ij}^{(k)}$.]

17.14. If $\mathbf{A} = \sum_{k=1}^{\infty} \mathbf{A}_k$ and $\mathbf{B} = \sum_{k=1}^{\infty} \mathbf{B}_k$ are two convergent series of m-by-n matrices and c_1, c_2 any numbers, then show that

$$c_1\mathbf{A} + c_2\mathbf{B} = \sum_{k=1}^{\infty} (c_1\mathbf{A}_k + c_2\mathbf{B}_k).$$

17.15. The **exponential matrix function** $e^{\mathbf{A}}$, where $\mathbf{A} \in \mathsf{M}_{n,n}$, is defined by the sum of the series

$$e^{\mathbf{A}} = \mathbf{E} + \frac{1}{1!}\mathbf{A} + \frac{1}{2!}\mathbf{A}^2 + \frac{1}{3!}\mathbf{A}^3 + \ldots$$

Show that this series converges for any (complex or real) square matrix $\mathbf{A} \in \mathsf{M}_{n,n}$. [Use problems 17.11 and 17.12 with $b_{ij}^{(k)} = n^{k-1}||\mathbf{A}||^k$.]

17.16. If $\mathbf{B} \in \mathsf{M}_{p,n}$ and $\mathbf{A} \in \mathsf{M}_{n,n}$ then show that

$$\mathbf{B}e^{\mathbf{A}} = \mathbf{B} + \frac{1}{1!}\mathbf{BA} + \frac{1}{2!}\mathbf{BA}^2 + \ldots$$

Deduce that if $\mathbf{A}$ and $\mathbf{C}$ commute, then $\mathbf{C}e^{\mathbf{A}} = e^{\mathbf{A}}\mathbf{C}$. [Use problem 4.24.]

17.17. Show that if $\mathbf{A} = \begin{pmatrix} 0 & 1 \\ -1 & 0 \end{pmatrix}$, then

$$e^{t\mathbf{A}} = \begin{pmatrix} \cos t & \sin t \\ -\sin t & \cos t \end{pmatrix}.$$

[Sum the series for $e^{t\mathbf{A}}$.]

17.18. We define the derivative of a matrix $\mathbf{A}(t) = [a_{ij}(t)]$ as $\frac{d}{dt}\mathbf{A}(t) = \frac{d}{dt}a_{ij}(t)$. Show that $\frac{d}{dt}e^{t\mathbf{A}} = \mathbf{A}e^{t\mathbf{A}}$. [Use problem 17.15 and 17.16 to calculate $\mathbf{A}e^{t\mathbf{A}}$.]

17.19. If $\mathbf{C}(t) = e^{t\mathbf{A}}e^{-t\mathbf{A}}$, then use $e^{\mathbf{0}} = \mathbf{E}$ and problems 17.10 and 17.16 to show that $\mathbf{C}(t) = \mathbf{E}$. Deduce that $e^{t\mathbf{A}}$ is nonsingular and $(e^{t\mathbf{A}})^{-1} = e^{-t\mathbf{A}}$.

17.20. Let $\mathbf{C}(t) = e^{t(\mathbf{A}+\mathbf{B})}e^{-t\mathbf{A}}e^{-t\mathbf{B}}$. If $\mathbf{A}$ and $\mathbf{B}$ commute, use problems 17.10 and 17.19 to show that

$$e^{\mathbf{A}+\mathbf{B}}e^{-\mathbf{A}}e^{-\mathbf{B}} = \mathbf{E}.$$

Deduce that

$$e^{\mathbf{A}+\mathbf{B}} = e^{\mathbf{A}}e^{\mathbf{B}}$$

if and only if $\mathbf{AB} = \mathbf{BA}$.

17.21. Show that the columns of $e^{t\mathbf{A}}$ are linearly independent solutions of $\{x\}' = \mathbf{A}\{x\}$, where $\mathbf{A}$ is *not necessarily diagonalizable*. [The columns of $e^{t\mathbf{A}}$ are thus a basis for the solution space.]

17.22. Show that $\{x\} = e^{(t-t_0)\mathbf{A}}\{c\}$ is the solution of the initial value problem

$$\{x\}' = \mathbf{A}\{x\}, \quad \{x(t_0)\} = \{c\}.$$

17.23. Let $\lambda_1, \ldots, \lambda_k$ be the distinct eigenvalues of the matrix $\mathbf{A} \in \mathsf{M}_{n,n}$ with multiplicities $m_1, \ldots, m_k$, respectively, and $q(\lambda)$ the polynomial

$$q(\lambda) = (-1)^n |\mathbf{A} - \lambda\mathbf{E}| = (\lambda - \lambda)^{m_1} \cdots (\lambda - \lambda_k)^{m_k}.$$

The polynomials $q_j(\lambda)$ are defined by

$$q_j(\lambda) = (\lambda - \lambda_1)^{m_1} \cdots (\lambda - \lambda_{j-1})^{m_{j-1}} (\lambda - \lambda_{j+1})^{m_{j+1}} \cdots (\lambda - \lambda_k)^{m_k}, \quad j = 1, \ldots k,$$

and $c_j(\lambda)$, $j = 1, \ldots, k$, are the coefficients of $(\lambda - \lambda_j)^{m_j}$ in the expansion

$$\frac{1}{q(\lambda)} = \frac{c_1(\lambda)}{(\lambda - \lambda_1)^{m_1}} + \cdots + \frac{c_k(\lambda)}{(\lambda - \lambda_k)^{m_k}}.$$

(i) Use problem 4.26 to show that

$$c_1(\mathbf{A}) q_1(\mathbf{A}) + \cdots + c_k(\mathbf{A}) q_k(\mathbf{A}) = \mathbf{E}.$$

(ii) Write

$$e^{t\mathbf{A}} = e^{\lambda_i t} e^{t(\mathbf{A} - \lambda_i \mathbf{E})}$$

and use the Cayley-Hamilton theorem and the definition of the matrix exponential function to prove that

$$p_i(\mathbf{A}) e^{t\mathbf{A}} = e^{\lambda_i t} p_i(\mathbf{A}) \sum_{j=1}^{m_i - 1} \frac{t^j}{j!} (\mathbf{A} - \lambda_i \mathbf{E}).$$

(iii) From (i) and (ii) deduce that

$$e^{t\mathbf{A}} = \sum_{i=1}^{k} e^{\lambda_i t} c_i(\mathbf{A}) p_i(\mathbf{A}) \sum_{j=1}^{m_i - 1} \frac{t^j}{j!} (\mathbf{A} - \lambda_i \mathbf{E}).$$

Note that the columns of the matrix $e^{t\mathbf{A}}$ give a basis for the solution space of $\{x\}' = \mathbf{A}\{x\}$ whether $\mathbf{A}$ is diagonalizable or not.

17.24. Use the formula given in problem 17.22 to solve the initial value problems $\{x\}' = \mathbf{A}\{x\}$, $x(t_0) = \{k\}$, where the nondiagonalizable matrix $\mathbf{A}$ and the vector $\{k\}$ are the following:

(a) $\begin{pmatrix} 1 & 2 \\ 0 & 1 \end{pmatrix}$, $x(0) = \begin{Bmatrix} -1 \\ 2 \end{Bmatrix}$; (b) $\begin{pmatrix} 1 & 1 \\ -1 & 3 \end{pmatrix}$, $x(0) = \begin{Bmatrix} 1 \\ 2 \end{Bmatrix}$;

(c) $\begin{pmatrix} 4 & 2 \\ -2 & 8 \end{pmatrix}$, $x(0) = \begin{Bmatrix} 3 \\ 1 \end{Bmatrix}$; (d) $\begin{pmatrix} 5 & -6 & -14 \\ 3 & -6 & -21 \\ -1 & 3 & 10 \end{pmatrix}$, $x(1) = \begin{Bmatrix} 1 \\ -1 \\ 0 \end{Bmatrix}$;

(e) $\begin{pmatrix} -1 & 0 & 2 \\ 2 & 1 & -2 \\ -2 & 0 & 3 \end{pmatrix}$, $x(-1) = \begin{Bmatrix} -2 \\ 0 \\ -1 \end{Bmatrix}$;

(f) $\begin{pmatrix} -2 & 14 & 34 \\ -1 & 8 & 16 \\ 0 & -1 & -1 \end{pmatrix}$, $x(1) = \begin{Bmatrix} 1 \\ 2 \\ 3 \end{Bmatrix}$.

17.25. Use the formula given in problem 17.22 to give a basis for the solution space of the systems in problem 17.2.

LECTURE 18

Inhomogeneous Systems of Differential Equations

Linear systems of inhomogeneous first-order differential equations with constant coefficients • The associated homogeneous system • Particular solutions • Representation of the general solution in terms of a particular solution and the general solution of the associated homogeneous system • The substitution $\{y(t)\} = \mathbf{K}\{z(t)\}$ and the reduced system • Solution of the reduced system and the resulting solution of the original system • Representation of the solution in terms of matrix multiplication • The method of variation of parameters • The initial value problem • Use of definite integrals • The convolution integral and solutions by means of convolution integrals • Problems

Let $\mathbf{A}$ be a given n-by-n matrix of constants and $\{b(t)\}$ be a given n-tuple of functions of the independent variable t. The subject of this lecture is linear **inhomogeneous systems** of differential equations with a constant diagonalizable coefficient matrix, such as

$$\frac{d}{dt}\{x(t)\} = \mathbf{A}\{x(t)\} + \{b(t)\}. \tag{18.1}$$

The linear homogeneous system

$$\frac{d}{dt}\{y(t)\} = \mathbf{A}\{y(t)\} \tag{18.2}$$

is referred to as the **associated homogeneous system** of the given system (18.1).

Linear inhomogeneous systems of algebraic equations were solved in lecture 7 by showing that the general solution was equal to a particular solution of the inhomogeneous system plus the general solution of the associated homogeneous system. The similarity we noted in the last lecture between linear homogeneous algebraic systems and linear homogeneous systems of differential equations suggests that we look for a similar situation in the case of the linear inhomogeneous system of differential equations (18.1). Suppose, therefore, that $\{x(t)\}_1$ and $\{x(t)\}_2$ are two solutions of Eq. (18.1). This means that

$$\frac{d}{dt}\{x(t)\}_1 = \mathbf{A}\{x(t)\}_1 + \{b(t)\}, \tag{18.3}$$

$$\frac{d}{dt}\{x(t)\}_2 = \mathbf{A}\{x(t)\}_2 + \{b(t)\}. \tag{18.4}$$

If we subtract Eq. (18.3) from Eq. (18.4) and set $\{y(t)\} = \{x(t)\}_2 - \{x(t)\}_1$, we obtain

$$\frac{d}{dt}\{y(t)\} = \mathbf{A}\{y(t)\}. \tag{18.5}$$

Thus, the difference of any two solutions of the linear inhomogeneous system (18.1) satisfies the associated homogeneous system (18.5). Since $\{x(t)\}_2 = \{x(t)\}_1 + \{y(t)\}$, we have the following result. *If $u(t)$ is a solution of the inhomogeneous system* (18.1), *then*

$$\{x(t)\} = \{u(t)\} + \{y(t)\} \tag{18.6}$$

is also a solution of Eq. (18.1) *for every function $\{y(t)\}$ that satisfies the associated homogeneous system* (18.2). We have also established that *if we find all solutions $\{y(t)\}$ of the associated homogeneous system, then all solutions of the inhomogeneous system are given by Eq.* (18.6). The results established in the last lecture tell us how to find all solutions of the associated homogeneous system whenever the coefficient matrix is diagonalizable. Thus, if the coefficient matrix is diagonalizable, knowledge of one solution of the inhomogeneous system allows us to construct its general solution, just as we found in the case of linear inhomogeneous algebraic equations.

Let $\lambda_1, \ldots, \lambda_n$ be the eigenvalues of the coefficient matrix $\mathbf{A}$ and let $\mathbf{K}$ be a matrix of associated eigenvectors of $\mathbf{A}$. The solution of the linear homogeneous problem was found by making the substitution $\{x(t)\} = \mathbf{K}\{z(t)\}$. Since we have to solve the associated homogeneous system of (18.1) anyway in order to solve (18.1), we shall try the same substitution

$$\{x(t)\} = \mathbf{K}\{z(t)\}. \tag{18.7}$$

When Eq. (18.7) is substituted into Eq. (18.1), we have

$$\mathbf{K}\frac{d}{dt}\{z(t)\} = \mathbf{A}\,\mathbf{K}\{z(t)\} + \{b(t)\};$$

that is, $\{z(t)\}$ satisfies the linear inhomogeneous system

$$\frac{d}{dt}\{z(t)\} = \mathbf{K}^{-1}\mathbf{A}\,\mathbf{K}\{z(t)\} + \mathbf{K}^{-1}\{b(t)\}. \tag{18.8}$$

If we define $\{w(t)\}$ by

$$\{w(t)\} = \mathbf{K}^{-1}\{b(t)\}, \qquad w_i(t) = \sum_{j=1}^{n} k^*_{ij} b_j(t), \tag{18.9}$$

and use the fact that $\mathbf{K}^{-1}\mathbf{A}\mathbf{K}=\mathbf{D}(\lambda_1, \ldots, \lambda_n)$, Eq. (18.8) becomes the **reduced system**

$$\frac{d}{dt}z_i(t)=\lambda_i z_i(t)+w_i(t), \quad i=1, \ldots, n. \tag{18.10}$$

It is a straightforward matter of calculation to show that all solutions of the linear inhomogeneous differential equation

$$\frac{d}{dt}u(t)=a\,u(t)+v(t)$$

are given by

$$u(t)=\exp(at)\left[c+\int_\beta^t v(\eta)\exp(-a\eta)d\eta\right]=c\,e^{at}+\int_\beta^t v(\eta)e^{a(t-\eta)}d\eta$$

where c and β are arbitrary constants. We note that, in the above formula, to carry out the integration we treat t as a constant and integrate with respect to η. Moreover, if the initial condition $u(t_0)=u_0$ is given, then we take $\beta=t_0$ *and* $c=u_0e^{-at_0}$. Thus, all solutions of Eq. (18.10) are given by

$$z_i(t)=c_ie^{\lambda_i t}+\int_\beta^t w_i(\eta)e^{\lambda_i(t-\eta)}d\eta.$$

We accordingly have

$$\{z(t)\}=\begin{Bmatrix} c_1e^{\lambda_1 t}+\int_\beta^t w_1(\eta)e^{\lambda_1(t-\eta)}d\eta \\ \vdots \\ c_ne^{\lambda_n t}+\int_\beta^t w_n(\eta)e^{\lambda_n(t-\eta)}d\eta \end{Bmatrix} \tag{18.11}$$

$$=\mathbf{D}(e^{\lambda_1 t}, \ldots, e^{\lambda_n t})\{c\}+\int_\beta^t \mathbf{D}(e^{\lambda_1(t-\eta)}, \ldots, e^{\lambda_n(t-\eta)}) \times\{w(\eta)\}d\eta$$

and hence Eq. (18.7) gives the general solution of Eq. (18.1):

$$\{x(t)\}=\mathbf{K}\{z(t)\}=\left[c_1e^{\lambda_1 t}+\int_\beta^t w_1(\eta)e^{\lambda_1(t-\eta)}d\eta\right]\{k\}_1 + \cdots +\left[c_ne^{\lambda_n t}+\int_\beta^t w_n(\eta)e^{\lambda_n(t-\eta)}d\eta\right]\{k\}_n \tag{18.12}$$

$$=\mathbf{K}\,\mathbf{D}(e^{\lambda_1 t}, \ldots, e^{\lambda_n t})\{c\}+\mathbf{K}\int_\beta^t \mathbf{D}(e^{\lambda_1(t-\eta)}, \ldots, e^{\lambda_n(t-\eta)}) \times\{w(\eta)\}d\eta$$

$$=\mathbf{K}\,\mathbf{D}(e^{\lambda_1 t}, \ldots, e^{\lambda_n t})\{c\}+\mathbf{K}\int_\beta^t \mathbf{D}(e^{\lambda_1(t-\eta)}, \ldots, e^{\lambda_n(t-\eta)}) \times\mathbf{K}^{-1}\{b(\eta)\}d\eta$$

where we have used Eq. (18.9). Since

$$\{y(t)\} = c_1 \exp(\lambda_1 t)\{k\}_1 + \ \ldots \ + c_n \exp(\lambda_n t)\{k\}_n$$
$$= \mathbf{K}\,\mathbf{D}(e^{\lambda_1 t}, \ldots, e^{\lambda_n t})\{c\}$$

is the general solution of the associated homogeneous equation, and

$$\begin{aligned}
&\mathbf{K}\int_\beta^t \mathbf{D}(e^{\lambda_1(t-\eta)}, \ldots, e^{\lambda_n(t-\eta)})\{w(\eta)\}d\eta \\
&= \mathbf{K}\int_\beta^t \mathbf{D}(e^{\lambda_1(t-\eta)}, \ldots, e^{\lambda_n(t-\eta)})\mathbf{K}^{-1}\{b(\eta)\}d\eta
\end{aligned} \tag{18.13}$$

is a particular solution of Eq. (18.1), we see that Eq. (18.12) give the general solution of the inhomogeneous problem as the sum of a particular solution and the general solution of the associated homogeneous problem, as we have already proved that it should. The last equation in (18.12) gives the solution $\{x(t)\}$ directly in terms of the eigenvalues and eigenvectors of the coefficient matrix $\mathbf{A}$ and the given n-tuple of functions $\{b(t)\}$. The integrals that occur in Eq. (18.13) are called **convolution integrals** and the particular solution (18.13) is called a **convolution solution**.

As an example, let us solve the linear inhomogeneous system

$$\frac{d}{dt}\{x(t)\} = \begin{pmatrix} 14 & -30 & 32 \\ -18 & 34 & -32 \\ -24 & 48 & -48 \end{pmatrix}\{x(t)\} + \begin{Bmatrix} 2t \\ 0 \\ t^2-2 \end{Bmatrix}.$$

A straightforward calculation gives

$$\lambda_1 = -8, \ \lambda_2 = 0, \ \lambda_3 = 8;$$

$$\{k\}_1 = \begin{Bmatrix} 3 \\ -1 \\ -3 \end{Bmatrix}, \ \{k\}_2 = \begin{Bmatrix} 2 \\ 2 \\ 1 \end{Bmatrix}, \ \{k\}_3 = \begin{Bmatrix} -1 \\ 3 \\ 3 \end{Bmatrix},$$

and hence

$$\mathbf{K} = \begin{pmatrix} 3 & 2 & -1 \\ -1 & 2 & 3 \\ -3 & 1 & 3 \end{pmatrix}, \qquad \mathbf{K}^{-1} = \frac{1}{8}\begin{pmatrix} -3 & 7 & -8 \\ 6 & -6 & 8 \\ -5 & 9 & -8 \end{pmatrix},$$

$$\{w(t)\} = \mathbf{K}^{-1}\{b(t)\} = \begin{Bmatrix} 2 - \frac{3}{4}t - t^2 \\ -2 + \frac{3}{2}t + t^2 \\ 2 - \frac{5}{4}t - t^2 \end{Bmatrix}.$$

The substitution $\{x(t)\}=\mathbf{K}\{z(t)\}$ gives us

$$\frac{d}{dt}\{z(t)\}=\mathbf{D}(-8, 0, 8)\{z\}+\begin{Bmatrix} 2-\frac{3}{4}t-t^2 \\ -2+\frac{3}{2}t+t^2 \\ 2-\frac{5}{4}t-t^2 \end{Bmatrix},$$

and we obtain

$$z_1(t)=e^{-8t}\left[c_1+\int\left(2-\frac{3}{4}t-t^2\right)e^{8t}dt\right]$$

$$z_2(t)=\left[c_2+\int\left(-2+\frac{3}{2}t+t^2\right)dt\right]$$

$$z_3(t)=e^{8t}\left[c_3+\int\left(2-\frac{5}{4}t-t^2\right)e^{-8t}\right]dt.$$

Thus, $\{x(t)\}=\mathbf{K}\{z(t)\}$ gives

$$\{x(t)\}=\left(c_1e^{-8t}-\frac{1}{8}\left(t^2+\frac{1}{2}t-\frac{33}{16}\right)\right)\begin{Bmatrix} 3 \\ -1 \\ -3 \end{Bmatrix}$$

$$+\left(c_2-2t+\frac{3}{4}t^2+\frac{t^3}{3}\right)\begin{Bmatrix} 2 \\ 2 \\ 1 \end{Bmatrix}$$

$$+\left(c_3e^{8t}+\frac{1}{8}\left(t^2+\frac{3}{2}t-\frac{29}{16}\right)\right)\begin{Bmatrix} -1 \\ 3 \\ 3 \end{Bmatrix}.$$

The method of solution given above is both simple and direct, and gives us a complete solution of the given system of linear inhomogeneous differential equations with constant coefficients. There is another method which can be used, and this method is important in a number of theoretical investigations. We have seen that knowledge of the general solution of the associated homogeneous equation (18.2) reduces the problem of solving the inhomogeneous system (18.1) to that of finding *one* solution of the inhomogeneous system; that is

$$\{x(t)\}=\{y(t)\}+\{u(t)\}, \tag{18.14}$$

where $\{y(t)\}$ satisfies

$$\frac{d}{dt}\{y(t)\}=\mathbf{A}\{y(t)\} \tag{18.15}$$

and $\{u(t)\}$ is *any one* solution of

$$\frac{d}{dt}\{u(t)\}=\mathbf{A}\{u(t)\}+\{b(t)\}. \tag{18.16}$$

Now, the general solution of the associated homogeneous equation (18.15) is given by

$$\{y(t)\} = \mathbf{K}\,\mathbf{D}(\exp(\lambda_1 t), \ldots, \exp(\lambda_n t))\{c\}, \qquad \mathbf{K}^{-1}\mathbf{A}\mathbf{K} = \mathbf{D}(\lambda_1, \ldots, \lambda_n). \tag{18.17}$$

We thus have to find a $\{u(t)\}$ that satisfies Eq. (18.16). Let us try to find a $\{u(t)\}$ of the form

$$\{u(t)\} = \mathbf{K}\,\mathbf{D}(\exp(\lambda_1 t), \ldots, \exp(\lambda_n t))\{v(t)\}. \tag{18.18}$$

A straightforward calculation based upon Eq. (18.18) gives

$$\begin{aligned}\frac{d}{dt}\{u(t)\} &= \mathbf{K}\,\mathbf{D}(\lambda_1\exp(\lambda_1 t), \ldots, \lambda_n\exp(\lambda_n t))\{v(t)\}\\ &\quad + \mathbf{K}\,\mathbf{D}(\exp(\lambda_1 t), \ldots, \exp(\lambda_n t))\frac{d}{dt}\{v(t)\}\\ &= \mathbf{K}\,\mathbf{D}(\lambda_1, \ldots, \lambda_n)D(\exp(\lambda_1 t), \ldots, \exp(\lambda_n t))\{v(t)\}\\ &\quad + \mathbf{K}\,\mathbf{D}(\exp(\lambda_1 t), \ldots, \exp(\lambda_n t))\frac{d}{dt}\{v(t)\}.\end{aligned}$$

Thus, substituting Eqs. (18.19) and (18.18) into Eq. (18.16), we have

$$\begin{aligned}&\mathbf{K}\,\mathbf{D}(\lambda_1, \ldots, \lambda_n)\,\mathbf{D}(\exp(\lambda_1 t), \ldots, \exp(\lambda_n t))\{v(t)\}\\ &\quad + \mathbf{K}\,\mathbf{D}(\exp(\lambda_1 t), \ldots, \exp(\lambda_n t))\frac{d}{dt}\{v(t)\}\\ &= \mathbf{A}\,\mathbf{K}\,\mathbf{D}(\exp(\lambda_1 t), \ldots, \exp(\lambda_n t))\{v(t)\} + \{b(t)\}\\ &= (\mathbf{K}\,\mathbf{D}(\lambda_1, \ldots, \lambda_n)\mathbf{K}^{-1})\mathbf{K}\,\mathbf{D}(\exp(\lambda_1 t), \ldots, \exp(\lambda_n t))\{v(t)\}\\ &\qquad + \{b(t)\}\\ &= \mathbf{K}\,\mathbf{D}(\lambda_1, \ldots, \lambda_n)\mathbf{D}(\exp(\lambda_1 t), \ldots, \exp(\lambda_n t))\{v(t)\} + \{b(t)\},\end{aligned}$$

since $\mathbf{A} = \mathbf{K}\mathbf{D}(\lambda_1, \ldots, \lambda_n)\mathbf{K}^{-1}$. The substitution (18.18) thus reduces Eq. (18.16) to the particularly simple system

$$\mathbf{K}\,\mathbf{D}[\exp(\lambda_1 t), \ldots, \exp(\lambda_n t)]\frac{d}{dt}\{v(t)\} = \{b(t)\}. \tag{18.20}$$

Solving for $d\{v(t)\}/dt$ yields

$$\frac{d}{dt}\{v(t)\} = \mathbf{D}[\exp(-\lambda_1 t), \ldots, \exp(-\lambda_n t)]\mathbf{K}^{-1}\{b(t)\}, \tag{18.21}$$

and hence a simple integration gives us

$$\{v(t)\} = \int_\beta^t \mathbf{D}[\exp(-\lambda_1\eta), \ldots, \exp(-\lambda_n\eta)]\mathbf{K}^{-1}\{b(\eta)\}d\eta. \tag{18.22}$$

Thus, when Eq. (18.22) is substituted into Eq. (18.18) the equations (18.14), (18.17), and (18.18) give

$$\{x(t)\} = \mathbf{K}\,\mathbf{D}(e^{\lambda_1 t}, \ldots, e^{\lambda_n t})\{c\} + \mathbf{K}\int_{\beta}^{t} \mathbf{D}(e^{\lambda_1(t-\eta)}, \ldots, e^{\lambda_n(t-\eta)})\,\mathbf{K}^{-1}\{b(\eta)\}d\eta, \tag{18.23}$$

which is just exactly the same as the last of Eq. (18.12). This method of solving inhomogeneous systems is known as the method of *variation of parameters*.

What now remains is to study initial value problems:

$$\frac{d}{dt}\{x(t)\} = \mathbf{A}\{x(t)\} + \{b(t)\}, \tag{18.24}$$

$$\{x(\alpha)\} = \{q\}, \tag{18.25}$$

where α is the initial value of the independent variable and $\{q\}$ is a given column matrix of numbers which are the initial values of the dependent variables. The general solution of Eq. (18.24) is given by Eq. (18.23), where $\{c\}$ is an arbitrary constant vector, β an arbitrary constant, and both $\{c\}$ and β are to be determined by the given initial conditions of any particular initial value problem. Hence, when we use Eq. (18.23) with $\beta = \alpha$ to evaluate $\{x(t)\}$ at $t = \alpha$, the initial conditions (18.25) become

$$\{q\} = \{x(\alpha)\} = \mathbf{K}\,\mathbf{D}(e^{\lambda_1\alpha}, \ldots, e^{\lambda_n\alpha})\{c\}. \tag{18.26}$$

When we solve these equations for $\{c\}$, we then have

$$\{c\} = \mathbf{D}(e^{-\lambda_1\alpha}, \ldots, e^{-\lambda_n\alpha})\mathbf{K}^{-1}\{q\}. \tag{18.27}$$

When $\{c\}$ is substituted into Eq. (18.23) we then obtain the desired solution of the initial value problem:

$$\{x(t)\} = \mathbf{K}\,\mathbf{D}(e^{\lambda_1(t-\alpha)}, \ldots, e^{\lambda_n(t-\alpha)})\mathbf{K}^{-1}\{q\} + \mathbf{K}\int_{\alpha}^{t} \mathbf{D}(e^{\lambda_1(t-\eta)}, \ldots, e^{\lambda_n(t-\eta)})\mathbf{K}^{-1}\{b(\eta)\}d\eta. \tag{18.28}$$

As a first example of a nonhomogeneous initial value problem let us consider again the system

$$\frac{d}{dt}\{x(t)\} = \begin{pmatrix} 14 & -30 & 32 \\ -18 & 34 & -32 \\ -24 & 48 & -48 \end{pmatrix}\{x(t)\} + \begin{Bmatrix} 2t \\ 0 \\ t^2-2 \end{Bmatrix}$$

with the initial condition $\{x(0)\} = [1, 0, 0]^T$. Since the general solution to the system has already been obtained in terms of the arbitrary constants c_1, c_2 and c_3 (see page 212) all we have to do is determine these constants so that the corresponding particular solution satisfies $\{x(0)\} = [1, 0, 0]^T$. By substituting the given initial condition in the general solution we obtain:

$$\begin{Bmatrix}1\\0\\0\end{Bmatrix}=\{x(0)\}=\left(c_1+\frac{33}{128}\right)\begin{Bmatrix}3\\-1\\-3\end{Bmatrix}+c_2\begin{Bmatrix}2\\2\\1\end{Bmatrix}+\left(c_3-\frac{29}{128}\right)\begin{Bmatrix}-1\\3\\3\end{Bmatrix}$$

$$=\begin{Bmatrix}3c_1+2c_2-c_3+1\\ -c_1+2c_2+3c_3-\dfrac{120}{128}\\ -3c_1+c_2+3c_3-\dfrac{186}{128}\end{Bmatrix};$$

that is,

$$\begin{Bmatrix}3c_1+2c_2-c_3\\ -c_1+2c_2+3c_3-\dfrac{120}{128}\\ -3c_1+c_2+3c_3-\dfrac{186}{128}\end{Bmatrix}=\begin{Bmatrix}0\\0\\0\end{Bmatrix},$$

from which

$$c_1=-\frac{81}{128},\quad c_2=\frac{96}{128},\quad c_3=-\frac{51}{128}$$

and the required solution is

$$\{x(t)\}=\left(-\frac{81}{128}e^{-8t}-\frac{1}{8}\left(t^2+\frac{1}{2}t-\frac{33}{16}\right)\right)\begin{Bmatrix}3\\-1\\-3\end{Bmatrix}$$

$$+\left(\frac{96}{128}-2t+\frac{3}{4}t^2+\frac{1}{3}t^3\right)\begin{Bmatrix}2\\2\\1\end{Bmatrix}$$

$$+\left(-\frac{51}{128}e^{8t}+\frac{1}{8}\left(t^2+\frac{3}{2}t-\frac{29}{16}\right)\right)\begin{Bmatrix}-1\\3\\3\end{Bmatrix} \tag{18.29}$$

$$=\frac{1}{8}\begin{pmatrix}\dfrac{51}{16}e^{8t}-\dfrac{243}{16}e^{-8t}+20-35t+8t^2+\dfrac{16}{3}t^3\\ -\dfrac{153}{16}e^{8t}+\dfrac{81}{16}e^{-8t}+\dfrac{9}{2}-27t+16t^2+\dfrac{16}{3}t^3\\ -\dfrac{153}{16}e^{8t}+\dfrac{243}{16}e^{-8t}-\dfrac{90}{16}-10t+12t^2+\dfrac{8}{3}t^3\end{pmatrix}.$$

Alternatively, we can use Eq. (18.28) directly with $\alpha=0$ since the initial condition is given at this point. The eigenvalues λ_i and the matrices $\mathbf{K}$, $\mathbf{K}^{-1}$, $\mathbf{K}^{-1}\{b(t)\}$ have already been calculated (see page 211) so that (18.28) gives the required solution in the form

$$\{x(t)\} = \begin{Bmatrix} 3 & 2 & -1 \\ -1 & 2 & 3 \\ -3 & 1 & 3 \end{Bmatrix} \mathbf{D}(e^{-8t}, 1, e^{8t}) \frac{1}{8} \begin{Bmatrix} -3 & 7 & -8 \\ 6 & -6 & 8 \\ -5 & 9 & -8 \end{Bmatrix} \begin{Bmatrix} 1 \\ 0 \\ 0 \end{Bmatrix}$$

$$+ \begin{Bmatrix} 3 & 2 & -1 \\ -1 & 2 & 3 \\ -3 & 1 & 3 \end{Bmatrix} \int_0^t \mathbf{D}(e^{-8(t-\eta)}, 1, e^{8(t-\eta)})$$

$$\times \frac{1}{8} \begin{pmatrix} -3 & 7 & -8 \\ 6 & -6 & 8 \\ -5 & 9 & -8 \end{pmatrix} \begin{pmatrix} 2\eta \\ 0 \\ \eta^2 - 2 \end{pmatrix} d\eta$$

$$= \frac{1}{8} \begin{pmatrix} 5e^{8t} - 9e^{-8t} + 12 \\ -15e^{8t} + 3e^{-8t} + 12 \\ -15e^{8t} + 9e^{-8t} + 6 \end{pmatrix} + \frac{1}{8} \begin{pmatrix} 3 & 3 & -1 \\ -1 & 2 & 3 \\ -3 & 1 & 3 \end{pmatrix}$$

$$\times \int_0^t \begin{pmatrix} (-8\eta^2 - 6\eta + 16)e^{-8(t-\eta)} \\ 8\eta^2 + 12\eta - 16 \\ (-8\eta^2 - 10\eta + 16)e^{8(t-\eta)} \end{pmatrix} d\eta$$

$$= \frac{1}{8} \begin{pmatrix} 5e^{8t} - 9^{-8t} + 12 \\ -15e^{8t} + 3e^{-8t} + 12 \\ -15e^{8t} + 9e^{-8t} + 6 \end{pmatrix}$$

$$+ \frac{1}{8} \begin{pmatrix} 3 & 2 & -1 \\ -1 & 2 & 3 \\ -3 & 1 & 3 \end{pmatrix} \begin{pmatrix} -t^2 - \frac{1}{2}t + \frac{33}{16} - \frac{33}{16}e^{-8t} \\ \frac{8}{3}t^3 + 6t^2 - 16t \\ t^2 + \frac{3}{2}t - \frac{29}{16} + \frac{29}{16}e^{8t} \end{pmatrix}$$

$$= \frac{1}{8} \begin{pmatrix} \frac{51}{16}e^{8t} - \frac{243}{16}e^{-8t} + 20 - 35t + 8t^2 + \frac{16}{3}t^3 \\ -\frac{153}{16}e^{8t} + \frac{81}{16}e^{-8t} + \frac{9}{2} - 27t + 16t^2 + \frac{16}{3}t^3 \\ -\frac{153}{16}e^{8t} + \frac{243}{16}e^{-8t} - \frac{90}{16} - 10t + 12t^2 + \frac{8}{3}t^3 \end{pmatrix},$$

which is the same result as Eq. (18.29).

The general formula (18.28), though useful for theoretical purposes, is not convenient when applied to particular problems in which the coefficient matrix **A** has *real* eigenvalues. One should rather derive the general solution to the corresponding *reduced system* (18.10) and then obtain the required particular solution to the original problem by using Eq. (18.7) and the initial conditions. This was the way followed in the first example where, in order to determine the arbitrary constants, we had to solve an algebraic system.

We now show an *alternative way for the calculation of the arbitrary constants.* Let us consider the initial value problem

$$\frac{d}{dt}\{x(t)\}=\begin{pmatrix} 6 & 1 & -2 \\ -24 & -8 & 12 \\ -8 & -4 & 6 \end{pmatrix}\{x(t)\}+\begin{Bmatrix} t \\ t^2 \\ t+1 \end{Bmatrix}, \qquad \{x(1)\}=\begin{Bmatrix} 2 \\ 0 \\ 1 \end{Bmatrix}.$$

In the usual way we calculate

$$\lambda_1=2,\ \lambda_2=4,\ \lambda_3=-2$$

$$\mathbf{K}=\begin{pmatrix} 1 & -1 & 0 \\ 0 & 2 & 2 \\ 2 & 0 & 1 \end{pmatrix},\ \mathbf{K}^{-1}=\begin{pmatrix} -1 & -\tfrac{1}{2} & 1 \\ -2 & -\tfrac{1}{2} & 1 \\ 2 & 1 & -1 \end{pmatrix}.$$

By substituting $\{x(t)\}=\mathbf{K}\{z(t)\}$, hence $\{z(t)\}=\mathbf{K}^{-1}\{x(t)\}$, we obtain the *reduced system*

$$\frac{d}{dt}\{z(t)\}=\mathbf{D}(2, 4, -2)\{z(t)\}+\begin{pmatrix} -\dfrac{1}{2}t^2+1 \\ -\dfrac{1}{2}t^2-t+1 \\ t^2+t-1 \end{pmatrix},$$

and also the *initial conditions for the reduced system*

$$\{z(1)\}=\mathbf{K}^{-1}\{x(1)\}=\begin{Bmatrix} -\dfrac{5}{2} \\ -\dfrac{9}{2} \\ 5 \end{Bmatrix}.$$

Thus the original problem has been reduced to the three first-order linear initial value problems

$$\frac{dz_1}{dt}=2z_1-\left(\frac{1}{2}t^2-1\right), \quad z_1(1)=-\frac{5}{2};$$

$$\frac{dz_2}{dt}=4z_2-\left(\frac{1}{2}t^2+t-1\right), \quad z_2(t)=-\frac{9}{2};$$

$$\frac{dz_3}{dt}=-2z_3+(t^2+t-1), \quad z_3(t)=5;$$

with solutions

$$z_1(t)=e^{2t}\left[-\frac{5}{2}e^{-2}+\int_1^t\left(-\frac{1}{2}\eta^2+1\right)e^{-2\eta}d\eta\right]=-\frac{21}{8}e^{2(t-1)}+\frac{1}{8}(2t^2+2t-3),$$

$$z_2(t)=e^{4t}\left[-\frac{9}{2}e^{-4}+\int_1^t\left(-\frac{1}{2}\eta^2-\eta+1\right)e^{-4\eta}d\eta\right]$$

$$=-\frac{305}{8}e^{2(t-1)}+\frac{1}{8}(8t^2+20t-11),$$

$$z_3(t)=e^{-2t}\left[5e^2+\int_1^t(t^2+t-1)e^{2\eta}d\eta\right]=5e^{-2(t-1)}+\frac{1}{2}(t^2-1).$$

Now that we know $\{z(t)\}$, it is a simple matter to calculate

$$\{x(t)\}=\mathbf{K}\{z(t)\}=\begin{pmatrix} -\frac{21}{8}e^{2(t-1)}+\frac{305}{64}e^{4(t-1)}+\frac{1}{64}(8t^2-4t-13) \\ -\frac{305}{32}e^{4(t-1)}+10e^{-2(t-1)}+\frac{1}{32}(40t^2+20t-43) \\ -\frac{21}{4}e^{2(t-1)}+5e^{-2(t-1)}+\frac{1}{4}(4t^2+2t-5) \end{pmatrix},$$

So far we have given examples in which the coefficient matrix $\mathbf{A}$ has real eigenvalues and we have seen that the simplest method is to use the reduced system (18.10). If $\mathbf{A}$ has complex eigenvalues, $\mathbf{K}^{-1}$ has complex entries so that at least some of the λ_i and $w_i(t)$ in Eq. (18.10) are complex. Though the reduced system can be solved in this case too, if we want to avoid solving equations which involve complex quantities, we may use the general formula (18.28). This is one case in which this formula offers an advantage in solving specific initial value problems. As a final example let us consider

$$\frac{d}{dt}\{x(t)\}=\begin{pmatrix}1 & -1\\ 1 & 1\end{pmatrix}\{x(t)\}+\begin{Bmatrix}e^t\\ e^{2t}\end{Bmatrix},\qquad \{x(1)\}=\begin{Bmatrix}1\\ 2\end{Bmatrix}=\{q\}.$$

An easy calculation gives

$$\lambda_1=1+i,\ \lambda_2=1-i,$$

$$\mathbf{K}=\begin{pmatrix}i & -i\\ 1 & 1\end{pmatrix},$$

$$\mathbf{K}^{-1}=\frac{1}{2}\begin{pmatrix}-i & 1\\ i & 1\end{pmatrix}.$$

By substituting in Eq. (18.28) we obtain

$$\{x(t)\}=\begin{pmatrix}i & -i\\ 1 & 1\end{pmatrix}\mathbf{D}(e^{(1+i)(t-1)},\ e^{(1-i)(t-1)})\frac{1}{2}\begin{pmatrix}-i & 1\\ i & 1\end{pmatrix}\begin{pmatrix}1\\ 2\end{pmatrix}$$

$$+\begin{pmatrix}i & -i\\ 1 & 1\end{pmatrix}\int_1^t\mathbf{D}(e^{(1+i)(t-\eta)},\ e^{(1-i)(t-\eta)})\frac{1}{2}\begin{pmatrix}-i & 1\\ i & 1\end{pmatrix}\begin{pmatrix}e^{\eta}\\ e^{2\eta}\end{pmatrix}d\eta,$$

or, if we write **K** under the integral sign and carry out the algebra

$$\{x(t)\}=\frac{1}{2}\begin{pmatrix}(1+2i)e^{(1+i)(t-1)}+\overline{(1+2i)e^{(1+i)(t-1)}}\\(2-i)e^{(1+i)(t-1)}+\overline{(2-i)e^{(1+i)(t-1)}}\end{pmatrix}$$
$$+\frac{1}{2}\int_1^t\begin{pmatrix}(e^\eta+ie^{2\eta})e^{(1+i)(t-\eta)}+\overline{(e^\eta+ie^{2\eta})e^{(1+i)(t-\eta)}}\\(e^{2\eta}-ie^\eta)e^{(1+i)(t-\eta)}+\overline{(e^{2\eta}-ie^\eta)e^{(1+i)(t-\eta)}}\end{pmatrix}d\eta$$

Each entry of the above matrices is the sum of a complex number plus its conjugate (see problem 17.1) hence *both matrices are real.* If we use the formula $e^{x+iy}=e^x\cos y+ie^x\sin y$, we obtain

$$(1+2i)e^{(1+i)(t-1)}=e^{t-1}[\cos(t-1)-2\sin(t-1)]$$
$$+ie^{t-1}[\sin(t-1)+2\cos(t-1)],$$
$$(2-i)e^{(1+i)(t-1)}=e^{t-1}[2\cos(t-1)+\sin(t-1)]$$
$$+ie^{t-1}[2\sin(t-1)-\cos(t-1)],$$
$$(e^\eta+ie^{2\eta})e^{(1+i)(t-\eta)}=e^{t-\eta}[e^\eta\cos(t-\eta)-e^{2\eta}\sin(t-\eta)]$$
$$+ie^{t-\eta}[e^{2\eta}\cos(t-\eta)+e^\eta\sin(t-\eta)],$$
$$(e^{2\eta}-ie^\eta)e^{(1+i)(t-\eta)}=e^{t-\eta}[e^{2\eta}\cos(t-\eta)+e^\eta\sin(t-\eta)]$$
$$+ie^{t-\eta}[e^{2\eta}\sin(t-\eta)-e^\eta\cos(t-\eta)].$$

From the above and $z+\bar{z}=2Re(z)$ we derive

$$\{x(t)\}=e^{t-1}\begin{pmatrix}\cos(t-1)-2\sin(t-1)\\2\cos(t-1)+\sin(t-1)\end{pmatrix}$$
$$+e^t\int_1^t\begin{pmatrix}\cos(t-\eta)-e^\eta\sin(t-\eta)\\e^\eta\cos(t-\eta)+\sin(t-\eta)\end{pmatrix}d\eta$$
$$=e^{t-1}\begin{pmatrix}\cos(t-1)-2\sin(t-1)\\2\cos(t-1)+\sin(t-1)\end{pmatrix}$$
$$+\frac{1}{2}e^t\begin{pmatrix}-e^t+e[\sin(t-1)+\cos(t-1)]+\sin(t-1)\\e^t+1+e[\sin(t-1)-\cos(t-1)]-\cos(t-1)\end{pmatrix}.$$

Problems

18.1. By using the corresponding reduced system, solve the system $d\{x(t)\}/dt=\mathbf{A}\{x(t)\}+\{b(t)\}$ where $\mathbf{A}$ and $\{b(t)\}$ are respectively

(a) $\begin{pmatrix}8 & 8\\-3 & -2\end{pmatrix},\begin{pmatrix}t\\t^2\end{pmatrix}$; (b) $\begin{pmatrix}1 & 2\\4 & -1\end{pmatrix},\begin{pmatrix}e^t\\3^t\end{pmatrix}$;

(c) $\begin{pmatrix}-6 & -1 & 2\\24 & 8 & -12\\8 & 4 & -6\end{pmatrix},\begin{pmatrix}t\\0\\e^t\end{pmatrix}$; (d) $\begin{pmatrix}-2 & 0 & 0\\1 & 0 & -2\\2 & 4 & -6\end{pmatrix},\begin{pmatrix}te^t\\e^{2t}\\t^2\end{pmatrix}$;

(e) $\begin{pmatrix}0 & 2 & 1\\0 & 2 & 0\\4 & -4 & 0\end{pmatrix},\begin{pmatrix}t\\t^2e^t\\0\end{pmatrix}$; (f) $\begin{pmatrix}0 & 1 & -2\\0 & -2 & 0\\4 & 2 & -6\end{pmatrix},\begin{pmatrix}t^2\\3t\\e^t\end{pmatrix}$.

18.2. Solve the initial value problem $d\{x(t)\}/dt = \mathbf{A}\{x(t)\} + \{b(t)\}$, $\{x(t_0)\} = \{q\}$ where $\mathbf{A}$, $\{b(t)\}$, t_0, and $\{q\}$, are respectively

(a) $\begin{pmatrix} 4 & -6 \\ 2 & -4 \end{pmatrix}, \begin{Bmatrix} t \\ 3 \end{Bmatrix}, 0, \begin{Bmatrix} 1 \\ 2 \end{Bmatrix}$; (b) $\begin{pmatrix} 2 & -2 \\ 6 & -5 \end{pmatrix}, \begin{Bmatrix} e^t \\ t^2 \end{Bmatrix}, 1, \begin{Bmatrix} 0 \\ 5 \end{Bmatrix}$;

(c) $\begin{pmatrix} 2 & 1 \\ -1 & 2 \end{pmatrix}, \begin{Bmatrix} te^t \\ 3t \end{Bmatrix}, a, \begin{Bmatrix} b \\ a+b \end{Bmatrix}$; (d) $\begin{pmatrix} 5 & -9 \\ 3 & -7 \end{pmatrix}, \begin{Bmatrix} \cos t \\ t \end{Bmatrix}, 3, \begin{Bmatrix} 1 \\ 0 \end{Bmatrix}$;

(e) $\begin{pmatrix} -5 & 18 & 42 \\ 6 & -17 & -42 \\ -3 & 9 & 22 \end{pmatrix}, \begin{pmatrix} e^{3t} \\ te^t \\ t^2 \end{pmatrix}, -1, \begin{pmatrix} 0 \\ 1 \\ 2 \end{pmatrix}$;

(f) $\begin{pmatrix} 1 & -1 & -2 \\ 1 & 1 & -1 \\ 0 & 0 & -1 \end{pmatrix}, \begin{pmatrix} \cos t \\ e^t \sin t \\ t^2 \end{pmatrix}, -2, \begin{pmatrix} 1 \\ 0 \\ 1 \end{pmatrix}$;

(g) $\begin{pmatrix} 10 & -4 & 2 \\ -12 & 8 & -5 \\ -48 & 24 & -14 \end{pmatrix}, \begin{pmatrix} e^{2t} \\ \sin t \\ e^t \cos t \end{pmatrix}, 0, \begin{pmatrix} 1 \\ 0 \\ 0 \end{pmatrix}$;

(h) $\begin{pmatrix} 0 & -1 & -1 \\ -1 & 0 & 1 \\ 0 & 0 & -1 \end{pmatrix}, \begin{pmatrix} \sin t \\ \cos t \\ 3 \end{pmatrix}, \pi, \begin{pmatrix} -2 \\ 1 \\ 0 \end{pmatrix}$.

LECTURE 19

An Example from Control Theory

Control of physical systems governed by differential equations • The control target • A control law and controllability by a control law • Use of eigenvalue theory to find control parameters • The family of control parameters that give a controllable process • The cost function • Optimal control • Solution of the optimal control problem •

This last lecture is devoted to the study of a problem of both mathematical and physical interest and provides an introduction to a very important discipline, namely control theory.

The laws which govern most physical systems are differential equations which tell us how the physical systems evolve with time. Usually, these differential equations (physical laws) contain two kinds of terms. Terms of the first kind are fixed by the physics of the system. These terms can not be changed without changing the given physical system into a new system altogether. Terms of the second kind describe what we can do to the physical system, such as add something to it, or subtract something from it, or hit it with a hammer, or what have you. Control theory studies how to choose the terms of the second kind so that we can force the physical system to do what we want it to do.

The physical system we pick for examination is governed by the following simple differential equation:

$$\frac{d}{dt}x(t) - a\,x(t) = f(t). \tag{19.1}$$

The terms on the left-hand side of Eq. (19.1) are the terms of the first kind which describe the physics of the system. Thus, the number a is given to us by the physics of the problem. The term $f(t)$ on the right-hand side of Eq. (19.1) is a term of the second kind; a function of t which we can choose by the way we act on the given physical system. A physical example in which the law (19.1) occurs is that in which $x(t)$ represents the amount of algae in a body of water. Equation (19.1) says that the amount of algae produced per unit time is equal to a times the amount of algae that is already present plus $f(t)$ which represents the rate at which we increase the algae. Thus, the number a is the birth rate minus the death rate of algae, which is fixed by the life processes of algae cells. We assume that the number a is positive. The function $-f(t)$ can then be interpreted as the rate at which we kill algae cells by the control measures we wish to employ. If we do nothing to the system, that is, if we take $f(t)=0$, then the solution of Eq. (19.1) is given by

$$x(t)=x_0e^{at}, \tag{19.2}$$

where x_0 denotes the amount of algae present at $t=0$. Thus, with no control, the algae population will grow exponentially large as time increases. This is obviously not a desirable situation in terms of the overall ecology of the body of water. We must accordingly do something other than just adopt a policy of indifference—$(f(t)=0)$. We thus want to prevent the runaway growth of the algae and we would like to do it in such a fashion that the number of algae approaches a given number X as time increases. The *target number* X of algae is determined by the optimal ecological balance of the body of water. This gives us a requirement for the choice of the control variable $f(t)$, namely, that $f(t)$ be chosen so that

$$\lim_{t\to\infty} x(t)=X \tag{19.3}$$

for each value of x_0.

There are many ways of choosing the function $f(t)$ so as to achieve the condition (19.3). It is thus necessary to narrow down the possible choices so as to obtain a manageable problem. Suppose that we build a "black box" which will choose the function $f(t)$ by the differential equation

$$\frac{d}{dt}f(t)=\alpha\, x(t)+\beta\, f(t). \tag{19.4}$$

This "black box law" says that we sample $x(t)$ and $f(t)$ at time t, form the combination $\alpha\, x(t)+\beta\, f(t)$, and then produce $f(t)$ at the rate given by Eq. (19.4). The "black box law" given by Eq. (19.4) is referred to as the *control law* for the choice of $f(t)$. The simplicity of the control law is dictated by the ease with which it can be achieved by appropriate hardware. What we now have to do is to make sure that the control law (19.4) will actually allow us to achieve the desired condition (19.3); that is, is $x(t)$ *controllable* by the control law (19.4) so as to achieve the condition (19.3)? The control law (19.4) contains the two undetermined parameters α and β, and hence we must study whether $x(t)$ is controllable by some choice of α and β so that we satisfy the condition (19.3). We thus have to study the following system of equations:

$$\frac{d}{dt}x(t)=a\,x(t)+f(t), \tag{19.5}$$

$$\frac{d}{dt}f(t)=\alpha\,x(t)+\beta\,f(t), \tag{19.6}$$

$$x(0)=x_0, \tag{19.7}$$

$$\lim_{t\to\infty} x(t)=X \text{ for all } x_0. \tag{19.8}$$

If this system of equations has a solution, then $x(t)$ is *controllable* by the control law (19.6).

The system of differential equations (19.5) and (19.6) can be written in the equivalent form

$$\frac{d}{dt}\begin{Bmatrix} x(t) \\ f(t) \end{Bmatrix}=\begin{pmatrix} a & 1 \\ \alpha & \beta \end{pmatrix}\begin{Bmatrix} x(t) \\ f(t) \end{Bmatrix}, \tag{19.9}$$

so that the coefficient matrix of the system is

$$\mathbf{A}=\begin{pmatrix} a & 1 \\ \alpha & \beta \end{pmatrix}. \tag{19.10}$$

Our study of systems of first-order linear differential equations tells us that the solution of Eq. (19.9) will be given by

$$\begin{Bmatrix} x(t) \\ f(t) \end{Bmatrix}=c_1e^{\lambda_1 t}\{k\}_1+c_2e^{\lambda_2 t}\{k\}_2, \tag{19.11}$$

where λ_1 and λ_2 are the eigenvalues of $\mathbf{A}$ and $\{k\}_1$ and $\{k\}_2$ are associated eigenvectors of $\mathbf{A}$. The only situation in which $x(t)$ given by Eq. (19.11) can satisfy the condition (19.8) and not oscillate in time (i.e., $\mathbf{A}$ has real eigenvalues) occurs when

$$\lambda_1=0, \quad \lambda_2=-\mu^2\leq 0, \tag{19.12}$$

in which case Eq. (19.11) becomes

$$\begin{Bmatrix} x(t) \\ f(t) \end{Bmatrix}=c_1\{k\}_1+c_2e^{-\mu^2 t}\{k\}_2. \tag{19.13}$$

The characteristic polynomial of $\mathbf{A}$ is given by

$$p(\lambda)=\det(\mathbf{A}-\lambda\mathbf{E})=\lambda^2-(a+\beta)\lambda+a\beta-\alpha, \tag{19.14}$$

and hence the conditions (19.12) on the eigenvalues of $\mathbf{A}$ give us the results

$$\alpha=a\beta=-a(a+\mu^2), \quad \beta=-(a+\mu^2). \tag{19.15}$$

Thus, for each choice of μ, the conditions (19.15) determine α and β and hence the coefficient matrix $\mathbf{A}$ so that we satisfy the conditions (19.12).

This is quite different from what we have done before. In the previous lectures we were given the matrix **A** and then solved the system of differential equations with **A** as coefficient matrix. Here, we have determined entries of the matrix **A** so that the solutions will have a desired form, namely Eq. (19.13). One kind of problem is just as easy as the other since the theory tells us what the solution looks like in terms of the eigenvalues and the eigenvectors of the coefficient matrix. We can thus fix the properties of the solution and find the corresponding coefficient matrix, or we can find the solution for a given coefficient matrix, with equal ease.

It now remains to complete this part of the problem. With α and β given by Eq. (19.15), the matrix **A** is given by

$$\mathbf{A}=\begin{pmatrix} a & 1 \\ -a(a+\mu^2) & -(a+\mu^2)\end{pmatrix}, \tag{19.16}$$

and hence we have

$$\lambda_1=0, \qquad \lambda_2=-\mu^2$$
$$\{k\}_1=\begin{Bmatrix} 1 \\ -a\end{Bmatrix}, \qquad \{k\}_2=\begin{Bmatrix} 1 \\ -(a+\mu^2)\end{Bmatrix} \tag{19.17}$$

and that $\mu\neq 0$. The requirement $\mu\neq 0$ comes from the fact that $\mu=0$ implies $\{k\}_1=\{k\}_2$, which says that **A** would not be diagonalizable in this case. When we substitute Eqs. (19.17) into Eq. (19.13), we have the explicit solution

$$\begin{Bmatrix} x(t) \\ f(t)\end{Bmatrix}=c_1\begin{Bmatrix} 1 \\ -a\end{Bmatrix}+c_2e^{-\mu^2 t}\begin{Bmatrix} 1 \\ -(a+\mu^2)\end{Bmatrix}, \quad \mu\neq 0.$$

The initial and final conditions (19.7) and (19.8) then give $c_1=X$, $c_2=x_0-X$ and hence

$$\begin{Bmatrix} x(t) \\ f(t)\end{Bmatrix}=X\begin{Bmatrix} 1 \\ -a\end{Bmatrix}+(x_0-X)e^{-\mu^2 t}\begin{Bmatrix} 1 \\ -(a+\mu^2)\end{Bmatrix}, \tag{19.18}$$

satisfies all of the equations (19.5) through (19.8). We note that Eq. (19.18) states that μ can not vanish if $x_0\neq X$. The solution (19.18) also tells us the initial value of $f(t)$:

$$f(0)=\mu^2 X-(a+\mu^2)x_0. \tag{19.19}$$

We have thus shown that $x(t)$ is controllable by the control law $df/dt=-a(a+\mu^2)x-(a+\mu^2)f$ for any value of the constant μ other than $\mu=0$. We thus not only have controllability of $x(t)$, we have infinitely many ways of controlling $x(t)$ with the given control law.

Now that we have established that the control law

$$df/dt=-a(a+\mu^2)x-(a+\mu^2)f \tag{19.20}$$

will control $x(t)$, we can go a little further into the problem. In the actual world, whatever is done costs something either directly or indirectly. For the problem we have just finished investigating, you would expect to pay something for providing $f(t)$, and it would cost you something when $x(t)$ is not at its desired value X. To be specific, we will assume that the *cost* that is involved in the process involving $x(t)$ and $f(t)$ is given by

$$C=\int_0^\infty\left[A\left|\frac{df(t)}{dt}\right|+B(x(t)-X)^2\right]dt \tag{19.21}$$

where A and B are given positive numbers. Thus, the cost per unit time due to $f(t)$ is $A|df/dt|$ and the cost per unit time due to $x(t)\neq X$ is $B[x(t)-X]^2$. Since the parameter μ is still at our disposal, we obviously would like to pick μ so that the cost of the control will be as small as possible. We thus want to minimize the cost with respect to the undetermined control parameter μ. This is the basic problem referred to as *optimal control*: control a process so that the desired result is achieved and do it in such a way as to minimize the cost. When Eq. (19.18) is used to evaluate the integrand on the right-hand side of Eq. (19.21), we have

$$A\left|\frac{df}{dt}\right|+B(x-X)^2=A\mu^2(a+\mu^2)|x_0-X|e^{-\mu^2 t}+B(x_0-X)^2e^{-2\mu^2 t},$$

and hence the cost is given by

$$C(\mu^2)=A(a+\mu^2)|x_0-X|+\frac{B(x_0-X)^2}{2\mu^2}. \tag{19.22}$$

Differentiating $C(\mu^2)$ with respect to μ^2 gives

$$\frac{dC(\mu^2)}{d(\mu^2)}=A|x_0-X|-\frac{B(x_0-X)^2}{2\mu^4}. \tag{19.23}$$

Thus, $C(\mu^2)$ has a stationary value at

$$\mu^2=\sqrt{\frac{B}{2A}}|x_0-X|, \tag{19.24}$$

which is easily seen to be the minimal value for $C(\mu^2)$. The *optimal control* is thus given by [see Eq. (19.20)]

$$\frac{df}{dt}=-(ax+f)\left(a+\sqrt{\frac{B}{2A}}|x_0-X|\right), \tag{19.25}$$

and the cost of this optimal control is

$$C\left(\sqrt{\frac{B}{A}}|x_0-X|\right)=|x_0-X|(Aa+\sqrt{2AB|x_0-X|}). \tag{19.26}$$

We end by observing that the optimal control given by Eq. (19.25) is obviously contingent upon the choice of the control law

$$\frac{df}{dt}=\alpha x+\beta f,$$

and the cost function

$$\int_0^{\infty}\left(A\left|\frac{df}{dt}\right|+B(x-X)^2\right)dt.$$

If we change the control law or if we have a different cost function, then the solution of the optimal control problem given above will no longer hold. In fact, the problem may even cease to be controllable.

Answers to Selected Problems

1.2. (b) $x_1 = 2,\ x_2 = 1,\ x_3 = -1$ (d) $x_1 = 1 + \frac{1}{5}a,\ x_2 = \frac{3}{5}a,\ x_3 = a$

(e) $x_1 = i,\ x_2 = 2i,\ x_3 = 1 + i$

1.3. (b) $a = -10,\ x_1 = \frac{1}{2}(b - 1),\ x_2 = \frac{1}{2}(9b - 23),\ x_3 = b$

(d) $a = 7,\ x_1 = -3b + 5c + 2,\ x_2 = b,\ x_3 = c$

(f) $a = -2,\ x_1 = -\frac{2}{2+i}(2b + 4 - i),\ x_2 = b,\ x_3 = \frac{2-3i}{2+i}b + \frac{2-i}{2+i}$

2.2. (a) $\mathbf{x} + 2\mathbf{y} = \begin{Bmatrix} 2 \\ 5 \\ 8 \\ 11 \end{Bmatrix},\ 3\mathbf{x} - \mathbf{y} = \begin{Bmatrix} -1 \\ 1 \\ 3 \\ 5 \end{Bmatrix},\ \mathbf{x} - i\mathbf{y} = \begin{Bmatrix} -i \\ 1 - 2i \\ 2 - 3i \\ 3 - 4i \end{Bmatrix}$

(c) $\mathbf{x} + 2\mathbf{y} = \begin{Bmatrix} -5 + 10i \\ 4 + 2i \\ -5 \\ 5 - 2i \end{Bmatrix},\ 3\mathbf{x} - \mathbf{y} = \begin{Bmatrix} -15 - 5i \\ 5 - i \\ -6 \\ 8 + i \end{Bmatrix},\ \mathbf{x} - i\mathbf{y} = \begin{Bmatrix} 0 \\ 3 - i \\ 1 + 3i \\ 2 - i \end{Bmatrix}$

(e) $\mathbf{x} + 2\mathbf{y} = \begin{Bmatrix} -9 \\ 8 \\ 8 \\ -3 \end{Bmatrix},\ 3\mathbf{x} - \mathbf{y} = \begin{Bmatrix} 8 \\ -4 \\ 3 \\ 1 \end{Bmatrix},\ \mathbf{x} - i\mathbf{y} = \begin{Bmatrix} 1 + 5i \\ -4i \\ 2 - 3i \\ 1 + 2i \end{Bmatrix}$

2.3. (a) $\begin{Bmatrix} 1 \\ -3 \end{Bmatrix}$ (c) $\begin{Bmatrix} -3 \\ -\frac{1}{2} \end{Bmatrix}$ (e) $\begin{Bmatrix} \frac{5}{2} \\ -4 \\ -\frac{1}{2} \end{Bmatrix}$

2.4. (a) No (c) Yes, $\mathbf{b} = \mathbf{a}_1 + \mathbf{a}_2$ (f) $\mathbf{b} = i\mathbf{a}_1 + 2\mathbf{a}_2$

2.8. (b) $a = 0$ $\begin{Bmatrix} 1 \\ 1 \\ 1 \\ 0 \end{Bmatrix},\ \begin{Bmatrix} 0 \\ -1 \\ 1 \\ 0 \end{Bmatrix}$

2.19. (a) $\mathbf{x} = \lambda \begin{Bmatrix} 1 \\ 2 \\ 3 \end{Bmatrix},\ \begin{matrix} x_1 = \lambda \\ x_2 = 2\lambda \\ x_3 = 3\lambda \end{matrix}$ (c) $\mathbf{x} = \begin{Bmatrix} 2 \\ -6 \\ 8 \end{Bmatrix} + \lambda \begin{Bmatrix} 1 \\ -3 \\ 4 \end{Bmatrix},\ \begin{matrix} x_1 = 2 + \lambda \\ x_2 = -6 - 3\lambda \\ x_3 = 8 + 4\lambda \end{matrix}$

(e) $\mathbf{x} = \lambda \begin{Bmatrix} 8 \\ 3 \\ -9 \end{Bmatrix},\ \begin{matrix} x_1 = 8\lambda \\ x_2 = 3\lambda \\ x_3 = -9\lambda \end{matrix}$

2.26. (a) $\mathbf{x} = m \begin{Bmatrix} 1 \\ -2 \\ 4 \end{Bmatrix} + n \begin{Bmatrix} 3 \\ -4 \\ 0 \end{Bmatrix},\ \begin{matrix} x_1 = m + 3n \\ x_2 = -2m - 4n \\ x_3 = 4m \end{matrix}$

(c) $\mathbf{x} = m\begin{Bmatrix} 1 \\ 2 \\ -3 \end{Bmatrix} + n\begin{Bmatrix} 3 \\ 0 \\ -5 \end{Bmatrix}$, $\begin{matrix} x_1 = m + 3n \\ x_2 = 2m \\ x_3 = -3m - 5n \end{matrix}$

(e) $\mathbf{x} = \begin{Bmatrix} 0 \\ 1 \\ -1 \end{Bmatrix} + m\begin{Bmatrix} 3 \\ 5 \\ 9 \end{Bmatrix} + n\begin{Bmatrix} 1 \\ -1 \\ 2 \end{Bmatrix}$, $\begin{matrix} x_1 = 3m + n \\ x_2 = 1 + 5m - n \\ x_3 = -1 + 9m + 2n \end{matrix}$

3.1. (a) $\mathbf{x} \circ \mathbf{y} = 0$, $||\mathbf{x}|| = \sqrt{14}$, $||\mathbf{y}|| = \sqrt{13}$

(c) $\mathbf{x} \circ \mathbf{y} = -4$, $||\mathbf{x}|| = \sqrt{13}$, $||\mathbf{y}|| = 2\sqrt{5}$

(e) $\mathbf{x} \circ \mathbf{y} = 1 - 14i$, $||\mathbf{x}|| = \sqrt{11}$, $||\mathbf{y}|| = \sqrt{39}$

3.2. (a) $\begin{Bmatrix} \frac{1}{\sqrt{14}} \\ \frac{2}{\sqrt{14}} \\ \frac{-3}{\sqrt{14}} \end{Bmatrix}, \begin{Bmatrix} 0 \\ \frac{-3}{\sqrt{13}} \\ \frac{-2}{\sqrt{13}} \end{Bmatrix}$ (c) $\begin{Bmatrix} \frac{3}{\sqrt{13}} \\ \frac{-2}{\sqrt{13}} \\ 0 \end{Bmatrix}, \begin{Bmatrix} 0 \\ \frac{1}{\sqrt{5}} \\ \frac{-2}{\sqrt{5}} \end{Bmatrix}$ (e) $\begin{Bmatrix} \frac{1+i}{\sqrt{11}} \\ 0 \\ \frac{3i}{\sqrt{11}} \end{Bmatrix}, \begin{Bmatrix} \frac{i}{\sqrt{39}} \\ \frac{2+3i}{\sqrt{39}} \\ \frac{5}{\sqrt{39}} \end{Bmatrix}$

3.3. (a) 0 (c) $-2/\sqrt{65}$

4.1. (a) $\begin{pmatrix} 2 & -3 & 0 \\ 0 & 6 & 8 \end{pmatrix}$ (c) $\begin{pmatrix} -15 & 4 & -7 \\ 0 & 10 & 0 \\ -1 & -6 & 13 \end{pmatrix}$ (e) $\begin{pmatrix} -2 \\ -15 \\ -1 \end{pmatrix}$

4.2. (a) $(19 \quad 24)$ (c) $\begin{pmatrix} 8 \\ -3 \\ 30 \end{pmatrix}$ (f) $\begin{pmatrix} 6 & 0 & 3 \\ -9 & 0 & 3 \\ 8 & 0 & 14 \end{pmatrix}$

(h) $\begin{pmatrix} -56 & 35 & 49 \\ 40 & -25 & -35 \\ -24 & 15 & 21 \end{pmatrix}$

4.3. (a) $\begin{pmatrix} 0 & 0 \\ 0 & 0 \end{pmatrix}$ (c) $\begin{pmatrix} 0 & 0 \\ 0 & 0 \end{pmatrix}$ (e) $\begin{pmatrix} 0 & 0 \\ 0 & 0 \end{pmatrix}$

4.4. (a) $\begin{pmatrix} 0 & 1 & 3 \\ 1 & 3 & 0 \\ 0 & 0 & 4 \end{pmatrix}\begin{Bmatrix} x_1 \\ x_2 \\ x_3 \end{Bmatrix} = \begin{pmatrix} 1 \\ 0 \\ 2 \end{pmatrix}$ (c) $\begin{pmatrix} 1 & 0 & 1 \\ 7 & 2 & 0 \\ 6 & 0 & 1 \end{pmatrix}\begin{Bmatrix} x_1 \\ x_2 \\ x_3 \end{Bmatrix} = \begin{pmatrix} 1 \\ 0 \\ 2 \end{pmatrix}$

(d) $\begin{pmatrix} 6 & 2 & 0 \\ 3 & -1 & -2 \end{pmatrix}\begin{Bmatrix} x_1 \\ x_2 \\ x_3 \end{Bmatrix} = \begin{pmatrix} 0 \\ 1 \end{pmatrix}$

5.1. (a) $2c_1 + 3c_2 + 6c_3 = 0$, $3c_1 - c_2 + 8c_3 = 0$

(c) $14c_2 - 3c_3 = 0$, $3c_1 + 7c_2 + 10c_3 = 0$

(e) $6c_1 + c_4 = 0$, $8c_2 + c_4 = 0$, $3c_2 + 4c_3 + 7c_4 = 0$

5.2. (a) Independent (c) $\frac{1}{2}\begin{Bmatrix} 6 \\ 4 \end{Bmatrix} + \begin{Bmatrix} -2 \\ 4 \end{Bmatrix} - \begin{Bmatrix} 1 \\ 6 \end{Bmatrix} = \begin{Bmatrix} 0 \\ 0 \end{Bmatrix}$

(e) $2\begin{Bmatrix}0\\1\\2\end{Bmatrix}-\begin{Bmatrix}3\\-1\\4\end{Bmatrix}-\begin{Bmatrix}-3\\3\\0\end{Bmatrix}=\begin{Bmatrix}0\\0\\0\end{Bmatrix}$

6.1. (a) $\begin{pmatrix}1&0&0\\0&1&0\\0&0&1\end{pmatrix}$ (b) $\begin{pmatrix}1&\frac{3}{2}&\frac{1}{2}\\0&0&0\\0&0&0\\0&0&0\end{pmatrix}$ (e) $\begin{pmatrix}1&0&0&0\\0&1&2&-1\\0&0&0&0\end{pmatrix}$

6.2. (a) $\begin{Bmatrix}1\\0\\0\end{Bmatrix},\begin{Bmatrix}0\\1\\0\end{Bmatrix},\begin{Bmatrix}0\\0\\1\end{Bmatrix}$ (b) $\begin{Bmatrix}6\\5\\17\\7\end{Bmatrix}$ (e) $\begin{Bmatrix}1\\-1\\1\end{Bmatrix},\begin{Bmatrix}2\\4\\-3\end{Bmatrix}$

7.1. (a) $c\mathbf{u}_1+2c\mathbf{u}_2+0\mathbf{u}_3=\mathbf{0}$ (d) $2c\mathbf{u}_1-3c\mathbf{u}_2-c\mathbf{u}_3=\mathbf{0}$

(f) $-c\mathbf{u}_1+\frac{2}{3}c\mathbf{u}_2-c\mathbf{u}_3=\mathbf{0}$

7.3. (a) No (c) Yes (e) No

7.4. (a) $a=4,\ \begin{Bmatrix}-1\\12\\16\end{Bmatrix}=2\begin{Bmatrix}1\\3\\2\end{Bmatrix}+3\begin{Bmatrix}-1\\2\\4\end{Bmatrix}$

(c) $a=-2,\ \begin{Bmatrix}1\\7\\0\end{Bmatrix}=2\begin{Bmatrix}2\\11\\3\end{Bmatrix}-3\begin{Bmatrix}1\\5\\2\end{Bmatrix}$

7.5. (a) $\mathbf{A}_R=\begin{pmatrix}0&1&0\\0&0&1\\0&0&0\end{pmatrix},\ \begin{pmatrix}1&0&0\\0&\frac{1}{2}&0\\0&0&1\end{pmatrix}\begin{pmatrix}1&0&0\\0&1&0\\-1&0&1\end{pmatrix}\times$

$\times\begin{pmatrix}\frac{1}{2}&0&0\\0&1&0\\0&0&1\end{pmatrix}\begin{pmatrix}0&1&0\\1&0&0\\0&0&1\end{pmatrix}=\begin{pmatrix}0&\frac{1}{2}&0\\\frac{1}{2}&0&0\\0&-\frac{1}{2}&1\end{pmatrix}=\mathbf{S}_A$

(c) $\mathbf{A}_R=\begin{pmatrix}1&0&0\\0&1&0\\0&0&1\end{pmatrix},\ \begin{pmatrix}1&0&0\\0&1&1\\0&0&1\end{pmatrix}\begin{pmatrix}1&0&-2\\0&1&0\\0&0&1\end{pmatrix}\times$

$$\times\begin{pmatrix}1 & 0 & 0\\ 0 & \frac{1}{2} & 0\\ 0 & 0 & 1\end{pmatrix}\begin{pmatrix}1 & 0 & 0\\ -1 & 1 & 0\\ 0 & 0 & 1\end{pmatrix}\begin{pmatrix}\frac{1}{3} & 0 & 0\\ 0 & 1 & 0\\ 0 & 0 & 1\end{pmatrix}$$

$$=\begin{pmatrix}\frac{1}{3} & 0 & -2\\ -\frac{1}{6} & \frac{1}{2} & 1\\ 0 & 0 & 1\end{pmatrix}=\mathbf{S}_A$$

(e) $\mathbf{A}_R=\begin{pmatrix}1 & 0 & 0\\ 0 & 1 & 0\\ 0 & 0 & 1\end{pmatrix}$, $\mathbf{S}_A=\begin{pmatrix}\frac{7}{3} & -\frac{4}{9} & -\frac{2}{3}\\ -2 & 0 & 1\\ \frac{2}{3} & \frac{1}{9} & -\frac{1}{3}\end{pmatrix}$

$$=\begin{pmatrix}1 & 0 & 0\\ 0 & 1 & -3\\ 0 & 0 & 1\end{pmatrix}\begin{pmatrix}1 & 0 & 2\\ 0 & 1 & 0\\ 0 & 0 & 1\end{pmatrix}\begin{pmatrix}1 & 0 & 0\\ 0 & 1 & 0\\ 0 & 0 & -\frac{1}{3}\end{pmatrix}\times$$

$$\times\begin{pmatrix}1 & 0 & 0\\ 0 & 1 & 0\\ 0 & -1 & 1\end{pmatrix}\begin{pmatrix}1 & -2 & 0\\ 0 & 1 & 0\\ 0 & 0 & 1\end{pmatrix}\begin{pmatrix}1 & 0 & 0\\ 0 & \frac{1}{3} & 0\\ 0 & 0 & 1\end{pmatrix}\begin{pmatrix}1 & 0 & 0\\ 0 & 1 & 0\\ -2 & 0 & 1\end{pmatrix}$$

7.6. (a) $\begin{pmatrix}-\frac{5}{2} & \frac{3}{2}\\ 2 & -1\end{pmatrix}$ (c) $\begin{pmatrix}\frac{5}{8} & -\frac{1}{16} & \frac{1}{16}\\ -\frac{3}{8} & -\frac{1}{16} & \frac{1}{16}\\ \frac{3}{16} & \frac{9}{32} & -\frac{1}{32}\end{pmatrix}$

(f) $\begin{pmatrix}5 & -2 & 0\\ -2 & 1 & 0\\ -1 & -1 & 1\end{pmatrix}$

7.7. (a) Inconsistent. $[x_1, x_2]^T = c[-1, 2]^T$, basis of solution space $[-1, 2]^T$, basis of row space $[2, 1]$.

(c) $[x_1, x_2, x_3, x_4]^T = c[3, 4, 2, -1]^T + [-5, 19, -6, 0]^T$.

(e) Inconsistent. $[x_1, x_2, x_3]^T = c[1, -2, 1]^T$, basis of solution space $[1, -2, 1]^T$, basis of row space $[1, 0, -1]$, $[0, 1, 2]$.

7.8. (a) Unique $[x_1, x_2]^T = [1/2, 0]^T$.

(b) Not unique. One dimensional. $[x_1, x_2]^T = [2/3, 0]^T + x[1/3, 1]^T$. Particular solution of inhomogeneous $[x_1, x_2]^T = [2/3, 0]^T$. General solution of homogeneous $[x_1, x_2]^T = x[1/3, 1]^T$. Basis of solution space of homogeneous $[1/2, 1]^T$. Basis of row space of **A** $[3, -1]$.

(f) Not unique. Two dimensional. $[x_1, x_2, x_3, x_4]^T = [1/2, 1/4, 0, 0]^T + x[-1/2, -5/4, 1, 0]^T + y[3/2, -11/4, 0, 1]^T$. Particular solution of inhomogeneous $[1/2, 1/4, 0, 0]^T$. General solution of homogeneous $[x_1, x_2, x_3, x_4]^T = x[-1/2, -5/4, 1, 0]^T + y[3/2, -11/4, 0, 1]^T$. Basis of solution space of homogeneous $[-1/2, -5/4, 1, 0]^T$, $[3/2, -11/4, 0, 1]^T$. Basis of row space of **A** $[1, 2, 3, 4]$, $[0, 4, 5, 11]$.

8.1. (a) $\mathbf{B} = \begin{pmatrix} -3-2x & 2-2y \\ 2+x & -1+y \\ x & y \end{pmatrix}$ (b) $\mathbf{B} = \begin{pmatrix} -3 & 2 \\ 2 & -1 \end{pmatrix}$ unique.

(d) **B** does not exist. (h) $\mathbf{B} = \begin{pmatrix} \frac{1}{2} & -\frac{3}{4} & \frac{1}{4} \\ -\frac{3}{4} & -\frac{1}{8} & \frac{3}{8} \\ \frac{1}{4} & \frac{3}{8} & -\frac{1}{8} \end{pmatrix}$ unique.

8.2. (a) **B** does not exist. (b) $\mathbf{B} = \begin{pmatrix} -3 & 2 \\ 2 & -1 \end{pmatrix}$

(d) $\mathbf{B} = \begin{pmatrix} -2+x & 1-2x & x \\ \frac{3}{2}+y & -\frac{1}{2}-2y & y \end{pmatrix}$ (h) $\mathbf{B} = \begin{pmatrix} \frac{1}{2} & -\frac{3}{4} & \frac{1}{4} \\ -\frac{3}{4} & -\frac{1}{8} & \frac{3}{8} \\ \frac{1}{4} & \frac{3}{8} & -\frac{1}{8} \end{pmatrix}$

8.3. (a) $\begin{pmatrix} 1 & 2 & 0 \\ 2 & 3 & 1 \end{pmatrix} = \begin{pmatrix} 1 & 2 \\ 2 & 3 \end{pmatrix}\begin{pmatrix} 1 & 0 & 2 \\ 0 & 1 & -1 \end{pmatrix}$,

$\begin{pmatrix} 1 & 2 \\ 2 & 3 \end{pmatrix} = \begin{pmatrix} 1 & 0 \\ 2 & 1 \end{pmatrix}\begin{pmatrix} 1 & 0 \\ 0 & -1 \end{pmatrix}\begin{pmatrix} 1 & 2 \\ 0 & 1 \end{pmatrix}$

(b) $\begin{pmatrix} 1 & 2 \\ 2 & 3 \end{pmatrix} = \begin{pmatrix} 1 & 2 \\ 2 & 3 \end{pmatrix}\begin{pmatrix} 1 & 0 \\ 0 & 1 \end{pmatrix}$, $\begin{pmatrix} 1 & 2 \\ 2 & 3 \end{pmatrix} = \begin{pmatrix} 1 & 0 \\ 2 & 1 \end{pmatrix}\begin{pmatrix} 1 & 0 \\ 0 & -1 \end{pmatrix}\begin{pmatrix} 1 & 2 \\ 0 & 1 \end{pmatrix}$

$\mathbf{S}^{-1} = \begin{pmatrix} 1 & 2 \\ 2 & 3 \end{pmatrix} = \mathbf{A}$ is unique.

(d) $\begin{pmatrix} 1 & 2 \\ 3 & 4 \\ 5 & 6 \end{pmatrix} = \begin{pmatrix} 1 & 2 & 0 \\ 3 & 4 & 0 \\ 5 & 6 & 1 \end{pmatrix}\begin{pmatrix} 1 & 0 \\ 0 & 1 \\ 0 & 0 \end{pmatrix}$, $\begin{pmatrix} 1 & 2 & 0 \\ 3 & 4 & 0 \\ 5 & 6 & 1 \end{pmatrix} = \begin{pmatrix} 1 & 0 & 0 \\ 3 & 1 & 0 \\ 0 & 0 & 1 \end{pmatrix} \times$

$\times \begin{pmatrix} 1 & 0 & 0 \\ 0 & 1 & 0 \\ 5 & 0 & 1 \end{pmatrix}\begin{pmatrix} 1 & 0 & 0 \\ 0 & -2 & 0 \\ 0 & 0 & 1 \end{pmatrix}\begin{pmatrix} 1 & 0 & 0 \\ 0 & 1 & 0 \\ 0 & -4 & 1 \end{pmatrix}\begin{pmatrix} 1 & 2 & 0 \\ 0 & 1 & 0 \\ 0 & 0 & 1 \end{pmatrix}$

(i) $\begin{pmatrix} 1 & 2 & 3 & 4 \\ 2 & 5 & 6 & 8 \\ 3 & 6 & 10 & 12 \end{pmatrix} = \begin{pmatrix} 1 & 2 & 3 \\ 2 & 5 & 6 \\ 3 & 6 & 10 \end{pmatrix} \begin{pmatrix} 1 & 0 & 0 & 4 \\ 0 & 1 & 0 & 0 \\ 0 & 0 & 1 & 0 \end{pmatrix},$

$$\begin{pmatrix} 1 & 2 & 3 \\ 2 & 5 & 6 \\ 3 & 6 & 10 \end{pmatrix} = \begin{pmatrix} 1 & 0 & 0 \\ 2 & 1 & 0 \\ 0 & 0 & 1 \end{pmatrix} \begin{pmatrix} 1 & 0 & 0 \\ 0 & 1 & 0 \\ 3 & 0 & 1 \end{pmatrix} \begin{pmatrix} 1 & 2 & 0 \\ 0 & 1 & 0 \\ 0 & 0 & 1 \end{pmatrix} \begin{pmatrix} 1 & 0 & 3 \\ 0 & 1 & 0 \\ 0 & 0 & 1 \end{pmatrix}$$

8.4. (a) $\begin{pmatrix} -\frac{5}{7} & \frac{3}{7} \\ \frac{4}{7} & -\frac{1}{7} \end{pmatrix}$ (c) $\begin{pmatrix} -5 & 2 \\ 3 & -1 \end{pmatrix}$ (d) $\begin{pmatrix} -5 & 3 & 1 \\ 6 & -3 & -2 \\ -2 & 1 & 1 \end{pmatrix}$

8.5. (a) $\begin{Bmatrix} x_1 \\ x_2 \end{Bmatrix} = \begin{pmatrix} -\frac{5}{3} & 3 \\ \frac{2}{3} & -1 \end{pmatrix} \begin{Bmatrix} 1 \\ 2 \end{Bmatrix} = \begin{Bmatrix} 13/3 \\ -4/3 \end{Bmatrix}$

(c) $\begin{Bmatrix} x_1 \\ x_2 \end{Bmatrix} = \begin{pmatrix} \frac{1}{2} & \frac{1}{5} \\ \frac{1}{4} & 0 \end{pmatrix} \begin{Bmatrix} 1 \\ 5 \end{Bmatrix} = \begin{Bmatrix} \frac{3}{2} \\ \frac{1}{4} \end{Bmatrix}$

(e) $\begin{Bmatrix} x_1 \\ x_2 \\ x_3 \end{Bmatrix} = \begin{pmatrix} 0 & \frac{1}{3} & -\frac{4}{15} \\ 1 & 0 & -\frac{2}{5} \\ 0 & 0 & \frac{1}{5} \end{pmatrix} \begin{Bmatrix} -3 \\ 2 \\ 1 \end{Bmatrix} = \begin{Bmatrix} \frac{6}{15} \\ -\frac{17}{5} \\ \frac{1}{5} \end{Bmatrix}$

9.1. (a) $\begin{pmatrix} 1 & \frac{5}{2} & \frac{3}{2} \\ \frac{5}{2} & 4 & \frac{5}{2} \\ \frac{3}{2} & \frac{5}{2} & 2 \end{pmatrix}, \begin{pmatrix} 0 & -\frac{1}{2} & \frac{3}{2} \\ \frac{1}{2} & 0 & \frac{5}{2} \\ -\frac{3}{2} & -\frac{5}{2} & 0 \end{pmatrix}$, $\operatorname{tr}(\mathbf{A}) = 7$

(c) $\begin{pmatrix} 3 & \frac{11}{2} & 0 \\ \frac{11}{2} & 2 & \frac{3}{2} \\ 0 & \frac{3}{2} & 4 \end{pmatrix}, \begin{pmatrix} 0 & -\frac{3}{2} & 0 \\ \frac{3}{2} & 0 & -\frac{3}{2} \\ 0 & \frac{3}{2} & 0 \end{pmatrix}$, $\operatorname{tr}(\mathbf{A}) = 9$

(e) $\begin{pmatrix} 1 & 0 & \frac{7}{2} \\ 0 & 2 & 0 \\ \frac{7}{2} & 0 & 3 \end{pmatrix}, \begin{pmatrix} 0 & 0 & -\frac{1}{2} \\ 0 & 0 & 0 \\ \frac{1}{2} & 0 & 0 \end{pmatrix}$, $\operatorname{tr}(\mathbf{A}) = 6$

9.2. (b) $\begin{pmatrix} 3 & 0 & 0 \\ 0 & 3 & 0 \\ 0 & 0 & 3 \end{pmatrix} + \begin{pmatrix} -1 & 0 & 1 \\ 0 & 0 & 2 \\ 2 & 0 & 1 \end{pmatrix}$

(d) $\begin{pmatrix} \frac{7}{3} & 0 & 0 \\ 0 & \frac{7}{3} & 0 \\ 0 & 0 & \frac{7}{3} \end{pmatrix} + \begin{pmatrix} -\frac{7}{3} & 1 & 2 \\ 3 & -\frac{7}{3} & 0 \\ 0 & 5 & \frac{14}{3} \end{pmatrix}$

(f) $\begin{pmatrix} \frac{7}{3} & 0 & 0 \\ 0 & \frac{7}{3} & 0 \\ 0 & 0 & \frac{7}{3} \end{pmatrix} + \begin{pmatrix} -\frac{4}{3} & 2 & 3 \\ 2 & \frac{2}{3} & 4 \\ 5 & 0 & \frac{2}{3} \end{pmatrix}$

9.3. (b) $\begin{pmatrix} 3 & 0 & 0 \\ 0 & 3 & 0 \\ 0 & 0 & 3 \end{pmatrix} + \begin{pmatrix} -1 & 0 & \frac{3}{2} \\ 0 & 0 & 1 \\ \frac{3}{2} & 1 & 1 \end{pmatrix} + \begin{pmatrix} 0 & 0 & -\frac{1}{2} \\ 0 & 0 & 1 \\ \frac{1}{2} & -1 & 0 \end{pmatrix}$

(c) $\begin{pmatrix} 3 & 0 & 0 \\ 0 & 3 & 0 \\ 0 & 0 & 3 \end{pmatrix} + \begin{pmatrix} 0 & \frac{11}{2} & 0 \\ \frac{11}{2} & -1 & \frac{3}{2} \\ 0 & \frac{3}{2} & 1 \end{pmatrix} + \begin{pmatrix} 0 & -\frac{3}{2} & 0 \\ \frac{3}{2} & 0 & -\frac{3}{2} \\ 0 & \frac{3}{2} & 0 \end{pmatrix}$

(f) $\begin{pmatrix} \frac{7}{3} & 0 & 0 \\ 0 & \frac{7}{3} & 0 \\ 0 & 0 & \frac{7}{3} \end{pmatrix} + \begin{pmatrix} -\frac{4}{3} & 2 & 4 \\ 2 & \frac{2}{3} & 2 \\ 4 & 2 & \frac{2}{3} \end{pmatrix} + \begin{pmatrix} 0 & 0 & -1 \\ 0 & 0 & 2 \\ 1 & -2 & 0 \end{pmatrix}$

9.4. (a) $\begin{Bmatrix} x_1 \\ x_2 \\ x_3 \end{Bmatrix}^T \begin{pmatrix} 1 & 0 & 0 \\ 0 & 1 & 0 \\ 0 & 0 & 1 \end{pmatrix} \begin{Bmatrix} x_1 \\ x_2 \\ x_3 \end{Bmatrix}$ (c) $\begin{Bmatrix} x_1 \\ x_2 \end{Bmatrix}^T \begin{pmatrix} 3 & 3 \\ 3 & 2 \end{pmatrix} \begin{Bmatrix} x_1 \\ x_2 \end{Bmatrix}$

(e) $\begin{Bmatrix} x_1 \\ x_2 \\ x_3 \\ x_4 \end{Bmatrix}^T \begin{pmatrix} 3 & 0 & 0 & 3 \\ 0 & 0 & 2 & 0 \\ 0 & 2 & 0 & 0 \\ 3 & 0 & 0 & 0 \end{pmatrix} \begin{Bmatrix} x_1 \\ x_2 \\ x_3 \\ x_4 \end{Bmatrix}$

9.5. a, d, e.

10.1. (a) $\begin{vmatrix} 3 & 5 \\ 5 & 7 \end{vmatrix} = -4, \quad \begin{vmatrix} 1 & 2 \\ 5 & 6 \end{vmatrix} = -4, \quad \begin{vmatrix} 1 & 3 \\ 3 & 5 \end{vmatrix} = -4$

(c) $\begin{vmatrix} 3 & 0 \\ 0 & 6 \end{vmatrix} = 18, \quad \begin{vmatrix} 1 & 0 \\ 0 & 5 \end{vmatrix} = 5, \quad \begin{vmatrix} 1 & 2 \\ 3 & 0 \end{vmatrix} = -6$

(e) $\begin{vmatrix} 0 & 7 \\ 1 & 0 \end{vmatrix} = -7, \quad \begin{vmatrix} 8 & 4 \\ 1 & 3 \end{vmatrix} = 20, \quad \begin{vmatrix} 8 & 0 \\ 0 & 7 \end{vmatrix} = 56$

10.2. (a) -14 (c) -5 (e) 194

11.1 (a) $2\begin{vmatrix} 5 & 3 \\ 0 & -7 \end{vmatrix} = -70$ (c) $-\begin{vmatrix} 1 & 0 & 3 \\ 0 & 3 & 2 \\ 0 & 0 & 4 \end{vmatrix} = -12$

(e) $10\begin{vmatrix} 1 & 7 & 8 & 2 \\ 0 & 1 & 3 & 1 \\ 0 & 0 & -3 & -1 \\ 0 & 0 & 0 & 5 \end{vmatrix} = -150$

11.2 (a) $x_1 = \begin{vmatrix} 3 & -2 \\ 8 & 1 \end{vmatrix} : \begin{vmatrix} 3 & -2 \\ 5 & 1 \end{vmatrix} = \frac{19}{13}$, $x_2 = \begin{vmatrix} 3 & 3 \\ 5 & 8 \end{vmatrix} : \begin{vmatrix} 3 & -2 \\ 5 & 1 \end{vmatrix} = \frac{9}{13}$

(c) $x_1 = \begin{vmatrix} 0 & -1 \\ 3 & 1 \end{vmatrix} : \begin{vmatrix} 3 & -1 \\ -1 & 1 \end{vmatrix} = \frac{3}{2}$,

$x_2 = \begin{vmatrix} 3 & 0 \\ -1 & 3 \end{vmatrix} : \begin{vmatrix} 3 & -1 \\ -1 & 1 \end{vmatrix} = \frac{9}{2}$

(e) $x_1 = \begin{vmatrix} 1 & 1 & -2 \\ 0 & -1 & -1 \\ 1 & -2 & 0 \end{vmatrix} : \begin{vmatrix} 0 & 1 & -2 \\ 6 & -1 & -1 \\ 1 & -2 & 0 \end{vmatrix} = -\frac{5}{21}$,

$x_2 = \begin{vmatrix} 0 & 1 & -2 \\ 6 & 0 & -1 \\ 1 & 1 & 0 \end{vmatrix} : \begin{vmatrix} 0 & 1 & -2 \\ 6 & -1 & -1 \\ 1 & -2 & 0 \end{vmatrix} = -\frac{13}{21}$,

$x_3 = \begin{vmatrix} 0 & 1 & 1 \\ 6 & -1 & 0 \\ 1 & -2 & 1 \end{vmatrix} : \begin{vmatrix} 0 & 1 & -2 \\ 6 & -1 & -1 \\ 1 & -2 & 0 \end{vmatrix} = -\frac{17}{21}$

12.1. (a) $p(\lambda) = (\lambda - 4)(\lambda - 2)$; $\lambda_1 = 4$, $\lambda_2 = 2$; $N(\lambda_1) = 1$, $N(\lambda_2) = 1$;

basis of $N(\lambda_1)$ $\left\{\begin{matrix} 3 \\ 4 \end{matrix}\right\}$, basis of $N(\lambda_2)$ $\left\{\begin{matrix} 1 \\ 2 \end{matrix}\right\}$;

$$\begin{pmatrix} 1 & -\frac{1}{2} \\ -2 & \frac{3}{2} \end{pmatrix}\begin{pmatrix} 8 & -3 \\ 8 & -2 \end{pmatrix}\begin{pmatrix} 3 & 1 \\ 4 & 2 \end{pmatrix} = \begin{pmatrix} 4 & 0 \\ 0 & 2 \end{pmatrix}.$$

(c) $p(\lambda) = (\lambda - 6)^2$; $\lambda_1 = \lambda_2 = 6$; $N(\lambda_1) = N(\lambda_2) = 1$; basis of $N(\lambda_1)$ $= N(\lambda_2)$ $\left\{\begin{matrix} 1 \\ 1 \end{matrix}\right\}$; not diagonalizable.

(d) $p(\lambda) = \lambda^2 + 4$; $\lambda_1 = \overline{\lambda}_2 = 4i$, $\lambda_2 = -4i$; $N(\lambda_1) = N(\lambda_2) = 1$; basis for $N(\lambda_1)$ $\left\{\begin{matrix} \frac{1}{2} + i \\ 1 \end{matrix}\right\}$, basis for $N(\lambda_2)$ $\left\{\begin{matrix} \frac{1}{2} - i \\ 1 \end{matrix}\right\}$;

$$\begin{pmatrix} -\frac{1}{2}i & \frac{1}{2} + \frac{1}{4}i \\ \frac{1}{2}i & \frac{1}{2} - \frac{1}{4}i \end{pmatrix}\begin{pmatrix} 2 & -5 \\ 4 & -2 \end{pmatrix}\begin{pmatrix} \frac{1}{2} + i & \frac{1}{2} - i \\ 1 & 1 \end{pmatrix} = \begin{pmatrix} 4i & 0 \\ 0 & -4i \end{pmatrix}.$$

(g) $p(\lambda) = -(\lambda-2)(\lambda-1)^2$; $\lambda_1 = 2, \lambda_2 = \lambda_3 = 1$; $N(\lambda_1) = 1, N(\lambda_2) = N(\lambda_3) = 2$; basis for $N(\lambda_1)$ $\begin{Bmatrix} 0 \\ 1 \\ 2 \end{Bmatrix}$, basis for $N(\lambda_2) = N(\lambda_3)$ $\begin{Bmatrix} 2 \\ -1 \\ 0 \end{Bmatrix}, \begin{Bmatrix} 2 \\ 0 \\ 1 \end{Bmatrix}$;

$$\begin{pmatrix} -\frac{1}{2} & -1 & 1 \\ -\frac{1}{2} & -2 & 1 \\ 1 & 2 & -1 \end{pmatrix}\begin{pmatrix} 1 & 0 & 0 \\ -\frac{1}{2} & 0 & 1 \\ -1 & -2 & 3 \end{pmatrix}\times$$

$$\times\begin{pmatrix} 0 & 2 & 2 \\ 1 & -1 & 0 \\ 2 & 0 & 1 \end{pmatrix} = \begin{pmatrix} 2 & 0 & 0 \\ 0 & 1 & 0 \\ 0 & 0 & 1 \end{pmatrix}.$$

12.2. (a) $x_1'(t) = 8x_1(t) - 3x_2(t)$
$x_2'(t) = 8x_1(t) - 2x_2(t)$

(f) $x_1'(t) = 5x_1(t) - 6x_2(t) - 14x_3(t)$
$x_2'(t) = 3x_1(t) - 6x_2(t) - 21x_3(t)$
$x_3'(t) = -x_1(t) + 3x_2(t) + 10x_3(t)$

12.3. (a) One. Not diagonalizable. (b) One. Not diagonalizable.
(e) Two. Not diagonalizable.

13.1. (b) $p(\lambda) = \lambda^2 - 1$; $\lambda_1 = 1, \lambda_2 = -1$; $m_1 = m_2 = 1$; $d_1 = d_2 = 1$; basis of $N(\lambda_1)$ $\begin{Bmatrix} 3 \\ 1 \end{Bmatrix}$, basis of $N(\lambda_2)$ $\begin{Bmatrix} 1 \\ 1 \end{Bmatrix}$;

$$\begin{pmatrix} \frac{1}{2} & -\frac{1}{2} \\ -\frac{1}{2} & \frac{3}{2} \end{pmatrix}\begin{pmatrix} 2 & -3 \\ 1 & -2 \end{pmatrix}\begin{pmatrix} 3 & 1 \\ 1 & 1 \end{pmatrix} = \begin{pmatrix} 1 & 0 \\ 0 & -1 \end{pmatrix}.$$

(e) $p(\lambda) = (\lambda - 5)^2$; $\lambda_1 = 5$; $m_1 = 2$; $d_1 = 1$; basis of $N(\lambda_1)$ $\begin{Bmatrix} -1 \\ 1 \end{Bmatrix}$; not diagonalizable.

(j) $p(\lambda) = -(\lambda-3)^2(\lambda+3)$; $\lambda_1 = 3, \lambda_2 = -3$; $m_1 = 2, m_2 = 1$; $d_1 = 2, d_2 = 1$; basis of $N(\lambda_1)$ $\begin{Bmatrix} 1 \\ 2 \\ 0 \end{Bmatrix}, \begin{Bmatrix} 0 \\ -3 \\ 2 \end{Bmatrix}$, basis of $N(\lambda_2)$ $\begin{Bmatrix} 2 \\ 4 \\ 1 \end{Bmatrix}$;

$$\begin{pmatrix} \frac{11}{3} & -\frac{4}{3} & -2 \\ \frac{2}{3} & -\frac{1}{3} & 0 \\ -\frac{4}{3} & \frac{2}{3} & 1 \end{pmatrix}\begin{pmatrix} 19 & -8 & -12 \\ 32 & -13 & -24 \\ 8 & -4 & -3 \end{pmatrix}\times$$

$$\times\begin{pmatrix}1 & 0 & 2\\ 2 & -3 & 4\\ 0 & 2 & 1\end{pmatrix}=\begin{pmatrix}3 & 0 & 0\\ 0 & 3 & 0\\ 0 & 0 & -3\end{pmatrix}.$$

(r) $p(\lambda)=(\lambda-1)^2(\lambda+1)^2$; $\lambda_1=1, \lambda_2=-1$; $m_1=m_2=2$; $d_1=d_2=2$; basis of $N(\lambda_1)\begin{Bmatrix}2\\0\\1\\0\end{Bmatrix},\begin{Bmatrix}-6\\1\\-3\\1\end{Bmatrix}$, basis of $N(\lambda_2)\begin{Bmatrix}1\\0\\1\\0\end{Bmatrix},\begin{Bmatrix}-8\\1\\-3\\2\end{Bmatrix}$;

$$\begin{pmatrix}1 & 1 & -1 & 2\\ 0 & 2 & 0 & -1\\ -1 & 2 & 2 & -2\\ 0 & -1 & 0 & 1\end{pmatrix}\begin{pmatrix}3 & -20 & -4 & 20\\ 0 & 3 & 0 & -2\\ 2 & -10 & -3 & 10\\ 0 & 4 & 0 & -3\end{pmatrix}\times$$

$$\times\begin{pmatrix}2 & -6 & 1 & -8\\ 0 & 1 & 0 & 1\\ 1 & -3 & 1 & -3\\ 0 & 1 & 0 & 2\end{pmatrix}=\begin{pmatrix}1 & 0 & 0 & 0\\ 0 & 1 & 0 & 0\\ 0 & 0 & -1 & 0\\ 0 & 0 & 0 & -1\end{pmatrix}.$$

(t) $p(\lambda)=(1-\lambda)^4$; $\lambda_1=1$; $m_1=4$; $d_1=2$; basis of $N(\lambda)$ $\begin{Bmatrix}1\\0\\0\\0\end{Bmatrix}$, $\begin{Bmatrix}0\\0\\1\\0\end{Bmatrix}$; not diagonalizable.

14.1. (a) $\begin{Bmatrix}1\\0\end{Bmatrix},\begin{Bmatrix}0\\4\end{Bmatrix};\begin{Bmatrix}1\\0\end{Bmatrix},\begin{Bmatrix}0\\1\end{Bmatrix}.$

(d) $\begin{Bmatrix}3\\0\\4\end{Bmatrix},\begin{Bmatrix}-\frac{36}{25}\\2\\\frac{27}{25}\end{Bmatrix};\begin{Bmatrix}\frac{3}{5}\\0\\\frac{4}{5}\end{Bmatrix},\begin{Bmatrix}\frac{-36}{5\sqrt{181}}\\\frac{10}{\sqrt{181}}\\\frac{27}{5\sqrt{181}}\end{Bmatrix}.$

(f) $\begin{Bmatrix}3\\1\\0\end{Bmatrix},\begin{Bmatrix}1/5\\-3/5\\3\end{Bmatrix};\begin{Bmatrix}3/\sqrt{10}\\2/\sqrt{10}\\0\end{Bmatrix},\begin{Bmatrix}1/\sqrt{235}\\-3/\sqrt{235}\\15/\sqrt{235}\end{Bmatrix}.$

14.2. (a) $\begin{pmatrix}-\frac{1}{5} & \frac{2}{5}\\ \frac{2}{5} & \frac{1}{5}\end{pmatrix}\begin{pmatrix}7 & 4\\ 4 & 1\end{pmatrix}\begin{pmatrix}-1 & 2\\ 2 & 1\end{pmatrix}=\begin{pmatrix}-1 & 0\\ 0 & 9\end{pmatrix}$; $\mathbf{K}_2=\mathbf{K}_1$;

$$\begin{pmatrix} -\frac{1}{\sqrt{5}} & \frac{2}{\sqrt{5}} \\ \frac{2}{\sqrt{5}} & \frac{1}{\sqrt{5}} \end{pmatrix}\begin{pmatrix} 7 & 4 \\ 4 & 1 \end{pmatrix}\begin{pmatrix} -\frac{1}{\sqrt{5}} & \frac{2}{\sqrt{5}} \\ \frac{2}{\sqrt{5}} & \frac{1}{\sqrt{5}} \end{pmatrix}=\begin{pmatrix} -1 & 0 \\ 0 & 9 \end{pmatrix}$$

$$\begin{pmatrix} -\frac{1}{\sqrt{5}} & \frac{2}{\sqrt{5}} \\ \frac{2}{3\sqrt{5}} & \frac{1}{3\sqrt{5}} \end{pmatrix}\begin{pmatrix} 7 & 4 \\ 4 & 1 \end{pmatrix}\begin{pmatrix} -\frac{1}{\sqrt{5}} & \frac{2}{3\sqrt{5}} \\ \frac{2}{\sqrt{5}} & \frac{1}{3\sqrt{5}} \end{pmatrix}=\begin{pmatrix} -1 & 0 \\ 0 & 1 \end{pmatrix}$$

(c) $$\begin{pmatrix} \frac{1}{5} & -\frac{2}{5} \\ \frac{2}{5} & \frac{1}{5} \end{pmatrix}\begin{pmatrix} 5 & 2 \\ 2 & 2 \end{pmatrix}\begin{pmatrix} 1 & 2 \\ -2 & 1 \end{pmatrix}=\begin{pmatrix} 1 & 0 \\ 0 & 6 \end{pmatrix}; \mathbf{K}_2 = \mathbf{K}_1;$$

$$\begin{pmatrix} \frac{1}{\sqrt{5}} & -\frac{2}{\sqrt{5}} \\ \frac{2}{\sqrt{5}} & \frac{1}{\sqrt{5}} \end{pmatrix}\begin{pmatrix} 5 & 2 \\ 2 & 2 \end{pmatrix}\begin{pmatrix} \frac{1}{\sqrt{5}} & \frac{2}{\sqrt{5}} \\ -\frac{2}{\sqrt{5}} & \frac{1}{\sqrt{5}} \end{pmatrix}=\begin{pmatrix} 1 & 0 \\ 0 & 6 \end{pmatrix};$$

$$\begin{pmatrix} \frac{1}{\sqrt{5}} & -\frac{2}{\sqrt{5}} \\ \frac{2}{\sqrt{30}} & \frac{1}{\sqrt{30}} \end{pmatrix}\begin{pmatrix} 5 & 2 \\ 2 & 2 \end{pmatrix}\begin{pmatrix} \frac{1}{\sqrt{5}} & \frac{2}{\sqrt{30}} \\ -\frac{2}{\sqrt{5}} & \frac{1}{\sqrt{30}} \end{pmatrix}=\begin{pmatrix} 1 & 0 \\ 0 & 1 \end{pmatrix}$$

(d) $$\begin{pmatrix} -\frac{1}{9} & \frac{4}{9} & -\frac{1}{9} \\ -\frac{4}{9} & -\frac{2}{9} & \frac{5}{9} \\ \frac{2}{9} & \frac{1}{9} & \frac{2}{9} \end{pmatrix}\begin{pmatrix} 5 & -2 & -4 \\ -2 & 8 & -2 \\ -4 & -2 & 5 \end{pmatrix}\times$$

$$\times\begin{pmatrix} -1 & -1 & 2 \\ 2 & 0 & 1 \\ 0 & 1 & 2 \end{pmatrix}=\begin{pmatrix} 9 & 0 & 0 \\ 0 & 9 & 0 \\ 0 & 0 & 0 \end{pmatrix};$$

$$\begin{pmatrix} -\frac{1}{5} & \frac{2}{5} & 0 \\ \frac{4}{45} & \frac{2}{45} & -\frac{1}{9} \\ \frac{2}{9} & \frac{1}{9} & \frac{2}{9} \end{pmatrix}\begin{pmatrix} 5 & -2 & -4 \\ -2 & 8 & -2 \\ -4 & -2 & 5 \end{pmatrix}\times$$

$$\times\begin{pmatrix} -1 & 4 & 2 \\ 2 & 2 & 1 \\ 0 & -5 & 2 \end{pmatrix}=\begin{pmatrix} 9 & 0 & 0 \\ 0 & 9 & 0 \\ 0 & 0 & 0 \end{pmatrix};$$

$$\begin{pmatrix} -\frac{1}{\sqrt{5}} & \frac{2}{\sqrt{5}} & 0 \\ \frac{4}{\sqrt{45}} & \frac{2}{\sqrt{45}} & \frac{-5}{\sqrt{45}} \\ \frac{2}{3} & \frac{1}{3} & \frac{2}{3} \end{pmatrix} \begin{pmatrix} 5 & -2 & -4 \\ -2 & 8 & -2 \\ -4 & -2 & 5 \end{pmatrix} \times$$

$$\times \begin{pmatrix} -\frac{1}{\sqrt{5}} & \frac{4}{\sqrt{45}} & \frac{2}{3} \\ \frac{2}{\sqrt{5}} & \frac{2}{\sqrt{45}} & \frac{1}{3} \\ 0 & \frac{-5}{\sqrt{45}} & \frac{2}{3} \end{pmatrix} = \begin{pmatrix} 9 & 0 & 0 \\ 0 & 9 & 0 \\ 0 & 0 & 0 \end{pmatrix}$$

15.1. (a) positive definite, (c) indefinite,

(d) positive semi-definite, (h) negative definite,

(j) negative semi-definite

15.2. (a) positive definite for $a > 1$; positive semi-definite for $a = 1$; indefinite for $0 < a < 1$; negative semi-definite for $a = 0$; negative definite for $a < 0$.

(c) positive definite for $a > 2$; positive semi-definite for $a = 2$; indefinite for $0 < a < 2$; negative semi-definite for $a = 0$; negative definite for $a < 0$.

15.3. (c) $\begin{pmatrix} 1 & 3 & -1 \\ 0 & 1 & 0 \\ 2 & 4 & 2 \end{pmatrix} \begin{pmatrix} a_1 & 0 & 0 \\ 0 & a_2 & 0 \\ 0 & 0 & a_3 \end{pmatrix} \begin{pmatrix} \frac{1}{2} & -\frac{5}{2} & \frac{1}{4} \\ 0 & 1 & 0 \\ -\frac{1}{2} & \frac{1}{2} & \frac{1}{4} \end{pmatrix}$

$$= \begin{pmatrix} \frac{a_1 + a_3}{2} & 3a_2 - \frac{5a_1 + a_3}{2} & \frac{a_1 - a_3}{4} \\ 0 & a_2 & 0 \\ a_1 - a_3 & -5a_1 + 4a_2 + a_3 & \frac{a_1 + a_3}{2} \end{pmatrix}$$

(e) $\begin{pmatrix} 1 & 0 & 2 \\ 2 & -3 & 4 \\ 0 & 2 & 1 \end{pmatrix} \begin{pmatrix} a_1 & 0 & 0 \\ 0 & a_2 & 0 \\ 0 & 0 & a_3 \end{pmatrix} \begin{pmatrix} \frac{11}{3} & -\frac{4}{3} & -2 \\ \frac{2}{3} & -\frac{1}{3} & 0 \\ -\frac{4}{3} & \frac{2}{3} & 1 \end{pmatrix}$

$$= \begin{pmatrix} \frac{1}{3}(11a_1 - 8a_3) & \frac{4}{3}(-a_1 + a_3) & 2(-a_1 + a_3) \\ \frac{2}{3}(11a_1 - 3a_2 - 8a_3) & \frac{8}{3}(-a_1 + a_3) + a_2 & 4(-a_1 + a_3) \\ \frac{4}{3}(a_2 - a_3) & \frac{2}{3}(-a_2 + a_3) & a_3 \end{pmatrix}$$

15.4. (a) $\begin{pmatrix} a_1 + 4a_2 & -2a_1 + 2a_2 \\ -2a_1 + 2a_2 & 4a_1 + a_2 \end{pmatrix}$; . (c) $\begin{pmatrix} a_1 + 4a_2 & -2a_1 + 2a_2 \\ -2a_1 + 2a_2 & 4a_1 + a_2 \end{pmatrix}$

(d) $\begin{pmatrix} a_1 + 16a_2 + 4a_3 & -2a_1 + 8a_2 + 2a_3 & -20a_2 + 4a_3 \\ -2a_1 + 8a_2 + 2a_3 & 4a_1 + 4a_2 + a_3 & -10a_2 + 2a_3 \\ -20a_2 + 4a_3 & -10a_2 + 2a_3 & 25a_2 + 4a_3 \end{pmatrix}$

15.5. (a) $\mathbf{P} = \begin{pmatrix} \frac{4}{5} & \frac{3}{5} \\ \frac{3}{5} & \frac{17}{10} \end{pmatrix}$, $\tilde{\mathbf{P}} = \begin{pmatrix} \frac{17}{10} & \frac{3}{5} \\ \frac{3}{5} & \frac{4}{5} \end{pmatrix}$, $\mathbf{0} = \begin{pmatrix} \frac{4}{5} & \frac{3}{5} \\ -\frac{3}{5} & \frac{4}{5} \end{pmatrix}$

15.6. (b) $\mathbf{A}^3 = 9\mathbf{A}^2 - 24\mathbf{A} + 18\mathbf{E}$; $\mathbf{A}^4 = 57\mathbf{A}^2 - 198\mathbf{A} + 162\mathbf{E}$;
$f_1(\mathbf{A}) = 19\mathbf{E} - 22\mathbf{A} + 8\mathbf{A}^2$; $f_2(\mathbf{A}) = 146\mathbf{E} - 175\mathbf{A} + 50\mathbf{A}^2$

(d) $\mathbf{A}^3 = 7\mathbf{A}^2 + 3\mathbf{A} + 9\mathbf{E}$; $\mathbf{A}^4 = 52\mathbf{A}^2 + 30\mathbf{A} + 63\mathbf{E}$
$f_1(\mathbf{A}) = 10\mathbf{E} + 5\mathbf{A} + 6\mathbf{A}^2$; $f_2(\mathbf{A}) = 56\mathbf{E} + 26\mathbf{A} + 47\mathbf{A}^2$

16.1. (a) $\{x\} = \begin{pmatrix} \frac{1}{\sqrt{10}} & \frac{3}{\sqrt{10}} \\ \frac{3}{\sqrt{10}} & \frac{-1}{\sqrt{10}} \end{pmatrix} \{y\}$, $\Phi^*(\{y\}) = 10y_1^2 + 20y_2^2$

(c) $\{x\} = \begin{pmatrix} \frac{3}{5} & -\frac{4}{5} \\ \frac{4}{5} & \frac{3}{5} \end{pmatrix} \{y\}$, $\Phi^*(\{y\}) = 25y_1^2$

(f) $\{x\} = \begin{pmatrix} \frac{2}{3} & \frac{1}{3} & \frac{2}{3} \\ -\frac{2}{3} & \frac{2}{3} & \frac{1}{3} \\ -\frac{1}{3} & -\frac{2}{3} & \frac{2}{3} \end{pmatrix} \{y\}$, $\Phi^*(\{y\}) = 9y_1^2 + 18y_2^2 - 9y_3^2$

16.2. (a) $\mathbf{T} = \frac{1}{2\sqrt{10}} \begin{pmatrix} 0 & -4 \\ 5 & -3 \end{pmatrix}$; $y_1^2 + y_2^2$, $y_1^2 - y_2^2$

(b) $\mathbf{T} = \frac{1}{3\sqrt{10}} \begin{pmatrix} 5 & 5 \\ 1 & 7 \end{pmatrix}$; $y_1^2 + y_2^2$, $2y_1^2 + y_2^2$

(c) $\mathbf{T} = \frac{1}{9} \begin{pmatrix} 7 & -1 & -2 \\ -1 & \frac{17}{2} & -1 \\ -2 & -1 & 7 \end{pmatrix}$; $y_1^2 + y_2^2 + y_3^2$; $y_2^2 + y_3^2$

16.3. (a) $\mathbf{T} = \dfrac{1}{4\sqrt{5}}\begin{pmatrix} 1 & 5 \\ 7 & -5 \end{pmatrix}$; $\ddot{r}_1 - r_1 = 0, \ddot{r}_2 + r_2 = 0$

(c) $\mathbf{T} = \dfrac{1}{6\sqrt{5}}\begin{pmatrix} 0 & 6 \\ 10 & -8 \end{pmatrix}$; $\ddot{r}_1 + r_1 = 0, \ddot{r}_2 - r_2 = 0$

17.3. (a) $\dfrac{d}{dt}\{x(t)\} = \begin{pmatrix} 3 & 5 \\ 2 & 3 \end{pmatrix}\{x(t)\}.$

(c) $\dfrac{d}{dt}\{x(t)\} = \begin{pmatrix} 0 & -3 & -5 \\ 0 & 0 & 5 \\ 0 & 0 & 0 \end{pmatrix}\{x(t)\}.$

(e) $\dfrac{d}{dt}\{x(t)\} = \begin{pmatrix} 0 & 1 & -3 \\ 2 & 0 & -4 \\ 1 & -1 & -8 \end{pmatrix}\{x(t)\}.$

17.4. (a) $x_1' = 8x_1 - 3x_2, \quad x_2' = 8x_1 - 2x_2; \quad \lambda_1 = 4, \quad \lambda_2 = 2; \quad m_1 = m_2 = 1;$ $d_1 = d_2 = 1$; diagonalizable

$\mathbf{K} = \begin{pmatrix} 3 & 1 \\ 4 & 2 \end{pmatrix}$; $\{x(t)\} = c_1 e^{4t}\begin{Bmatrix} 3 \\ 4 \end{Bmatrix} + c_2 e^{2t}\begin{Bmatrix} 1 \\ 2 \end{Bmatrix}$; $e^{4t}\begin{Bmatrix} 3 \\ 4 \end{Bmatrix}, e^{2t}\begin{Bmatrix} 1 \\ 2 \end{Bmatrix}.$

(d) $x_1' = 2x_1 - 5x_2, \; x_2' = 4x_1 - 2x_2; \; \lambda_1 = 4i, \; \lambda_2 = -4i; \; m_1 = m_2 = 1;$ $d_1 = d_2 = 1$; diagonalizable

$\mathbf{K} = \begin{pmatrix} \frac{1}{2} + i & \frac{1}{2} - i \\ 1 & 1 \end{pmatrix}$; $\{x(t)\} = c_1\begin{Bmatrix} \cos 4t - 2\sin 4t \\ 2\cos 4t \end{Bmatrix}$

$+ c_2\begin{Bmatrix} 2\cos 4t + \sin 4t \\ 2\sin 4t \end{Bmatrix}.$

(g) $x_1' = x_1, \; x_2' = -\dfrac{1}{2}x_1 + x_3, \; x_3' = -x_1 - 2x_2 + 3x_3; \; \lambda_1 = 2, \lambda_2 = 1;$

$m_1 = 1, m_2 = 2; d_1 = 1, d_2 = 2$; diagonalizable

$\mathbf{K} = \begin{pmatrix} 0 & 2 & 2 \\ 1 & -1 & 0 \\ 2 & 0 & 1 \end{pmatrix}$; $\{x(t)\} = c_1 e^{2t}\begin{Bmatrix} 0 \\ 1 \\ 2 \end{Bmatrix} + c_2 e^{t}\begin{Bmatrix} 2 \\ -1 \\ 0 \end{Bmatrix} + c_3 e^{t}\begin{Bmatrix} 2 \\ 0 \\ 1 \end{Bmatrix}.$

17.5. (a) $\{x(t)\} = c_1 e^{t}\begin{Bmatrix} 3 \\ 1 \end{Bmatrix} + c_2 e^{-t}\begin{Bmatrix} 1 \\ 1 \end{Bmatrix}$; $e^{t}\begin{Bmatrix} 3 \\ 1 \end{Bmatrix}, e^{-t}\begin{Bmatrix} 1 \\ 1 \end{Bmatrix}$;

$\{x(t)\} = e^{t-1}\begin{Bmatrix} 3 \\ 1 \end{Bmatrix} - 2e^{1-t}\begin{Bmatrix} 1 \\ 1 \end{Bmatrix}.$

(d) $\{x(t)\} = c_1 e^{t}\begin{Bmatrix} 2 \\ 3 \\ -1 \end{Bmatrix} + c_2 e^{t}\begin{Bmatrix} 3 \\ 1 \\ 0 \end{Bmatrix} + c_3 e^{2t}\begin{Bmatrix} 2 \\ -2 \\ 1 \end{Bmatrix}$;

$e^{t}\begin{Bmatrix} 2 \\ 3 \\ -1 \end{Bmatrix}, e^{t}\begin{Bmatrix} 3 \\ 1 \\ 0 \end{Bmatrix}, e^{2t}\begin{Bmatrix} 2 \\ -2 \\ 1 \end{Bmatrix}$;

$$-19e^{t-1}\begin{Bmatrix}2\\3\\-1\end{Bmatrix}+24e^{t-1}\begin{Bmatrix}3\\1\\0\end{Bmatrix}-17e^{2t-2}\begin{Bmatrix}2\\-2\\1\end{Bmatrix}$$

(e) $\{x(t)\}=c_1e^{it}\begin{Bmatrix}i\\1\\0\end{Bmatrix}+c_2e^{-it}\begin{Bmatrix}-i\\1\\0\end{Bmatrix}+c_3e^{t}\begin{Bmatrix}1\\0\\1\end{Bmatrix};$

$$\begin{Bmatrix}-\sin t\\\cos t\\0\end{Bmatrix},\begin{Bmatrix}\cos t\\\sin t\\0\end{Bmatrix},\ e^t\begin{Bmatrix}1\\0\\1\end{Bmatrix};$$

$$-\cos 1\begin{Bmatrix}-\sin t\\\cos t\\0\end{Bmatrix}-\sin 1\begin{Bmatrix}\cos t\\\sin t\\0\end{Bmatrix}+\begin{Bmatrix}1\\0\\1\end{Bmatrix}.$$

18.1. (a) $x_1=2c_1e^{4t}+4c_2e^{2t}+t^2+\frac{7}{4}t+\frac{19}{16},$

$x_2=-c_1e^{4t}-3c_2e^{2t}-t^2-\frac{13}{8}t-\frac{31}{32}.$

(b) $x_1=c_1e^{3t}-c_2e^{-3t}-\frac{1}{4}e^t-\frac{2}{3}t,$

$x_2=c_1e^{3t}+2c_2e^{-3t}-\frac{1}{2}e^t+\frac{1}{3}t-\frac{1}{3}.$

(e) $x_1=c_1e^{2t}+c_2e^{2t}-c_3e^{-2t}-e^t\left(\frac{2}{3}t^2+\frac{8}{9}t+\frac{28}{27}\right)-\frac{1}{4},$

$x_2=c_1e^{2t}-e^t(t^2+2t+2),$

$x_3=2c_2e^{2t}+2c_3e^{-2t}+e^t\left(\frac{4}{3}t^2+\frac{16}{9}t+\frac{56}{27}\right)-t.$

18.2. (a) $x_1=-\frac{27}{8}e^{2t}+\frac{1}{8}e^{-2t}-t+\frac{17}{4},$

$x_2=-\frac{9}{8}e^{2t}+\frac{1}{8}e^{-2t}-\frac{1}{2}t+3.$

(c) $x_1=be^{2(t-a)}\cos(t-a)+(a+b)e^{2(t-a)}\sin(t-a)$

$+\int_a^t \eta e^{2t-\eta}[3e^{-\eta}\sin(t-\eta)+\cos(t-\eta)]d\eta,$

$x_2=-be^{2(t-a)}\sin(t-a)+(a+b)^{2(t-a)}\cos(t-a)$

$+\int_a^t \eta e^{2t-\eta}[3e^{-\eta}\cos(t-\eta)-\sin(t-\eta)]d\eta.$

(h) $x_1=-3e^{t-\pi}-2e^{\pi-t}+3,\quad x_2=3e^{t-\pi}+e^{\pi-t}+\sin t-3,$

$x_3=-3e^{\pi-t}+3.$

Books for Further Reading

We list below, in order of increasing difficulty, some of the texts that can be used for further reading. The books in the first part are mostly theoretical while the second part gives texts which deal mainly with applications of Linear Algebra.

W. L. FERRAR — *Algebra—A Textbook of Determinants, Matrices and Algebraic Forms,* Oxford, Clarendon Press, 1957.

A. C. AITKEN — *Determinants and Matrices,* Interscience Publishers Inc., New York, 1959.

M. BOUCHER — *Introduction to Higher Algebra,* Dover, New York, 1964.

W. L. FERRAR — *Finite Matrices,* Oxford, Clarendon Press, 1960.

L. MIRSKY — *An Introduction to Linear Algebra,* Oxford, Clarendon Press, 1963.

H. W. TURNBULL — *The Theory of Determinants, Matrices and Invariants,* Dover, New York, 1960.

C. C. MacDUFFEE — *The Theory of Matrices,* Chelsea, New York, 1st corrected ed., 1947; 2nd corrected ed., 1962.

H. G. CAMPBELL — *Linear Algebra with Applications,* Appleton-Century-Crofts, New York, 1961.

R. A. FRAZIER, W. J. DUNCAN, and A. R. COLLAR — *Elementary Matrices,* Cambridge University Press, 1965.

A. LICHNEROWICZ — *Algèbre et Analyse Lineaires,* Masson, Paris, 1947.

Index

DOMINIC G. B. EDELEN is currently Professor of Mathematics and Astronomy at the Center for the Application of Mathematics at Lehigh University, Bethlehem, Pennsylvania, and Chairman of the Undergraduate Applied Mathematics Group. Prior to this position, he taught at Purdue University, was a staff mathematician at the RAND Corporation, and held the positions of staff engineer and research and development scientist in industry. Dr. Edelen has also authored three books on mathematical physics. He is a fellow of the Royal Astronomical Society and a member of the Tensor Society of Japan and the Board of Editors of the International Journal of Engineering Science. He holds B.E.S., M.S.E. and Ph.D. degrees from Johns Hopkins University.

Presently, ANASTASIOS D. KYDONIEFS is teaching at the Center for the Application of Mathematics, Lehigh University, Bethlehem, Pennsylvania. In addition to his teaching experience, he has been a senior research assistant and a university research fellow at the University of Nottingham, England. Born in Greece, Dr. Kydoniefs received his B.Sc. degree from the University of Athens, Greece and his M.Sc. and Ph.D. degrees from the University of Nottingham, England.